Broken
not
Shattered

Broken
not
Shattered

BASED ON A TRUE STORY

Always Keep faith — *Kyna Bryn*

KYNA BRYN

BEANE
Books

Publisher: Lisa Beane, Beane Books
Cover Design: Mallory Beane, Mallory Lauren Photography
Photographer: Mallory Beane, Mallory Lauren Photography
Copy Editor: Pamela Waite, Waite Editing
Interior Design: Pamela Waite, Waite Editing

We hope you enjoy this book from Beane Books. Our goal is to produce high quality books and products for your enjoyment. We guide those who want to write and those who otherwise may never have had the opportunity to write and tell their story.

Beane Books can bring authors to your live event. For more information or to book an event, contact Lisa Beane of Beane Books at lisa@beanenatural.com.

BeaneNATURAL, LLC
Beane Books
Fairfield, OH, USA
lisa@beanenatural.com

Beane Books is an imprint of BeaneNATURAL, LLC
First Edition October, 2016
ISBN 978-0-9981562-0-0

For information visit:
www.brokennotshattered.com

Published in the USA

DEDICATION

This book is dedicated to my beautiful daughter.

She has inspired me in more ways than I can begin to put into words. When we face our biggest challenges always remember that you are never alone.

Strength comes from within and your faith will always carry you through your darkest moments.

Never give up on yourself. You are meant for great things, but only you can make the decision and take action to make those things come to life.

I would also like to thank all of those who believed in me when I had a hard time believing in myself.

"PASSIONATE... COURAGEOUS...WOMAN of FAITH... determined to share her story with the world is how I would describe the author. She will go to all ends of the earth to get this book into the hands of those who need it the most in hopes that this story will change the lives and outcomes of others who have lived a life similar to that in the book."
Lisa Beane, Publisher - Beane Books

Table of Contents

Chapter ONE

MONDAY, March 9, 2015: I woke up ready to take on the day. My family was always teasing me about being a morning person as if that's a bad thing. Honestly, I do usually wake up in the best of moods. Every morning I make a cup of hot tea then I spend time reflecting on what I am going to do first. I pick from the normal list of things such as prayer, bible study, exercise or working on that days to-do list.

My one and only child, Bree, is a typical 15-year-old young lady. She can do anything she puts her mind to and I believe that wholeheartedly. At this point in time, Bree was home schooled and loved the freedom of it. I've always been a little strict when it came to her studies and grades, but she always worked hard to keep them up. On this particular day, around 1:30 in the afternoon, Bree and I realized we needed a couple of things from the store for dinner. Bree stayed behind to do her school work while I jumped in my truck and headed down the road. As I pulled near the stop sign I noticed a woman trying to cross the street.

I thought to myself that the woman looked like she was in her late-70s. She was wearing a large, down-filled, very loud blue trench coat and I literally stopped about ten feet back from the stop sign when I saw her. As I continued to watch her I noticed she was struggling just to get across the street. I began to think about how sad her story must be. I assumed she must be homeless by the way she appeared. Her trench coat was very dirty and she looked so rough. Then I thought, "Zara, don't end up like that. Don't be alone, homeless, looking so rough and walking the streets when you're older." And in that instant I questioned myself: Why did I stop the truck so far back? As if this stranger I had never seen or met before could have somehow given me a disease or had some gross smell that could affect me. I was in my truck, it was cold out and my windows were up. Reflecting on it now I realize I was simply being a judgmental bitch.

It took this woman awhile to get across the street. As I continued to watch her I noticed she was having a really hard time moving and she kept looking at the street sign as if she was lost. At that moment my heart ached and I realized that I needed to help her. I let my foot off the brake and slowly rolled my truck up to the stop sign. I rolled my window down and asked her if she was okay. She looked at me with deep desperation and said, "NO, I'm not."

She began to lean on the stop sign as if it were her only anchor to stay standing. Then she proceeded to tell me she was trying to find the store that someone had told her was down in this direction. She said that she just wanted chips and it was the only thing that made her leave her house. I asked her if I could offer her a ride and she didn't hesitate. It took her a couple of minutes to get into my truck, but once inside I knew that God had placed her there at that exact moment. The second the passenger side door to my truck shut the woman began sharing her testimony with me.

I listened carefully as she explained that her mother had just passed away only two months earlier and she was all alone now. She told me about how she had worked for the prison system for a long time and she somehow ended up with a head injury. Her memory was only good for about one to two minutes and yes, only minutes. This woman was not joking. Once I got her to the store I waited for about ten minutes for her to come out, but she was still nowhere to be seen. I decided to go in and check on her to make sure she was okay. As I stood back and watched her scramble through the purse she had been carrying it looked as if she had four wallets, all of which were pretty empty. After a few moments I assumed she was searching for the money she had already given the clerk. She had received her change and was even holding it, but she didn't remember that she had paid.

The clerk was looking over her as if he simply just wanted her to get out of the way so he could help the next person in line. So I went over to her, talked to the clerk and he reassured my assumption that she was, in fact, holding her change. I helped her gather all her things, noticing she hadn't even gotten chips, and took her back out to the truck. At that precise moment I felt determined to help this woman find her way home. After we got into my truck I asked her what her address was. I was thrown off a little when I realized it was right down the street from my home. My first thought of her was very off, especially when you consider that at first glance I judged her as a homeless woman. Who am I to judge anyone?

One thing I have learned is that none of us have an authority or the right to judge anyone at any time, for any reason. It doesn't matter if you have money or if you are poor. It doesn't matter if you're black, white, brown, green, yellow; it doesn't matter your race. It doesn't matter if you are a man or a woman. It doesn't even matter what your sexual preference is; whether you're into same sex, opposite sex, the freaky Fifty Shades of Grey sex, it doesn't matter. We all face problems. We all have our challenges. None of us are better than the other. Our world is so consumed with judging and it's wrong to use the Bible as if it's been provided to defend hate. Trying to portray how awesome and together you are while tearing others down or judging others only hurts yourself. I feel it holds you back from your happiness and from your own designed purpose in this world.

As I drove out of the parking lot this sweet old woman continued to share her story with me. She shared how she really hated the house she was living in now because the bills were just too high. Which, of course, I could completely relate with and I am sure most of us can. I considered how much harder it must be to be older, alone, having only that one income to rely on and it never being enough to cover the cost of living. Don't get me wrong, I have lived in a tent at one point in my life, but it was when I was younger. At this time in my life things were really good, as far as our income went. Our fridge was full, bills paid and we were able to do extras like a movie or going out for dinners here and there.

The woman continued talking about her home and how it was drafty and very cold. At that time I was living in Indiana and we had a few really rough winters with extremely cold temperatures. The funny thing though was throughout each complaint she would throw out a praise. She would say things like, "My house is just too big for me, but I know Jesus is with me," or, "This house takes all my money and I don't have much, but I know God is watching over me." I was truly captivated by her.

As I drove down the street searching for the address she gave me I realized that she said she lived at 904. The house numbers only went to 600. She seemed to get a little frustrated, but I told her it was no problem and that I wasn't going to leave her until I got her home. I asked her if she had an I.D. in her purse and she excitedly answered, "Yes, I should." She continued thanking me and praising the Lord as she began searching for her I.D. After trying a few streets nearby to see if she recognized any of the houses she finally found it. It was interesting that she actually had the numbers correct she just had the street wrong.

The look of relief on her face when she saw her home was something I will never forget. As slow moving as she had been she almost jumped out of my truck, even leaving her purse behind. I grabbed her purse and caught up with her in enough time to grab her hand and help her get up the walkway. She opened the door to her home like she had been away for days. The woman went in so fast that I had to call her back to grab her purse. Since she was home safe I jumped back into my truck and headed to the store as planned.

After finishing at the store and arriving back at home I shared my experience with my daughter. I told her that I would like to take her sometime and go to the lady's home just to help in any way we could. My daughter not only agreed, but thought it would be a great idea. I really enjoyed that woman's company and stories. I felt awful when I realized that I didn't even get her name. As our day went on my daughter and I did our normal daily routine. She did school work as I cleaned and prepped for dinner.

My husband, Ty, was usually home from work around 6:30 p.m. I tried to make sure he had fresh, hot food when he got home even though by this time I didn't like cooking for him. Ty was someone I thought of as my best friend, my lover and a man that would always stand by my side. I used to call him my Prince because he is originally from Africa. He came to the United States in 2010 to attend college and further his education, or so he had claimed when we had met. I had never expected this man to come into my life when he did. Ty showed up in my life at a time I was weak and very lonely. He filled a void that I never thought anyone could fill.

As we sat down to eat dinner I began sharing my day with my husband. I started telling him about the sweet older woman I was blessed enough to help. I told him that Bree and I were planning to go visit her and offer her any help we could. All of a sudden, Ty looked at me and to my surprise he asked me, "Are you talking about an older woman wearing a long blue coat?" I quickly answered, "Yes." He went on to explain that he had seen the same woman that morning as he was leaving for work. He said that she looked like she was homeless and he was in a rush so he didn't think twice about stopping to check on her.

Can you imagine how many hours she was actually out wandering around lost? Ty left for work at 5:30 a.m. It was almost eight hours later when I picked her up. I thank the Lord for using me at that moment and for making me aware enough to not stay in judgment. We all have a tendency to judge others by sight or by simple differences. We need to take control of those negative thoughts. Is it easy? No way, but I believe it is possible. This may be something hard to grasp with the world being filled with so much hatred, but I am going to say it often throughout this book, "We were not put here to judge one another."

Now I am not claiming to be anyone special or someone with some great talent or knowledge. I do feel, however, that I am supposed to share my story, my victories and my failures with you. I do admit that I am 100% a lady with the mouth of an educated sailor. I am not the 'normal author' nor am I a woman with a perfect record of great choices. I am simply going to challenge you to step out of your comfort zone and embrace a concept of living differently by making the choice too. Your comfort zone can be a horrible place to get stuck because you can miss out on so much. We were never designed to sit aside and just rot, only focusing on ourselves and what we alone want. We have a much greater purpose and I believe loving one another without judgment is a key essential to discovering our individual purpose in this life.

Tuesday, March 10, 2015: "Time to rise and shine," I thought as I jump out of bed ready to take on another day headstrong, as usual. Looking forward to the day I woke up with positive thoughts and in a good mood. I thought it was going to be just another normal day, but that was further from the truth then I ever could have realized. As the morning moved along Bree and I decided to go see the sweet woman from the day before. I recalled that she never did get the potato chips at the store that she was after, so Bree and I decided to take her some.

Not sure if she would remember me we headed out unaware of what to expect. When my daughter and I walked up to the door I thought about what I was going to do if the woman didn't recognize me. Then I came up with the plan that if she didn't remember me I would tell her she had won some drawing and we were there to help clean or do any chores she needed done. Bree was first to the door and, after she knocked, a young lady opened the door and said, "Can I help you?" I stepped up and asked after the woman who lived there. The young woman just opened the door and pointed toward an area inside the home.

As we stepped inside there the sweet older woman was, looking well rested and eating her lunch. I turned to the young lady and asked after the woman's name, it was Margaret. I then looked at Margaret and asked her if she remembered me. She looked at me and said, "Yes, I remember you. You're the angel that picked me up and gave me a ride." I can't express in words how relieved I was that she remembered me. As we sat and visited with Margaret I asked her if it would be okay if my daughter and I came to visit as often as possible. She gladly accepted. I also asked Margaret if I could pray with her and she again accepted. After praying and visiting for a while I realized the young lady was Margaret's hospice care provider. I explained to her how I met Margaret and she told me that Margaret wasn't even supposed to leave the house.

When we left Margaret's home I began to cry when I thought about the fact that I even stepped on my brakes ten feet back from this beautiful woman just because at that moment her appearance was dirty, sad and lonesome. As if I don't have days I look the exact same. Have you ever felt like when you look in the mirror you're harder on yourself than anyone else is? Do you judge yourself when you stand before yourself? Now imagine, most of the time when you look at others what's the first thing you do? Are you doing the same thing and judging them because of their appearance? Even knowing that appearance doesn't define you we still tend to judge people based on what they look like.

Now just picture walking up to a mirror and saying, "You're gorgeous. You are looking so good today. You are blessed and are going to experience blessings today." Then make it your purpose to make as many people smile as often as possible and treat them the same way. Treat them as they are beautiful and they too are blessed. I triple dog dare you to try it for three days. Love yourself and others often; You will be amazed at what changes not only within you but around you.

I know it may be tough to hear, but none of us live in a fairytale. Most of us grow up on fairytales of being rescued by some Prince Charming and our lives being wonderful forever. That is simply not reality for many of us. Money has its problems, just ask anyone with wealth. Poor folks have their problems also. All of us face challenges and problems, but how we handle them makes a huge difference. Now I am not referring to just the big issues, I mean even small problems are still problems. My personal opinion is, please refer to the saying, 'opinions are like assholes and everybody has one', we are given only what we can handle. I believe, even when we don't realize how strong we are and think we are going to break, it is in those moments we can choose to grow or stay stuck and allow the darkness of our situation to consume us.

At this time in my life I was not only a stay-at-home mom, but I also owned and operated a small daycare. I did this in order to make some extra income. My family was blessed by all the children that came through our home every day. I, of course, kept a limit on how many children I had at one time. There are laws, not to mention if I went beyond four kids I was liable to pull my hair out. On this particular Tuesday I had three kids, which was pretty much my normal headcount. My little brother, Dakota, who lived down the street from us, ended up calling and needed to come over to do some laundry. I told him it wasn't a problem and cleaned out the dryer so everything was ready for his arrival.

Dakota got to the house later in the afternoon around three or four o'clock. Once my brother arrived he started his laundry and we began talking about how our day had been. We decided we would go ahead and get a bottle of alcohol to drink while he finished up his laundry. Bree was entertaining the kids and watching TV, so we did a quick run and grabbed a fifth of Kissed Caramel Vodka. All except one of the kids had been picked up before the first fifth was gone and, once we finished it, we decided to go ahead and grab another one.

Bree, and the one child left at the house ended up going to a game that night and she ended up staying all night with her friend after the last child had left. By the time Ty got home from work my brother had left and I was pretty drunk. Ty was, to say the least, pissed off. I don't remember too much after he got home. I remember sitting on the bed with Ty trying to get him to talk to me, but he was just hateful toward me. Ty was never shy about telling me what a worthless drunk I was anytime I drank. Even at times when he was drinking with me and I happened to get more drunk than him I was still, "Just a worthless drunk."

I remember Ty looking over this diagnostic tool he had ordered which had just arrived in the mail that day. I got angry at him for something he said and I ripped the diagnostic tool out of his hands and proceeded to break it over my thigh. That night was really blurry for me. Have you ever worn beer goggles? It was about three times worse than that. I had a few visions of taking picture frames off of our wall and throwing them down the hallway. They slammed against the door at the end of the hallway just shattering to pieces. Ty man-handled me a lot that night and that was why I kept my distance and was throwing pictures. Ty was getting his things together quickly and he was leaving, again. Before I knew it Ty was gone and the house was empty.

I have been through some crazy things in life, but that was the most violent bloody night I have ever experienced. I couldn't believe who I was or how I reacted. I hated the person Ty brought out of me. I have never been a violent woman, but Ty knew how to push every button inside of me like no one else ever could. I am a tough woman, don't get me wrong, but never to my man. Ty brought out a lot of anger in me. This was far from the first fight we had, but it was the worst one we ever had. As I sat on the stairs in the foyer I realized the only sound in our home was that of me crying. I tried to pull myself together as best as possible.

I felt like I was sobering up from the war that had just occurred because I felt like my mind was starting to work with my body again. Have you ever gotten so messed up where you're there, then you're not, then you're like, "WTF just happened?" I have. The professionals call them blackouts. You know when your friends come tell you what YOU did the night before? Not fun at all. This war took place in our home. A place that was supposed to be the safest place in the world for our family. I had a friend show up and as heavy tears fell to the floor I just shut the house down and headed over to Dakota's house.

When I walked into my little brother's house I didn't realize how beat up or how covered in blood I truly was. Dakota just looked at me and went straight to his dresser and grabbed his gun. Before I had a chance to really think I instantly tackled him in the stairwell and started hollering for his roommates. They quickly came and were able to get the gun out of his hand. All it took was Dakota to see me, the blood, the bruises, and that was it for him. He was ready to do whatever he had to protect me.

After everything calmed down, a few friends came over and hung out with us. My feet had deep cuts and my hands were also cut up. I vividly remember taking off my wedding rings and sitting them on the counter. My diamond was chipped and it was a horrific sight. What I once thought represented love was now resting in a puddle of blood and water. As I washed my hands I tried so hard to recall exactly what happened. I felt like I was in a daze. I could only remember bits and pieces. Even though I hadn't had a drink for hours by this time I was still having a hard time remembering. Why, what and how did everything get so bad so fast?

My feet began hurting really bad and I was making a mess because the blood wasn't stopping. What the hell was wrong with me? My mind just wouldn't slow down. Everyone around me was just shocked and couldn't believe the extent of my wounds. After Dakota's roommate cleaned and dressed most of my cuts as best she could, she was finally able to get the bleeding to stop. So what did Dakota and I decide to do? We decided why not get another fifth? At that point it couldn't really get much worse. I was done and, after we drank some more, I crashed out on the bed.

Wednesday, March 11, 2015: I woke up around a quarter to eight in the morning. Damn Dakota's snoring. He was sleeping on the couch, which was close to the bed I was sleeping on. I dragged myself out of bed and stumbled into the kitchen where I found my coat and shoes. I didn't know what I was going to do, but I knew something inside of me was different. I felt like there was a burning inside of me and I didn't understand what it was. I actually walked home that morning and I am not sure how I made it. I'm pretty sure there was still a little alcohol lingering in my system. Yes, I am being sarcastic. Obviously, after three fifths of alcohol the night before there may have been more than a little alcohol left in me.

I was in so much pain that even my fingernails hurt. It was insane. When I got home everything got worse. Our home, my home was a disaster. I didn't realize until I got home how bad things truly got out of hand. The house was covered in not only blood, but broken glass and eggs. Yes, I did say eggs. See, when Ty was getting everything he wanted so he could leave I began throwing eggs at him and telling him to just leave, somehow our front door was even broken.

All of a sudden little things were coming back to me. I recall sitting on our bed and Ty calling me names. Ty said he was leaving which always set me off. I remembered my husband trying to leave and me yelling at him to get out. I remembered pushing him and screaming at him. I remembered Ty strangling me and slamming me into our entertainment center. He just kept arguing and yelling at me which, because of drinking the two fifths of alcohol, just enticed my drunk ass to yell back. Being so drunk, I just took it as if he were challenging me. At that moment I was flooded with anger because, again, Ty ran away. He always ran away when something happened that he didn't like or agree with.

I instantly grabbed my phone and started blowing that man up by texting and calling him. When Ty finally answered his phone he stated that he was never coming home and that he was far away. I figured he was in Ohio because the last time he left that was where he went. I told Ty he was a grown man and he had to stop running away every time things got bad in our marriage. I told him he needed to come home and help me clean up the mess we had made. I was cut badly and I needed his help. I told him that it wasn't fair that he left again. This wasn't all my fault and I was willing to do whatever I needed on my side to make things right. I begged him and told him I would even go back on Antabuse, (a drug that makes you extremely ill if you drink alcohol). He refused to hear me or listen, which was also normal for Ty. So after he hung up on me I just focused on cleaning the house.

I struggled as best I could to clean everything downstairs. I knew I had kids coming after school and I didn't want them to see the house like that. I could barely stand the sight of it myself. It took everything I had to scrub the blood out of the carpets. I won't try to describe the pain of every movement to you because, frankly, I'm not sure I can. After I got everything cleaned up downstairs I tried to climb the stairs to see what mess needed cleaned up there.

When I made it to the top of the stairs I just sat down and began crying. The shame and hurt was so heavy. I simply sat there trying to figure out how the hell I got to this place in my life. At that point I didn't know what a normal life felt like. Was anything really like that even possible for me, anything normal? There are several things I may not remember from that night, but what I do know is God used those events to change my life forever. I couldn't bring myself to clean any of the upstairs. "The kids were never allowed up there anyway," I thought to myself.

I continued arguing with Ty on the phone about him coming home. Then it occurred to me that our gas bill was on a payment plan and $150 of it was sitting in one of Ty's bank accounts, which my name had been put on to look better for his citizenship application. I ran up to the bank in fear that he would leave Bree and I screwed and the gas would get shut off. Ty had $256 and some change in that account and the bitch in me took everything except the change. Ty texted after a short time upset about me taking his money, but I didn't respond to him. I knew about his other bank accounts and I knew that he would be just fine. The man was far from broke even though he acted like he was all the time. Once I had gotten back from the bank I was positive that no kids would notice the complete anarchy that had occurred the night before and I finally allowed my body to rest.

I didn't realize how beaten up I truly was until that moment when I finally brought my body to complete stillness. Truth is I had bruises down my arms all the way to my elbows. It honestly felt like I had broken both of them. My knees were just as bad. I was covered in bruises and cuts all over my body. This was by far the worst fight I had ever been in. This was also the only fight that ever made such a huge impact on my life. It lifted the clouds from my mind and exposed my heart as it had never been exposed before. As I sat there in pain I knew my life was not going to be the same ever again.

I began reevaluating all the choices I had made throughout the years. I started to become aware of the fact that each time I drank heavily I was taking a piece of my armor off. One piece at a time with the more I drank. I am unprotected when I get drunk. The best way I can explain it is everyone in my family knows when I have been drinking too much just by looking at me. They all say that I change. I suppose that is why alcohol is referred to as 'spirits'.

Alcohol and drugs have a tendency to make us change. While we may think it takes something away or helps us cope, the pain is actually just burrowing further into our souls. It destroys us and everyone around us and hurts more then it helps. You can believe it or not, but we are actually provided armor in order to be the warriors we are designed to be, but when we abuse ourselves with trying to numb the pain it leaves us naked without defenses. In case you're unaware of the armor you have access to:

"Wherefore take unto you the whole armor of God that ye may be able to withstand in the evil day, and having done all, to stand. Stand therefore, having your loins girt about with truth, and having on the breastplate of righteousness; And your feet shodwith the preparation of the gospel of peace; Above all, taking the shield of faith, wherewith ye shall be able to quench all the fiery darts of the wicked. And take the helmet of salvation, and the sword of the Spirit, which is the word of God."
(Ephesians 6:13-17)

I have never in all my years attacked my man, my love, my partner. Not until I was with Ty, which was a doomed marriage from day one. I never wanted or thought that I would be with someone who could bring out the meanest and worst part of me. Have you ever been with or even around someone that brought out the worst in you? With Ty it was as if he knew when and how to make me mad and he seemed to do it on purpose.

Finding the power to say no to whatever demon you struggle with, doesn't matter what it is, is not easy. Alcohol, drugs, sex, binge eating, pills, whatever you are fighting. Saying no and overcoming the issue actually makes you stronger and it gets easier the more often you say no. I fall on my face all the time. I simply get back up and dust myself off and try again. When you get knocked down it is your choice to stay there or to pick yourself up and start over.

Every one of us suffers, hurts and keep secrets in some way and at some point. For me, I found my freedom in breaking down every wall and allowing light to shine in every corner of my soul. I am standing in front of you now exposed, fragile and broken. I'm learning that it doesn't make me weak to be exposed. Honestly, I have never felt stronger now that I am putting everything out into the light and confessing the truth right here and right now with you.

As I continued sitting in my chair I began to reflect deeply on my life and the things that had led me to this point. I knew that there was no way I could have any kids come over to the house. I was having a hard enough time bending down just to sit on the toilet. So I called and other arrangements were made for the kids I was supposed to watch that day. For the rest of the day I just laid in my recliner and tried not to move. I really couldn't if I wanted too. I also made arrangements for my daughter to stay with her friend again. There was no way I could let her come home with the entire upstairs destroyed.

That night Dakota ended up coming over and staying with me. We talked about all the events that took place the night before. I began discovering that I had bruises on my ribs, strangle marks on my neck and some of the marks on my body that were simple self-defense wounds. The only explanation was that I just got thrown around and beat like a rag doll. I remembered my husband had strangled me, but I was still not sure about my ribs. I thought it may have been the entertainment center I was tossed into.

At this time Ty was actually a corrections officer at a prison and had been through training on restraining grown men. So forgive me if I felt there was a problem with the fact that I was covered with bruises, which also included a fat lip. I was wrong for being drunk, I am not denying that. I just felt that there were many other options Ty could have made that night that would have been much better. Leaving would have been the first one, but he preferred to stay and fight while calling me a drunk and worse names I won't write here. Reflecting back on all the events that took place that night it amazed me how obvious his reaction was to me and how it went just as Ty had planned.

Thursday, March 12, 2015: I felt more lost today than yesterday. I really didn't know what I was going to do. Ty was our home's main source of income. Even though Ty had only been working as a corrections officer for eight months now, he was giving me $1,200 a month to take care of the house and our bills. I was stressed about the bills, my home, my life and my marriage. Everything was falling apart. A very dear friend came over and helped me with cleaning the upstairs, all the glass and the broken entertainment center in my bedroom. It was such a mess and it seemed like everything was broken up there.

My friend started acting like Officer Benson, from *SVU (Special Victims Unit, TV show)*, as she began documenting everything from taking pictures of all my wounds to telling me that I needed to put all the clothes covered in blood in a bag to save them if I needed evidence. I just figured Ty was gone and we had no kids together, so to me there was nothing to fight over in a divorce. He came with a few bags and a goal. He left with his bags and his goal achieved. I had no interest in getting any law involved. I honestly praise God for sending me my friend that day. She helped me more than she could ever understand by just being there. What she did upstairs with cleaning and vacuuming was beyond appreciated. The house was almost back to normal, at least in appearance. I felt like God was telling me it was time to surrender and obey because I was destroying my life and had been for a long time.

I was 100% willing to take on the responsibility for 50% of our marital problems. Truth be told, Ty isn't shy to tell you what he thinks of you and that didn't exclude me, his wife. I felt like he was always keeping a score on me. To me trying to keep a scoreboard of the good and bad in your marriage is like holding a cactus in your hand and squeezing it. The only difference is you feel the pain in your heart not your hand. You allow the scoreboard to become your focus and there is no room for forgiveness. All you seem to focus on is the bad of whoever you're keeping score on. There is no way to move forward in a marriage if you are constantly holding onto every past mistake your partner has made. Even though I had forgiven Ty many times he could never let go of any mistake I made.

Are you aware that we are actually forgiven as many times as there are drops in the ocean? I find that amazing. Yet, for most of us, forgiving is the hardest thing to do. I believe that the Lord can make things easier and that he does want to pour out his blessings upon us. We, being of this world, can continue to get stuck in this circle of bad decisions and refuse to forgive not only those around us, but we refuse to forgive ourselves. Do you ever feel like just when you think you're getting your shit together and things are going to be okay you end up falling again or being knocked down? I know that is how I felt most of my life.

It reminds me of the book, _SHE (Safe Healthy Empowered)_, written by: Rebecca St. James and Lynda Hunter Bjorklund (2004, Tyndale Publishers, INC,), where Lynda talks about a story she had once read. She goes on to write:

"I once read a story about a chicken coop that caught fire. Once the flames had been extinguished, people who were sorting through the remains found a hen with her wings spread across the nest to protect her eggs. Though the mother perished, the protection she had provided allowed her eggs to make it safely through the danger."

It goes on to explain that Jesus provides a similar love for us. I don't know about anyone else, but sometimes I felt like I may be one of the eggs that was saved by the hen. However, the people sorting through the ashes just keep stepping on the hen and cracking my shell. Most of us fight so hard to pretend like everything is okay in our life so that no one knows the truth of how we feel inside. When we do that we are only battling ourselves. I have come to realize that by exposing every dark secret I have I am no longer overtaken by addiction, darkness, sadness or confusion. Surrender has become my strength. Once I surrendered trying to control everything in my life things have finally fallen into place. I am right where I am supposed to be at the right moment, right now.

"Trust in the Lord with all thine heart,
lean not unto thine own understanding" - Proverbs 3:5

Hello, my name is Zara Banks. I am a child of God, a mother, a writer, a Warrior, a citizen of Heaven and a survivor. I am broken. I make mistakes and I am not perfect in any way, shape or form. I have many tattoos and my tongue is pierced. I am not afraid to talk about sex and, again, I cuss like a well-educated sailor. I have now been divorced three times and I am just getting started here. However, it is my belief that because of God's mercy I am forgiven, I am loved and I am never alone. I am sharing my story not for fame, not for fortune, but in prayer that my testimony can help someone else realize they are worthy and can make it through this life no matter how hard it gets. No matter how low we fall to the bottom, no matter how many times we fail, every single one of us are worthy. You are worth the fight no matter what you have been through and no matter what has happened to you. The only person that can change you, is you. I suppose the only way to understand how I have gotten to where I am today is to take you back to the beginning.

Chapter TWO

Tuesday, September 5, 1978 - 1982: I was born in Pontiac, Michigan at 9:36 am. I entered the world at eight pounds, eleven and a half ounces, 21-1/2 inches long. At the time of my birth my mother was 23 years old and my father was 59 years old and, yes, that is 36 years difference between them. My mother already had my older brother, Derek, when she had met my father. Derek was almost three years old when my mother and father married. Then, shortly after my father adopted Derek, a year later there I was.

We lived in Michigan and moved twice in my first four years of life. I remember my mother telling me once that she married my father because she honestly thought he had money. He was older and owned a real estate business. My father offered the security she wanted and needed. See my mother loved my father, but she was never in love with my father. I don't recall much of my years from birth to four years old. One of the few memories I do recall was always listening to Casey Kasem on the countdown playing on each radio in the house every single Sunday. We were always dancing around the house and singing along to the music. Unfortunately, soon after my mother and my father married, the real estate office burned down and they were at square one. So a decision to move to Florida is what began our family's journey.

1982 - 1989: At four years old my family and I moved to Florida. We lived in Florida for eight years and moved into as many as six different homes. There was one home that had a pool in the backyard and there was also a huge lake off of the back yard. My family was standing there looking at the lake and I asked about going swimming in the lake instead

19

of the pool. My father said that perhaps sometime we could do that. It was crazy because at the same time an alligator came up near the center of the lake. We all agreed that swimming in there would be a bad idea. Eventually, the alligators somehow made it into our swimming pool. Needless to say we didn't live there for very long.

I didn't enjoy elementary school very much. I was always the oddball redhead in the class. I also had a mole that my mom always tried to convince me was a "beauty mark." Good luck telling that to the kids who call you 'mole face' every single day. It seemed to get bigger as I grew older and it was located on the right lower side of my chin. Eventually, the harassment became so bad and too much for me to bare. My mother ended up taking me to have it removed.

I was always small for my age which made me a great target for the kids to bully. I found out quickly that, as a child, other kids didn't like redheads with freckles. My physical education teacher would even tease me. He called me "Howdy Doody," all the time in front of everyone and it always made the other kids laugh. I didn't understand that reference until later in life; needless to say it wasn't intended to encourage me.

A huge issue that we seemed to battle consistently for a while was the fight with lice. When we lived in Florida I ended up getting it six times within a short time frame and my mom ended up chopping all my hair off. I then had spiked hair, a flat chest and was called a boy all the time. The kids were so mean to me that they would call me names and make fun of me on a constant basis. However, outside of school, Derek was four years older and he was always my rock. Growing up having Derek as a big brother was awesome. Of course we would torment one another, but what brother and sister doesn't? Stupid things like him tying me up at the top of the stairs then rolling me down them. Or the time he pushed me off the top bunk and broke my collar bone. He asked me if I wanted to play super-girl; I realized after he pushed me off the top bunk that apparently my flying powers failed me. Don't let me mislead you because I did my fair share of tormenting too. Our father did favor me a bit. I learned that when I would write Derek's name on things he would be the one to get in trouble.

One time I carved his name into our front door. I used a stool to give me height and make sure it looked like I couldn't have done it. Derek got into huge trouble for that. Honestly, without Derek and his friends I wouldn't have even had many friends at all. Even though most of the people I considered friends were actually my brother's friends they still always allowed me to play with them in all the sports. I usually played better than most of the guys, but not Derek, though, he was always good in sports.

In the year 1984, I was six years old. My mother and father had a family friend named Joe. I remember him as a creepy, dirty, homeless guy. To this day, I am still unsure why I would run to Joe every time he came around. He would lift me up right in front of my parents, holding me normally. You know how most of us hold a child; we put our hand on the child's thigh, cup the thigh and hold the child safely up. Joe would always hold me like that; but, what you couldn't see was his fingers. He would move his hand up my inner thigh slowly so no one would notice. He would then rub on and toy with my vagina with his long, hidden fingers. It didn't matter who was standing there it was happening. No one ever noticed, nor did I say a word. My mother claims she was uncomfortable with the man. Eventually she told me not to run and let him pick me up anymore. After a short time my father asked Joe not come to our home and I never saw him again. I also never thought about what he had done to me until years later.

Let me apologize now. I realize reading an explicit event like that may be tough for some of you, however, suck it up. Honestly, there has never been an easy transition for me so I ask you to forgive me for not giving you that either. I simply pray that me baring my soul to you will, in some way, help you understand. Although we can go through HELL, our Heavenly Father walks with us. He forgives not only us, but our trespassers.

My father made sure we always made it to church. I loved the atmosphere, plus, my brother and I were in Awanas and any of the other events involving church. I asked Jesus Christ to be my Savior at a young age, but I had no clue what that meant. I only did it to make my parents proud. Plus my older brother, Derek, went often so, in my eyes, I had to also.

As I sit here pondering the past I have to admit that in my youth one of my most favorite memories are of Christmas events. Our family was very big on gathering and having large Christmas parties. I loved that time of year because either we traveled to Grandma's in Michigan or the family came to see us. Our family holidays were always the best. The adults would party and do their thing while all of us kids (mainly cousins, etc.) got to play and do our thing. I used to fight with friends about Santa Claus all the time because my mom said he was real and so did society. I wanted to believe that he was real and would defend Santa anytime anyone said he wasn't. I was dedicated.

Later in life, little did I know I would feel like a complete ass when I realized that Santa wasn't real. Just seems to me we, as a whole, get too caught up in the pressure rather than the purpose. Santa has nothing to do with why any of our children should be behaving all year long. Honestly, I don't think we should be lying to our children. I know this may offend some of you, but it is the way I feel being a parent now. I do hope you're aware of the fact that you won't always agree with me throughout this book. I am unafraid to be the spoiler: Santa Claus, Tooth Fairy, Easter Bunny, all those non-visible deities, customs, traditions, whatever you may call them; THEY ARE NOT REAL! So ask yourself, why do you convince your child/children to believe in them? Simply because of a tradition or society has made it seem like the right thing to do?

During our Christmas get-togethers and other family events I was never really uncomfortable around any of my family until 1985 when I was seven years old. One of my mother's two brothers, Carl, came to Florida to live with us. I will never forget the night my parents were having their usual poker game night with some of their friends. My brother and I always loved when they had poker nights because all the adults would play their game with coins. When they were done the adults would always throw a bunch of the change under the table for us kids to find.

Then the next morning when Derek and I would wake up we would race and dive under the table, fighting to get the most money. This evening in particular, Derek and I were hanging out and fell asleep watching movies in our parent's room. I woke up for some reason and went to my mom who was sitting at the table still playing cards. She told me to go ahead and go sleep in my bed. My Uncle Carl had gone out and partied earlier that evening, so he wasn't home until everyone was asleep.

I was sleeping soundly when all of a sudden I woke up to being touched. My Uncle Carl was rubbing on my body; caressing me as if I were a grown woman. He reeked so bad of alcohol and I realized, as he started touching himself, that he had no clothes on. At the time I was so frozen with fear I couldn't move any part of my body; I could barely breathe. I was so afraid and didn't understand why he was touching me like that. As his fingers slid in and out of me he began masturbating. After cumming he ended up rubbing some of his cum on my lips. I'll never forget when he laid still finally, breathing heavy. It was only then that I finally found the courage to speak. I told him I had to go potty and he told me to go.

I remember just climbing in bed with my parents and acting as if I just had a bad dream. I cried myself to sleep that night. I don't recall the exact moment I told my mother what had happened with my Uncle Carl; however, I did tell her about it at some point. Carl moved out soon after. I recall all of us treating it as if I really did just have a bad dream. I do not remember any of us talking about it again. My memory of that night was literally tossed into a small treasure box and locked up. The key and box were then thrown into my mind to drift separately until the day the key and the lock came together again. On the outside our family appeared to really have everything together. When I look back now we were a pretty normal middle class family: minus the crazy sexual demons being passed along for generations.

"She sits in the Wonderland of her dreams. Sipping tea in enchantedforests of her mind. Away from the pain of reality."
-R.S. D'Amico

Outside of our personal family issues my family also knew of my struggles with the bullies, but no one could really help. Finally there came a day I was just over being bullied. At age nine I got into my first fist fight. Back then it was all about who left marks. Whoever had the most marks was the loser, meaning bruises, cuts, etc. Everyone that hadn't witnessed the fight said that the other girl had won. Truth is, her nail scratched me down the side of my face which left me with the most marks. I always felt so disgusting and, of course, none of the boys liked me as a girlfriend. I felt like the black sheep and, truth is, I was treated like one. I started getting the attitude of a tomboy. Okay, honestly, I became a straight tomboy. None of the girls ever liked me, but I found that the guys would be cool with me and accept me as one of them. I believe that was just another bonus of having Derek as my brother. I was good in sports, plus I wasn't afraid to pick up lizards and hang them off of my ears. With the boys I was accepted as an equal. I only had one or two female friends that truly cared for me. Most of the other girls wanted nothing to do with me or would just make fun of me.

Growing up in Florida for eight years was fun. We went to Disney World, SeaWorld and went on all kinds of adventures. Our house was always covered with family pictures of good times we shared. I even remember the weather being fabulous most of the time while we were there. All the neighborhood kids would come over and hang out at our house. Honestly, my mom was the mom everyone else's kid called 'mom.' Many of our friends thought she was the most awesome parent and wished she was their mother. As my father got older my mother was forced to work two jobs at certain times just to make ends meet. I knew my mother was unhappy and she had been for years. She always shared things with me she never should have.

I had a great hate toward my mother for a very long time because of the way she would treat my father. She was loud and always made fun of him in front of us, their friends and whomever else. She would make fun of their sex life or shall I say, lack of. It was strange because my father would rarely say anything about it, at least never in front of us kids. My parents never fought in front of us. They would always go to their bedroom if they were arguing or disagreeing about something.

One time my mother took me to the beach with some gentleman friend of hers. Now I am sure she had several affairs and this was just one of them. She looked at me after the man left to get something and said, "How would you like a new daddy?" I told her I wouldn't leave my dad, but she could do what she wanted. My mother has told me before that I am a big reason why she never left my father. It was because I wouldn't leave with her. She asked me several times growing up if I wanted to leave with her, but my answer was always the same. See, my mother always treated me as a friend not a daughter.

My father and I, however, were always close. He was one of few men in my life that never hurt me, nor tried too. I loved, respected and honored my father. He was like the grandpa who would share all of the old awesome stories of his past. He was a great inspiration, not to mention a wonderful father to me and my brother. My dad was even my show and tell at school. I would load up his pictures from when he served in World War II and share his story with my class. With my dad being so much older he was much more laid back. He had his moments of dishing out the punishments, but I was always his baby girl. I loved bragging about his age and the fact that his father served in World War I. It didn't take long before I learned that having an older father was just more ammo for bullies. I was teased and picked on for everything and by what seemed like everyone.

Then one day my mom and dad sat Derek and I down with news of a baby on the way. It was 1986 and I was eight years old. I remember the night as if it were yesterday. I sat on my bed alone that night and debated running away, killing myself or staying for the baby. I chose to stay long enough to see the baby and then make a final decision. It was on St. Patrick's Day of 1987, when my little brother, Dakota, was born. I was always there to take care of Dakota and to this day I still am. I looked after him as if he were my own.

Dakota and I have always been extremely close. When he was born I promised him I would always be there for him and I've stuck to that. I could go to school and tolerate the haters, judgments and comments from my peers, then go home and watch cartoons with Dakota and the world was okay. I knew that no matter what he loved me so I watched out for him at all times. My mother thought she was comforting me when I would get teased and come home crying. She would say things like, "Ugly ducklings grow up to be beautiful swans." I felt like she was saying I was ugly, but when I grew up I wouldn't be. I still feel like that's what it meant. I didn't understand why she would say that and it made me feel unworthy and even more unaccepted.

In 1987 the movie 'Dirty Dancing' came out. I know this because Derek made the comment to my mother about how he could dance like Patrick Swayze and my mom took it like a challenge. Soon after Derek and I were enrolled in Arthur Murray Dance Studio. Not too much of the dirty dancing, but we learned how to ballroom dance with the best of them. I was the youngest to be in that studio during the three years we took lessons. My mother and brother loved it and so did I. We were with the studio from 1986-1988. Derek and I were involved in many competitions and won several trophies.

Thinking back to it now, my mother really did do her best with the schedule she had to work with. She actually was the one who made all of our costumes, took us to every competition, not to mention video recorded all of them. I think for my mother it was a form of escape but, for me, I loved dancing. I enjoyed when I would hear praises of how of good I danced, it made me feel special. I loved dressing up, too. It was the only time I was allowed to wear heels and makeup, at least out in public. The only negative to learning how to Foxtrot, Waltz, Swing and Cha-Cha at the age of eight is finding a partner now, that as an adult knows those same dance moves.

While growing up, we did all kinds of awesome family things. One thing I always loved and appreciated was every single night we sat down for dinner together. Dad led us in prayer and our dinner would begin. We would all share our day with each other and we listened to one another. It was something I decided I wanted to do with my children when I got older. While in Florida, we also often went to a place called Moon Lake Beach. It was the best place to go swimming when I was a kid and all of us loved it.

Although my father was older he was extremely active. He would swim with all of us kids, run and the man was always fixing or building something around the house. Unfortunately, my father suffered from extremely bad sinus infections and had his sinuses drained several times. My mother and father decided that due to my father's health issues it would be best to move again. So in 1989 we loaded up and headed to Las Cruces, New Mexico. I was 11 years old at the time.

1989 - 1992: On our way to New Mexico we had CB's in order to communicate between the two vehicles. Dakota was in my mom's vehicle and I was riding with my dad. I always sang the 'Winnie the Pooh' song to Dakota and he was throwing a fit wanting me to sing to him. My mom came over the CB and told me to go ahead and sing for Dakota. I sang the whole song and soon realized that everyone tuned into our channel on the CB could hear me. There were many compliments and truckers making requests after that. All I could do was sit there with my face as red as my hair.

Traveling was always fun with our family. We would sing and play traveling games all the time; however, my favorite thing to do was play on the CB. I loved talking to all the truckers and learning their codes. I have never been shy to talk to strangers or try new things. On one of our stops we pulled into a McDonald's and it was pouring rain. I jumped out of the vehicle without my shoes and ran into the restaurant trying to stay as dry as possible. I quickly realized something was wrong. When I looked down I was standing in a small puddle of blood. My parents ended up getting us to a hotel for the night and my mom began 'surgery' on my foot.

When I jumped out of the vehicle I slammed my foot on a piece of glass so hard that my mom had to use a razor blade and tweezers to get it out. It took her almost an hour to finally get the glass out of my foot. I don't even want to imagine what the people in that hotel thought just hearing me yelling and not knowing what was actually going on. I am honestly surprised that no one called the cops. I was screaming the entire time at the top of my lungs while in tears, "No! Stop! Hurry! Get it out!" Can you imagine walking through a hotel and hearing someone screaming those words? My entire family made fun of me for that for years.

After my mother performed the hotel surgery we enjoyed the rest of the night. I was excited about moving to New Mexico. I convinced myself it would be better than Florida and all the mean kids I had dealt with for so long. When we got to Las Cruces my parents took us to a KOA Campground and we stayed there for a couple months while my parents looked for a house. I personally loved living at the campground. I've always loved the outdoors and I still do. Plus there was a pool and, when I was younger, you couldn't keep me out of the water. On my dad's birthday, which falls on the Fourth of July, I thought I had picked out the perfect present. I found a large beach towel with a full design of the United States flag on it. I thought my father would love it and he showed a gracious gratitude for his present.

It was years later when I found that same towel unused in the top of my parent's closet. When I asked why it was never used I was told that my father and my grandfather fought for what that flag represents. How could he ever use it to lay on or wipe his body on; he couldn't. It isn't just a flag, but it represents many who have fought and those still fighting for our freedom, for our Country. I learned a powerful lesson about respect and honor that day.

While we stayed at the campground I befriended a young lady who was pregnant with twins. She worked the grounds of the campground with her family. I don't recall her name, but she was from Mexico. She was in her very early twenties and didn't speak English at all. She and I would spend hours together just trying to understand one another. I would teach her English words and she would teach me Spanish words. She was really the first friend I had in New Mexico. I appreciated her friendship and the time she spent with me.

Soon it was time for what I had been dreading and yet feeling excited about, school. I started 6th grade in a middle school where there were very few white people. As you know, I am a redhead, the whitest of white people. It's a joke, not being racist. I was wrong to assume I would be accepted and it would be different than Florida. My first month in the school was tough and I was not accepted at all.

Something exciting did occur; I won two tickets to a concert. My mother and I went to see Debbie Gibson, whom I was a big fan of. We also went to see Randy Travis and Alan Jackson, at which time I was crushing on Mr. Jackson. I knew every song and loved listening to him all the time. I will never forget when he was done with his show and he took a bow. There were two projector screens on both sides of the stage and I was drooling over him the entire time he was on stage. When he took his bow he actually took his hat off and I was in shock. I couldn't believe with all that curly blond hair he was fairly bald on top. It didn't matter to me, he was my crush for a long time. I must admit some of my favorite times were going to concerts and fairs with my family. My mom always tried to make sure we had 'girl time' without the boys too.

Our family enjoyed spending time together in those days and, although at this time we were staying in a small camper, we always seemed to make it work. I only attended the new middle school for a short time while my parents found our new home. I had to change schools and had high hopes things would get better, but I think there were less white kids at the new school. Racism was a daily battle. It doesn't' always go one way, being white and disliked happens also. I experienced my first school lockdown because of threats of a drive by shooting and within the first month I was jumped almost daily. There was one time I was in the bathroom and these four girls came in and started taunting me. I was still new to the school and didn't really know anyone at all. These girls kicked my ass pretty bad. They pushed me around the bathroom and several of them kept throwing punches that connected to my head. Once they were done they just stood over me laughing. With tears flowing I finally stood up and I just pushed my way through them. I was determined to get help and started walking toward the principal's office. One of the girls started walking quickly next to me and started begging me not to tell. She kept saying she was sorry and kept walking with me as I continued to cry. I couldn't even look at her. I did end up in the office, but I didn't turn any of them in. As I sat there thinking about it I figured it would make things worse for me if I snitched. I still continued to get jumped through sixth grade and realized it was either I learned to fight or I would never make it.

The trailer my parents found was one of the nicest in Butterfield Park. It was also the only home with a stone fence surrounding it. On the next street over my brother, Derek, made friends with one of the neighbor kids who happened to have six siblings altogether. That family had such a strong impact on my life. I am still friends with all of them to this day. Then a couple houses away there was a bunch of other kids our ages.

I feel like it was a blessing how it all occurred. Derek made friends, then I made friends and Dakota made friends. There were girls and boys that were our ages and we all got along really well. Sleepovers were awesome and so much fun. The adventures all of us had were so memorable. We would stay up all night and we were surrounded by nothing but desert, so we could do pretty much whatever we wanted. All of us kids really ended up owning that small neighborhood. Plus not far from any of our homes was an old basketball court and small park. We played what we called street b-ball. By this time Derek stood almost six feet tall and was one of the best basketball players anywhere, at least in my eyes. The first few games I sat back and watched with all of the other girls. Derek knew I had some skill and I started standing up when it was time to start picking teams.

No one would pick me at first until I got a break and Derek was one of the captains. He picked me and it was on. I hustled, playing as hard as I could. My game was so tight that day I even surprised myself. I was making shots and shocking all of the boys. That was one time in my life

I knew Derek was proud to be my brother, he was proud of me. In street b-ball there are no fouls and there were some very rough plays, but my older brother had taught me how to play. After that I was never last to be picked again. It was crazy because I was a diehard fan of Michael Jordan and Derek loved Isaiah Thomas. The year 1991, when Chicago Bulls played the Detroit Pistons, our house was insanely loud and crazy fun. My brother was so mad at the end of that game and I was on top of the world. Chicago won in case you're wondering.

Soon after we got settled my mother started working for a Christian Gospel Rescue Mission that not only had a shelter for the homeless but a large thrift store also. After a short time my mother was the manager of the thrift store. The thrift store was what I ended up considering a little piece of Heaven on earth. I was able to have first pick of all and any clothes that came in. My mom never put a cap on how many clothes I could have, which may be why I own way too many clothes to this day.

As time passed by school was getting a little better. I was still getting in fights, but I was winning them more than losing. I started to think that I was pretty bad ass actually. I didn't really start many fights at all, but fights went off around me no matter where I was, whether in the hallways or on the bus. By this time I didn't fear to throw the first punch when someone would come at me and I wasn't as worried about fitting in, but I did try to get along with everyone that I could.

I recall this one big project in school where we had to help in our community. I took the project on like I was going to change the world. We had to do the project in groups so I used my mother's pull and made arrangements for my group to serve the homeless at the shelter. I called every single newspaper and every news channel that I could get ahold of. I spoke with several people and was actually able to convince the paper to come out and do a story on the girls that were in my group and myself. We ended up on the front page of the paper that week. It was, by far, a great experience and it was before my 12th birthday.

During the Christmas break of 1990, a little over a year of being in our new home, our family made the normal trip up north to Grandma's house for the holiday. While we were there our home in New Mexico was broken into by a local gang. Upon our return we found our home destroyed. The back door couldn't be closed or locked, due to the break in. I remember my father rigged up a rope from the handle to some kind of anchor in the house in order to make the door secure.

There were spray paintings all over the inside of our home and so many of our items broken, with a lot being stolen also. The house never felt right again. Honestly, it was weeks before I could even take a shower without someone sitting outside the door talking to me. It wasn't long after that my parents moved us to another home about a mile and a half away from Butterfield Park. The distance didn't stop us from seeing our friends. Derek and I always walked back and forth to hang out with everyone in Butterfield Park. There was this long tunnel that ran under the main highway that lead to the other side where Butterfield Park was and we always walked through it.

I would always get nervous or scared when I would walk through the tunnel alone. It was known as a hangout for some of the kids in local gangs and the homeless, but I never really saw anything except the graffiti left behind. Even though we lived outside of town, we had our own little community. Where we lived, White Sands Missile Range located in New Mexico, was actually on the other side of the Organ Mountains. We lived close to the base of the mountains on the opposite side of White Sands Missile Range.

I wasn't supposed to make the walk to Butterfield without Derek being with me, but I defied my mother's orders often. She worked so much that there were little repercussions and I rarely got caught breaking the rules. So against her wishes off I would go. As soon as I would get to the tunnel, which felt like a mile long to a 12 year old, I would just stand there staring at it. During the day it wasn't as bad because you could actually look through it to see if anyone was in there, but the slightest cloud made it way too dark for comfort.

I would usually run as fast as I could to get to the other side, but I always found myself singing, *"Jesus loves me this I know, for the Bible tells me so."* I would sing the entire song the whole time I was in the tunnel. Thinking back on it now, I did that often. Whenever I had bad dreams or would get nervous about something I would sing that song in my head and comfort would come to me. No matter what I was going through or what I went through, either from my own choices or by the path God has for me, I know our Heavenly Father has never forsaken me.

Toward the end of my seventh grade school year I was a force to be reckoned with. In the beginning I was being jumped and called out for being different; white, freckles, red hair, and flat chested. By this time, to top all of that off, I had braces and glasses. I was the biggest dork in the entire school by looks, but I had overcome being ashamed of who I was. I was still harassed at school, but less often and it didn't tear me down as much. I accepted that I didn't look like the other girls.

I soon discovered there was this huge drop in one of the roads, which was located in between Butterfield and our new trailer. If you've ever driven the roads in Branson, Missouri you'd know what I mean because the road dipped like the roads do there. This road was deep, all dirt and where kids would meet for fights. Everyone called it the 'pit'. It got to a point where girls would call me out and want to fight me just to fight. So we would schedule a time to meet at 'the pit' and everyone would know about it. I thought I was training myself, (keep in mind this was right before I turned 13 years old, summer 1991), and I would have Dakota, who was four years old at the time, ride on my back. I would have him wrap his legs around my waist and hold onto my ponytail for close to a mile walk. All the girls would go for the hair first and I thought that if it didn't hurt me they would have no control of me. I thought that by having Dakota hanging onto my hair the entire way would somehow, in some way, help me when some girl grabbed my hair.

After arriving at the pit I would sit my little brother at the top with the other kids, then I would go meet the girl at the bottom of the pit. Then it was fight on. I didn't lose often, but I'm pretty sure it had nothing to do with my young ignorant idea of self-training. Fighting became a norm for me. One night when Derek and I stayed at our friends in Butterfield some of my fighting skills came out.

It was Derek and all his buddies, then there was me and one or two girls. Somehow we ended up in one of our friend's backyards and the boys had boxing gloves. Now these are the same boys I would hard foul (slam on the ground, but you don't really count it as a foul) when we played street b-ball and they weren't afraid to do the same to me. I was always just one of the guys back then. Even though I was crushing on and liking boys at a young age, I accepted that they were not interested in me. So I stepped up and challenged one of the hottest guys in the group. All the girls thought he was a hottie, including myself, but I knew we were only friends and that was good enough for me.

Once all the guys counted us in, I went full force and within less than a minute the poor guy was on the ground knocked out. It was hilarious. I earned respect with the boys as often as I could. I thought the way to do that was to be as badass as I could at all times. One time, while playing our normal game of street b-ball, my team was struggling. On the opponent's side of the basketball court I somehow stole the ball and took it all the way down the court, made the shot and it was an incredible play.

All the guys started yelling and I will never forget the look in Derek's eyes. It took all but a couple minutes until I realized that when I stole the ball I did it with my wrist. My right hand up to my elbow swelled and I could barely move my fingers. I was so pumped up that the pain didn't even bother me. Derek bragged about the shot and told me how good I did the entire way to the hospital. I don't believe I even cried as I was so proud of myself for such an awesome play. It was moments like that when I knew how much I loved being Derek's little sister. His opinion of me meant a lot to me for a long time. When he was proud of me it felt like we were best friends.

Our new trailer was in a pretty good location for being in the middle of nowhere. We did have a small horse corral next door and the neighbors were friendly. On the other side of us and in front of us there was just field. Behind us was also a lot of field but, about a half mile back, there was another trailer which was empty. At one time when I was just tired of being picked on and fighting I decided I wasn't going to go to school. So the day before school I dug up a small spot in the middle of the field behind our house. I loaded up my spot with food, blankets and everything I thought I would need for the next day. So that very next morning I woke up and acted like I was going to school. Instead I headed to my little hidden fort in the backyard. I stayed under the blankets sleeping most of the time and ended up getting away with it so I did it several more times. I thought it was awesome to break in the house while everyone was gone to do my chores. My mom would get home a little after us kids, but she would always notice how everything was already done, which made her happy yet she couldn't figure out how everything was done so fast.

My mother recalls there being snow on the ground this particular day, however, I don't remember much snow in New Mexico at all. If we had a quarter inch of snow school was usually cancelled. The day I am referring to is a day the neighbors just happened to notice me sitting up in the field behind the house. I was hidden pretty well in my small fort but, if I sat up and you were paying attention, you could see my head. When my mother got the call from our neighbors and had to drive 20 minutes from work she was so mad at me. I got busted sleeping in the field and was in a lot of trouble. I never did that again needless to say.

In 1991 my parents allowed me to go with my friend from Butterfield Park and her family to Mexico. It was an experience I will never forget. I do not and did not speak Spanish, but I do understand how to communicate with people so I never had many issues with even small talk. I loved meeting and love to meet new people. I would talk to strangers anytime, anywhere, with no fear and did from a young age. I also had the biggest crush on my friend's brother who was actually Derek's best friend. He was maybe a year or two older than me. We had all spent so much time together playing street b-ball and just hanging out that I grew a deep love for him. However, I was always kept in the friend zone when it came to the boys.

I was still the fighting, complete tomboy and none of the guys were interested in me like that. Remember the whole 'ugly duckling' thing'? I never forgot it. I always reminded myself of the time my mother had said those words to me. There was once an occasion when a guy I really liked in school asked me out. I couldn't believe it and my heart fluttered. Then less than an hour later he broke up with me and said he did it for a bet. Everyone was laughing at me. I was so embarrassed and hurt. Normally I would just hold everything in and cry by myself. After I got home that day I ran into my room and broke down into tears.

Eventually, a family with two brothers and two sisters moved into the trailer behind us. The sisters were close to my age and one of the boys were closer to Derek's age. Dakota was always a part of everything; however, during these three years he was very young and had his own little buddies. When we lived in New Mexico I loved doing everything I could outside, as I do now. The two sisters that had moved in behind us were Ivy and Ashley.

From day one I tried hard to get Ivy to like me, but she was the kind of girl that was friendly but she was tough and a bully. Ashley was a complete opposite because she acted like a Barbie doll. I became friends with both of them, but Ivy always took advantage of me and bullied me. I had a strong hate for her because she would tease me really bad on the bus, which just encouraged other kids to do the same. It felt like Ivy found it funny to taunt me and pick on me in front of our peers. I can't express how many tears that chick made me cry. She was much stronger than I was and I knew I couldn't beat her in a fight so I took her abuse.

My mother received food stamps back then. You know, the older version that were actually paper bills? I would steal a hundred dollar packet every time she would get them then head to town with Ivy, Ashley and their mom. Somehow my mother never noticed the food stamps missing. I would just go to the store and buy bulks of candy with them. I would then take the candy to school in my little brother's Teenage Mutant Ninja Turtle suitcase and sell all of it in order to flip the stamps for cash. I tried to always have some kind of money in my pocket.

Ivy, Ashley, and I also used to play what we looked at as a game when we went to the mall. All three of us girls would see who could steal the most. I am talking about stealing clothes and other items that came to amounts like $1,250.00 or more. We just sat in the parking lot comparing the stolen goods and laughing about it. I have no idea why or how we weren't ever caught.

One of the things I loved the most when I was with Ivy and Ashley was when we would sleep on their trampoline. Laying out in the open and just looking at the stars is one thing everyone should do at least once. See, Ivy was pretty cool to me when it was just us and no one was around but, if there were others near us, she would become a bully and make fun of me for whatever she could come up with.

We still attended church almost every Sunday. Derek was always real involved with the youth group, but I just couldn't get into it. I knew that there was a God, but I wasn't sure what that meant or what God could want from me. I followed Derek to church often. Now I thank God for Derek's strong influence in the younger years of my life. I don't think he even realizes how much influence his decisions made on me when we were younger. Even though I would pray and sing to God when I was afraid or felt alone, I truly had no idea what it meant to be a child of God.

It was clear that no boy liked me as a girlfriend and I convinced myself that meant I wasn't lovable. It really affected the way I looked at myself. I am not talking about love from your mom or dad, I am talking about a boyfriend or even just a guy that likes you. I was such an outcast for so long I just adjusted to it. I was struggling to survive and couldn't wait to be out on my own and grown up. I just wanted to be older and independent. I thought that would change everything. My mother has always tried telling me I have a gypsy soul, which is ironic with where my choices ended up taking me. I was always more mature and older than my age. My mother always said I should have been born when she was and she should have been born when I was. In some ways I used to think she was right, but now I realize that I am right where God meant for me to be.

So by the middle of my eighth grade year in 1991 I was pretty confident in my fighting skills. You could say that I wasn't messed with too much. I had earned and beat my way to having respect or simply being feared, I didn't really care which it was. For the first time in my life I felt like I had friends and I wasn't being picked on daily. I wasn't popular by any means, but getting through a complete week without a fight or being made fun of was huge for me. In eighth grade it actually happened many times.

Chapter THREE

1992: Eighth grade was one of my best school years thus far. Kids didn't make fun of me as often and I really had friends. The boys still acted as if they weren't attracted to me, which made me continue to question whether I would ever have a boyfriend or not. In a way I just felt left out. Most of my friends were dating and some already having sex. I was convinced that I would never be anything but the ugly duckling. As the school year came to a close Derek was getting ready to graduate and had decided to join the Navy. My parents decided it was time to move to a different state yet again. Although I was upset about the move, I was also okay with the new adventure.

After my brother left it wasn't long till I found myself saying my goodbyes to everyone we knew. The guys that had been mine and Derek's friends actually acted as if they liked me. Ironic, now that my six-foot-tall brother was out of the state, the boys began acting different. I had no idea that most of them were simply intimidated by Derek. My best friend's brother, who I had a huge crush on, ended up asking me if I wanted to be in an orgy. I felt so stupid because I had no clue what it was, so I asked him. After he explained what it was, I admit, I was hurt. I really cared for him and it just threw me completely off guard. I just didn't see him acting or being like that with me. At this time I still had no memory of anything that had happened to me as a child, but this move in the summer of 1992 was about to change everything for me, forever.

My parents decided we were going to move to Tennessee. The road trip was fun for Dakota and me, as most road trips usually were. Once we made it to Tennessee, all of us unloaded the U-Haul into a storage unit and we headed up north to Michigan in order to spend time with the family. I didn't understand why my parents made the decision to move again, let alone to Tennessee. Once we arrived in Michigan, all of the plans changed. For some reason my parents decided we were going to move to Michigan instead of Tennessee. They found a house quickly in the Thumb area. My father and some others headed to Tennessee to get our things out of the storage unit and brought our things back up north.

We moved to a small town and everyone seemed to know one another. My grandparents actually owned property that wasn't very far from our new house. During that summer it was crazy meeting distant family I had never met before. Cousins and, of course, both my mother's brothers, Carl and Frank, were around us a lot more. There was nothing like the huge bonfires and crazy parties my family had. We would all gather at my grandparents' property and pitch tents. Some of the family even had campers parked on the property. We also had family that lived at the house next to the property, which was my grandfather's (who adopted my mother at age 2) sister's house. She lived there with her husband and son, Todd, who was just a couple of years older than me.

The property had what you could call a large gazebo. The building was built with a room that had a picnic table and was set up nice for gatherings. It was screened in and had electricity running to it. I remember the family throwing so many parties that summer. I loved it because I would go back and forth from the bonfire to the keg that was kept in the gazebo and then back. I was sent to get beer refills for the adults. My cousins and I would sneak drinks in between runs and I got pretty drunk on several occasions. I was only 13 years old at this time.

I was always the first to jump when Uncle Carl was going somewhere. He would always buy me things and I could cuss around him so I thought he was cool. I knew once I was alone with him that things were off. I didn't understand why, but every time I went with him I would have thoughts like *"Just try something, I will stab you in your eyes."* I thought I could defend myself against anyone. I had no fear of anything or anyone. I didn't understand why I felt so uncomfortable around my Uncle Carl. He had never done anything to me, so I had convinced myself. He never did try anything with me when I would go with him either. He would just spoil me by not telling me no when I would ask for things at the store. I knew I was uncomfortable around him when we were alone I just didn't understand why. It didn't stop me from hanging out with him though.

The property was very large and there were trails that all of us rode the four wheelers on. There was also a stream between the house and the property where we would hunt for frogs and snakes. I thought this side of my family was crazy. They didn't usually attend our 'normal' family functions. I admit that I loved the way they lived. See, my mother raised us to have manners. We were expected to eat properly with no elbows allowed on the table, eat with our mouths shut, etc. She was also determined to teach me to carry myself as a lady. The ballroom dancing really helped me with understanding what a classy woman was and how to carry myself as one.

Everything in our home had its place. We always lived with some kind of organization. Mother always said that she wanted us to know how to eat in a 'fancy' restaurant with proper manners. She claimed she wanted us to be able to fit in wherever life took us. She also taught us to be thankful for things, even things we didn't want. If we got a Christmas present we didn't like we were required to act excited and tell the person thank you. I am very grateful that my mother raised us with those morals.

On the contrary, my other half of the family is full of straight deer hunting, beer drinking, crazy hillbillies and, yes, there are many located in Michigan. One of the many distant cousins I have was three or four years old during this time. I remember his dad would pick him up by his hair and dangle him there. The kid would just laugh at you as he hung there, dangling. We are talking the jean overalls, barefoot, kids everywhere, loud, drunk, crazy family members. I had a small crush on Todd, my non-blood related cousin. He drank with the adults and I just thought he was so cool.

After a while I did start attending a church youth group, but I just liked going because of the cute boys. I wasn't used to all the boys actually looking at me like I was pretty and not like some outcast. At one point during the summer I fell asleep and woke up with DD cups. I know it seems drastic, but my breasts grew in quick over this summer. By the time my first day of school came I was well developed and wearing a 36DD bra. I was also able to do away with my eyeglasses and I was never called 'four eyes' again. Starting my freshman year I was actually attractive, well figured and I loved the attention I was getting.

Honestly, I missed Derek more than I had ever imagined I would have. As much as we argued growing up, Derek was someone I always looked up to. He was a great big brother and when he left things changed a lot. Derek was always my mother's favorite growing up. I always felt like that was obvious. I never knew until Derek left for the Navy how much I truly relied on him as an anchor for me. He was always there for me, even when I was just the annoying little sister. I knew my brother loved me and I loved him.

On September 5th I turned 14 years old. My style at this time was what some would call a 'wigger', meaning my pants sagged down to the middle of my butt. I carried myself as a badass and decided I was never going to take shit from anyone in school ever again. I didn't have any trouble adjusting once I started school. For some reason, many of the kids were drawn to me because I was from New Mexico and very different. In my freshmen year a lot of the kids were always asking me about New Mexico because they heard I knew people in gangs and had fought my way through middle school. This made me stand out among the 'small town' kids. I wasn't shy to share my stories about the things I had went through either. My mother had always told me when we moved, "It's a fresh start. You can be anyone you want to be." She would encourage me to recreate myself. It made it very confusing since all I was trying to do was find myself.

At one point I ended up trying out for the girls' basketball team and had such a positive attitude going into it. I knew how to play some basketball and I was good at it. My brother Derek even shipped me a pair of Air Jordan's for the tryouts, which meant the world to me. I realized once I started playing with the girls I could never be a part of the team. One girl fouled me and I instantly wanted to beat the crap out of her. It wasn't even a serious foul, but I had so much anger inside of me. Tears welled in my eyes as I tried to control my temper, but I ended up walking out of the tryouts. I couldn't handle any girl pushing me in any way, even if it was just a foul playing basketball. I played with the boys, fought with the girls and I was used to it being that way. I learned a lot about self-control during my freshmen year and, to this day, I practice self-control daily. I'm still growing and still learning as each day passes.

My style and attitude were a real problem for my mom. I was starting to rebel more than ever before. I was convinced there was no one that could stop me. I began acting out and my relationship with my mother got much worse. I would break curfew and do as I wanted. There were many nights I didn't even come home or snuck out and went drinking alcohol with my friends. I did as I pleased with no remorse. Mom tried to punish me, but the punishments never stuck. I could get my mom to change her mind the next day, sometimes within a few hours after she would ground me. Due to my choices in clothing style I remember my mom always yelling at me to pull up my pants. She would tell me she wouldn't go anywhere with me if I couldn't wear my clothes properly. I didn't care what she said. I had an anger and hatred towards her that I couldn't explain. Whatever my mother told me to do you could bet I would try and do the complete opposite.

I was really enjoying being a freshman in my new school. I was even an anchor on the morning news for our entire school. My face was on the TV each morning for a little while. I had so many kids come up to me and say I reminded them of Darlene from the television show, '*Roseanne*'. I was also getting a lot of attention from boys and I liked that a lot. My mom was still working all the time which left me free to run the streets and do what I wanted without answering to anyone most of the time.

It was around this time that I met Dawn who quickly became my best friend. From the moment we met we were inseparable. Dawn was my age, but she was way more experienced with guys than I was. She was a complete opposite of me. She was pretty and already used to all of the attention from the opposite sex. She wore makeup and dressed up nice, also, which was something I was not into. To me she seemed popular and she also had an older brother. Between the two of them their house was usually always a blast. Due to my mother trying to be more of a friend to me growing up it made it very easy to manipulate her and get most anything I wanted. If she would say no about something it would take me less than five minutes to convince her to say yes. It got so easy and obvious that my friends and I eventually made bets on how long it would take me to get my way.

Now that I'm a parent I see that was one of the biggest problems with my mother, she was never consistent. If she said, "No," I knew I could get her to say "Yes" more times than not. I took advantage of that as often as I could. I suggest that you be a parent and not a friend to your children. One of the books I read when I was pregnant was, "How to Behave So Your Children Will, Too!" Written by; Sal Severe, Ph.D. (1997, Greentree Publishing; page. 96). Dr. Severe goes on to explain:

> *"If you want self-disciplined children, you need to be consistent. You need to mean what you say. You need to follow through. You can significantly improve your children's behavior by being more positive and more consistent. All parents need to be more consistent. Consistency is the most important element in your relationship with your children. It is the most important ingredient, yet it is the most frequently omitted. If you change one thing about the way you discipline your children, be more consistent."*

Another added problem my mother and I had was she shared *Every-thing* with *Everyone*. It didn't matter who you were or if I was standing next to her, she would tell you everything I ever did wrong or she would complain and share her story of how miserable she was in life. It got worse as time went on. Many times she would share extremely personal information that no stranger needed to hear. She wasn't shy to discuss her sex life, or her lack of, or anything else that would embarrass most of us, especially as children.

A big part of the problem was many of her stories weren't even the way that things had happened. It drove me crazy when she would lie and she did it often. I remember one evening when my mother and I went for a walk. I ended up asking her about an incident that occurred when we lived in New Mexico. We were supposed to go to the KOA for our Easter egg hunt as we had done in the past. My mother told me at the time the Easter egg hunt had been cancelled. I was so disappointed that I ended up calling the KOA to ask why it was cancelled. Of course, I was told the time and day it was scheduled for. It hadn't been cancelled at all and I felt like my mom was wrong for lying to me. I wasn't supposed to lie because it was bad, so why could she?

As we walked and reflected on the event that had taken place a couple years prior. I asked her why she got so upset at me back then. Truth is, she beat my ass pretty bad when I confronted her about why she lied and why we couldn't go to the Easter egg hunt. As we continued to walk she explained to me that I was the child. She claimed that I didn't have a right to call her out on lies. My mother always talked to me as a friend and just as another adult. Yet, when I would return the same intelligence, I would be treated as a child or told to act like one. It was very confusing growing up.

I believe it was almost as if she couldn't help herself when it came to lying. I decided at the young age of 14 that I didn't ever want to be known as a liar. I didn't care if I got in trouble or not. I always tried to tell the truth. Many times before that moment and in that moment I thought about how I would never treat my children like she treated me. I didn't want to be anything like my mother, especially to my children, as she was to me in my youth.

Soon after my mother and I had that talk my best friend Dawn and her brother were throwing an awesome party at their house. There was this really pretty girl there and I didn't even know her name. I happened to be standing near her when she was telling Dawn about going into the woods near the house to have sex. As she shared with Dawn that she was a virgin and nervous I looked at her and started trying to talk her out of it. I have no idea why it bothered me so much. I didn't even know this girl, but I wanted to talk her out of making a mistake.

It didn't matter what I said. It truly made no difference. She went into the woods anyway. I couldn't ever forget her face when she walked out of the dark woods, it was covered with shame. I felt so bad for the girl, but I also felt like it was her own fault. Just remember, even when we are not making the right choices God still allows us to make the choice. The night went on and we continued to drink and have a blast. It was always fun hanging out with Dawn, her brother plus all of our friends. Of course, country life in Michigan is just as Kid Rock describes in his song 'Summer Time', so much fun and many good people to enjoy the nights with.

As time went on I began to grow a complete hatred for authority alto-gether, especially my mother's. I had no problem making that very clear to anyone that would listen, including her. A few days after the party my mother called some talk show. They were trying to put together a 'teens out of control' episode. They asked to speak with me and next thing I knew I was on a phone interview. I was honest with the person on the phone and I did admit that I drank often. I explained that I was still a virgin, but I always did what I wanted regardless. I described the party and the poor girl I tried to convince not to give her virginity away. In the end the woman on the phone expressed that I wasn't exactly what they were looking for. I thought it was funny that my mom was trying to get me on some show about wild teens. I didn't think I was that bad because I always told the truth. I always felt that if anyone needed help it was my mom, not me.

When my mother would ask what I did the night before I didn't lie to her. To this day I still try to always be honest and truthful. I'm not claiming to be perfect in any way and I'm not saying I have never lied,

I just really aim to stay real and honest at all times. I am a firm believer that the truth will set you free. I have stuck by that always. Although some of my mother's stories are farfetched, my father taught me that a person is only as good as their word. That is something that I now always consider before I even begin to speak.

As school went on I started dating this good looking guy who was on the track team. He was not part of the party friends I was hanging out with and didn't even fit in with any of them. Even my best friend, Dawn, didn't like him very much, but I did. His name was Brice and he was such a gentleman. He was tall, athletic and had a smile that just took my breath away. His lips were full and I fell for him quickly. Brice was the shy type and I am a loud upfront kind of person. We pushed boundaries with one another sexually, but we were both virgins. Neither of us were really ready to have sex yet; however, we explored one another and pushed the limits. Brice was really my first true boyfriend. I believe that I did love him, at least as much as I knew how to love.

His family was always wonderful and all accepted me. Brice also had sisters that I absolutely loved spending time with. At some point in our relationship Brice's grandmother passed away. Brice took it really hard and asked me to attend the funeral with him. He made a promise to me that day that I never forgot. Brice said that no matter where we were in life when my father passed away he would come to the funeral and be there for me. He made me promise to tell him when my father did pass and I promised I would tell him.

It wasn't long after Brice and I were dating that the holidays were upon us. My family and I did all the normal things. All of us loaded up and went to Grandma's in Southern Michigan. The family all came around as they usually did. I still enjoyed the holidays even though it didn't seem to be as much fun as it used to be when I was younger.

Even with the constant war between my mother and me we tried to pretend that everything was okay during Christmas. I felt like the way my mother treated me was with jealousy and hatred. To me she never really seemed to truly care for me, at least not when I was younger; however, on the outside, she always tried to make it look like we were a happy family. The pictures in our home, the events we would attend, all of it made us appear to be some 'normal, middle class family'. But we weren't okay, we weren't normal, our family had deep, dark secrets that were kept from the outside eyes, but that was soon to change.

Chapter FOUR

1993: Soon after New Year's Eve, Brice ended up asking me to my first formal dance. It was called the Snow Ball and I was so excited about going. My mother ended up putting curlers in my hair, which once taken out made me look like Annie, the older movie with the redhead that had an Afro. It took over two hours to wash and fix it. The price and hours women pay to be beautiful sometimes is insane. I was 50/50 on the gown. Part of me was excited to dress up fancy, but the other part of me was uncomfortable. It wasn't my style to dress up fancy back in those days, yet a part of me missed dressing up. It reminded me of when I danced at Arthur Murray Dance Studio. I loved the outfits and formals that were required during our Showcases yet, now, at this time, I was portraying some bad-ass chick who wasn't afraid of anything and a formal gown was not portraying that look at all. Brice always treated me with respect and I cared for him a great deal, yet, for some reason I ended up breaking up with him soon after we had gone to the dance.

Once Brice and I were broken up it wasn't long after that I met Travis. He was so handsome and looked just like Alan Jackson to me. A young Alan Jackson that is. He was good looking with long, curly blond hair and a great personality. It didn't take long after we met that we were dating and referring to one another as boyfriend and girlfriend. I instantly thought he was my true love, which I tended to do with any new man I began to date. As I mentioned earlier, I did attend youth group; however, by this time I didn't attend weekly, I only went once in a while. I used youth group as another place to go in order to get away from my mother.

49

There was one time that my youth group decided to go on a ski trip and I was invited. I had never been skiing before so I was ready for the new adventure. Once we arrived we were all left to pretty much fend for ourselves. I really wanted to try and learn how to ski and I was determined to learn. So I geared up and ended up going on the bunny hill all by myself. I actually ended up getting stuck. I made it to the top of the hill, but trying to maneuver the skis seemed impossible for me. I sat there for what felt like hours, but it was only about 15 or 20 minutes. No one offered to help me even though I sat and cried for a moment out of complete embarrassment. I was honestly angrier at myself for not knowing what I was doing and getting stuck in the first place. I barely made it up the hill on my own so coming down was not happening. I tried everything from sliding down on my butt to trying to stand up, but I could not figure out or get used to how to control the skis.

Eventually one of the three youth pastors that had accompanied my youth group finally noticed me stuck on the hill. He came up to get me and helped me slide down. When we made it to the bottom of the hill the youth pastor asked me if I wanted a hot cocoa. I told him yes and we headed toward the lodge. As soon as we were out of anyone's sight he tried to make a move on me. I couldn't believe it, but he tried to kiss me. For some reason, throughout my life men acted drawn to me. At this time I really didn't know how to react to it. It wasn't just guys my age, either, it was grown men more than it was boys my age.

As I turned away from him I felt so disgusted. This was a youth pastor I looked up to and had gone to for answers about life, someone I was supposed to be able to count on, but I accepted that was only an illusion. I spent the rest of the trip in the ski lodge talking to my boyfriend, Travis, on the phone. I told him everything that happened and he decided to stay on the phone with me until it was time to go home. I just kept feeding quarters to that pay phone in the ski lodge the entire time I was there. Once home from that trip I never went back to that church again, nor have I ever been skiing again.

Within a few days after returning from the ski trip I found myself at Travis' house. We had skipped school together and his parents were at work so Travis and I had the house to ourselves. Somehow we ended up in their bedroom making out in their bed. It ended up being the first time I ever had sex, which is something you never forget. My mind was like Allie from 'The Notebook' written by Nicholas Sparks. I didn't talk as much, but I kept thinking about a million things. I recall thinking about the fact that it was nothing like the movies made it look. It hurt and there was no passion involved at all. It was uncomfortable, and I remember feeling dirty the entire time. My boyfriend was slow and tried to be gentle, but the whole thing was just awkward for me. Travis talked to me and he tried to be as easy with me as possible. After the initial penetration it didn't hurt so much, however, the love between Travis and I was nothing compared to 'Noah and Allie'. Actually, Travis and I broke up soon after.

It wasn't long after Travis and I broke up that my mother and father ended up moving us again. This time the new house was only a block away from our old one so we didn't have to change schools. Now this house was really huge, but there was something off with it. My room was in its own separate part of the house that was a built-on addition. At night it scared the crap out of me a few times because, as soon as I would close my bedroom door, all I could hear was people walking around in the hallway and talking. It was almost as if a small party was going on right outside of my bedroom.

The first few nights I thought Dakota was messing with me, so the first few times I heard the noise I just opened my door real quick in order to bust him. No one was ever there. It was extremely creepy and made no sense to me. The so-called party happened all the time at night. As soon as my door shut the talking and walking in the hallway would start. I got used to the noise, but I never got used to realizing there was no explanation for it. Almost every friend I ever had stay the night at my house would hear it and freak out. I never saw anything, but if you were to ever stay the night in that house I am sure you would experience something similar.

51

Now my father was 73 years old at this time and he wasn't able to do very much. Physically he was there, but his memory was slipping away. One thing I loved doing with my dad was playing "Bitch" Rummy. We would play for hours. I always seen my father as very wise and I loved all of his stories about his life. It was amazing to me some of the things he experienced in his lifetime. He was also a very firm believer in Jesus Christ. I can honestly say that I don't think I ever heard my father even say a cuss word while I was in his presence. My father used words that didn't make any sense. He would say things such as, "Dag-nab it" and "dag-comet." I talked to my father often about everything. He always talked to me about believing in the Bible, in God's word, and he encouraged me to always search for understanding. I was taught that only when we seek truth does God then provide it. I believe there is nothing wrong with sharing the word, however, when you try to force God on others then you are stepping out of the purpose God intended by sending his son to give us choice.

Although I did listen and respect my father, I knew I had the right to make my own decisions. I chose to behave as one that partied and did what I wanted, right or wrong choices. My mom was acting like she didn't understand why I wasn't her idea of a normal teen. I felt like it was too late for her to try to be a mother to me. She raised me as her friend and to be independent and strong, which at times made me feel alone and weak. Mom wanted and needed me home all the time to watch Dakota and my dad, but I had no interest in helping her. I was actually getting to a point that I wasn't afraid to stand up against her. I refused, rebelled and had no respect for her. I came and went as I pleased at all hours and I truly became unreliable for my family. If I was told I couldn't do something, I would just sneak out and do it anyway. I didn't want to help my mother in any way because, at that time, I felt like I hated her and she hated me. In my eyes she was an evil enemy who was constantly trying to pull me down. I thought anywhere she wasn't, was better than where she was.

As time went by, I was getting pretty wild and could care less about the risks I took. I recall this guy who was in his early twenties that used to hang out at our school all the time. He had a Kawasaki Ninja and loved hitting on all of the younger girls. I, of course, ended up falling into his trap of flirtation. I met up with him a few times and we would ride his bike out to his place and have sex. He wasn't someone I even cared for, but I loved the bike rides. The freedom I felt from the wind blowing through my hair was indescribable. It was then that I fell in love with motorcycles and riding them. I have no idea how, but that guy was somehow even able to get into our school dances. It was crazy because I ended up in a 'dance off' with him at one of our school dances and I won. It really pissed that guy off and we didn't hang out much after that. I thought it was pretty funny at the time.

My mother really didn't know half the things I was doing. Truth is, my mother went through a lot in her life and has had sexual demons attached to her since she was a young child. Due to her trying to make me her friend and not her daughter I was beyond in my years and thought I knew everything I needed to be on my own. I couldn't understand my mom's anger when I would come home and she would ask me what I was doing and where I had been. I was always honest with her when she would actually ask. I was beyond determined not to lie because she always did. Of course, when my mother would ask, "Where were you all night?" at 14 years old I would reply with stories about getting drunk and partying all night. I didn't care if she was upset. I felt like I wasn't lying so it shouldn't matter.

In all reality I was just begging for someone to care enough to help me. So when she would get upset I would just laugh behind her back. She beat my ass several times, trust me. I believe that my mother just wanted and needed as much help as I did. She was, and perhaps is, just as lost as most of us tend to feel at certain points throughout this life. When we feel lost it is very real and can drag you through some dark places. Whatever it is that you choose, don't choose to remain in the darkness. Seek God and Jesus Christ, read self-help books, get counseling, anything but choosing to surrender and staying in that darkness. Alone you are not and there are so many others that can provide you with options to help. It starts with your decision to help yourself.

As time went on I continued to grow in anger and headed down a self-destructive path. Getting high and drinking was becoming a daily thing for me. I would stash beer in between my mattresses wake up and drink as much as I could before school. I drank so much that it didn't even matter what it was as long as it contained alcohol. I also started getting into a lot more trouble at school. I'll never forget this one time when I had drank vodka before going to school and the teacher smelled the alcohol on me. I had always gotten away with it before, so the fact that someone finally caught on didn't even bother me.

I was placed in a small room until my mother came to get me. I thought it was hilarious when the teacher opened the door to let me out. He said, "I could get intoxicated just by standing in this room." I didn't think it smelled that strong but, thinking back now, I'm sure it did. I easily got bored in school. Most of the work wasn't challenging to me at all and I was giving up. I didn't care about anything, especially myself. The only two people in the world that meant anything to me was my father and Dakota. I always made sure to tell both of them I loved them whenever I had the chance. Yet, I didn't realize how much I was hurting them also.

It was about this time that my mother put me into counseling. I found counseling interesting and, at first, it was just some counselor my mother had picked out of the phone book. Throughout a short time I went through addiction counseling, three group therapies and several individual counselors. I always felt like I was smarter than the counselors because I could get them to spend over half our time together talking about themselves. I thought I was some great manipulator because I was able to ask all the right questions or answer a question in a way to change any subject the counselor tried to touch on. I felt that the problem was my mother and she should have been the one sitting there, not me.

I found it funny that my mother felt like they didn't know what they were doing because almost every counselor would suggest that it was a family issue and not just me. When they would suggest family counseling she would change me to another counselor or to a group. It truly made my mom angry because she felt something was wrong with me alone. Truth is, I was so young and my mother would try to convince the counselors that I was this horrible child. Now that I had been having sex, that was the first thing my mother would talk to people about. And not just with counselors, either. We could be standing in a grocery store and she would share everything I ever did with anyone that would listen. She didn't care if I was standing there or not. I can't describe how much I resented that woman then. My mother would tell you about when I lost my virginity or stayed out all night, and it didn't matter if we were standing in the produce aisle at Walmart.

What was crazy is you could be a complete stranger and she would just start sharing these things. It was almost as if she wanted attention because I was acting out. It only got worse when a psychiatrist moved in next door. From the moment I was born I think my mom resented me. When I started developing and becoming a young lady my mother's resentment only got worse. It was as if she was jealous of me. In all truth, she has never faced any of the horrific abuse she herself had experienced and was exposed to.

It wasn't long until I actually had one counselor who was coming to my house to spend time with me there. She would take me out and we would go eat or just go for a walk in the park. One random day we were sitting in McDonald's and she asked me if I had ever been touched. I answered quickly, as I had so many times in the past, "NO!" I was shoving a bunch of french fries in my mouth when the counselor mentioned that my mother had told her something about my uncle touching me when I was younger.

In that very instant everything flooded my mind. The key found its way to the treasure box and it was opened right there in that moment. I remembered everything Joe and Carl had done to me. The smells, the touching, the way I felt scared; Everything. After that day the nightmares began to haunt me badly and my anger toward my mother was raging inside of me because a part of me blamed her. Sexually active doesn't even begin to describe how bad my acting out became. I was running to sex, embracing it, not ashamed at all of having sex. I even started to keep a list of the guys I was sleeping with in order to keep a count.

Getting guys to have sex with me was easy because I wasn't shy at all, but I was such a lost young lady. By the time summer came I was hanging out with some real bad boys all the time. Several of the guys I hung out with wanted to have sex with me, but I didn't have sex with most of them because they were friends. Dawn and I still hung out a lot, but she was a bit more active than I was with the guys we hung out with. As in middle school, I was just one of the guys to them; but, the difference was I chose to keep them in the friend zone not the other way around. I found other guys without any problem. I wasn't scared to pick up a stranger and take him somewhere to have sex. I think Dawn was hoping for love while I was just having sex.

Dawn and I were very close and we did everything together most of the time. I don't recall there being many dull moments when it came to us. We lived over three miles away from one another, but we would walk the distance almost every day. We both enjoyed walking all over town and, I think in part, we both enjoyed the attention we got when we walked. Honking and guys hooting and hollering at us happened all the time. I loved getting the attention. The attention somehow made me feel good about myself. I was always seeking acceptance and attention from those around me rather than realizing I was created with worth. Loving and accepting yourself is hard to do.

I had one friend that was a beautiful young Mexican girl. She remains a friend to this day. One day I went with her and some of her family to work in the fields picking cucumbers. I couldn't even last an entire day. I left at lunch because work wasn't something that interested me at all and picking cucumbers really isn't as easy as it may seem. It was a very physical job and I had no interest in it. This same friend also had a huge family. Most of them lived with or near one another. My friend's father had recently been released from prison, which I just found intriguing for some reason. I spent the night there several times, but there was a point when it was just too much for me to handle.

Her brother, who lived next door with his wife and child, would sneak into my friend's window once my friend was asleep. He and I would have sex right next to my friend and she never woke up. I actually had my first orgasm with him. The crazy thing is I was also having sex with her father. Although I enjoyed sex, I had no clue how to say no when a man came on strong; I would just give in and let him do what he wanted with my body. It became awkward when we were in their van going somewhere and her father would sneak little winks at me when no one was looking. Then her brother would look back when no one was looking and do the same thing. It was insane and uncomfortable to be in the same room with both of them. Eventually I stopped staying the night there all together.

Sometime during the same summer I ended up hanging out and drinking with my non-blood-related cousin Todd. Yes, I even had sex with him. I was having sex like sex was all I was created for. The first time may have been uncomfortable and hurt, but by this time I was enjoying it and fully addicted. I had a serious problem with saying no - I couldn't. I spent most of the summer very intoxicated or high and having sex. I don't even remember some of the men or boys that I had sex with during this time. To be honest, there are several events that occurred during this time that I don't remember at all.

One of my friends that hung out with all of us was a dealer and ended up pressuring me into having sex with him. I wanted a bag of pot (marijuana) and he wanted sex, so I went along with what he asked of me which was a trade - Weed for sex. We were never the same as friends after that. I felt so ashamed of myself. I also received my first tattoo at 14 years old. I was laying on top of a friend's kitchen table and it was extremely painful. My first tattoo was on my tummy and, although it hurt, I grew a complete love for the artwork.

In September I turned 15 years old and was now a sophomore in high school. My mother was at her wits end with me and me with her. We clashed about everything and there was nothing healthy about our relationship. Soon after school started my mother told me she wanted to take me somewhere for a surprise. Her and I got into the car and drove for almost two hours. She refused the entire time to tell me where she was taking me, but just kept encouraging me that it was somewhere fun that I would enjoy.

No matter how hard I tried talking her into telling me where we were headed she continued to refuse to divulge the location to me. We drove all the way to St. John's and we pulled into a psychiatric hospital. When we arrived, she pulled a suitcase that was already packed with my clothes out of the trunk. I can't even begin to express the thoughts I had about my mother at that moment. We went in and I was given an in-depth evaluation. After a few hours the results determined that I needed counseling but I wasn't qualified for in-treatment. I'll never forget how mad my mother was. She was so pissed that they wouldn't keep me.

She went off on the counselors and the doctor. She yelled at them because, when she had called and set the meeting up, someone told her over the phone they would keep me. I kept thinking that they should take note that she was the one needing to be kept there. She was so loud that, even though I was in the other room, I could hear everything she was saying. When we left my mother acted like nothing had happened and just talked as if we hadn't just went through all of that. She did that a lot. She could go crazy, yelling and hitting you, then, five minutes later, she was fine and it was like nothing ever happened. I learned it was better to just go along with it rather than argue with her.

After the incident at the psychiatric hospital I was over being around my mother completely. I was continually haunted by the nightmares and thoughts of what my uncle and Joe had done to me. They were consuming me. It became torturous and I couldn't sleep well without drinking or getting high. Since the psychiatric hospital wouldn't keep me, my mother eventually ended up taking me to a place in Northern Michigan; a home designed for runaways. Once we arrived I agreed to stay there. I ended up making friends with one of the girls that was actually from the town where we were staying. We made this elaborate plan to escape and 'run away from the runaway home'. We just thought it would be funny. After the last bed check, we climbed out of the window and disappeared into the night. We ended up going to a friend of hers that lived close. There were four adult men, my new female friend and myself.

That night was filled with a lot of drinking and smoking pot. There was also cocaine available; but, at that point in time, I was afraid of doing heavy drugs. I loved to party and get drunk, even high on marijuana, but when it came to anything else I always said no. I saw many of my friends trip on acid and do all kinds of other drugs that just brought about stupid things. I was honestly afraid of liking the drug too much. I had been in enough counseling to be aware of my addictive personality. At least that was what the counselors told me I had.

In the early hours of the morning, as I was sleeping in a chair in the living room, one of the guys started touching me. I woke up quickly. As I kicked him with my steel-toed boots, I called him out for putting his hands on me. I was so loud that I woke everyone in the house up. The guy just kept apologizing and saying that he didn't mean to offend me. The next day I ended up calling a friend and we made arrangements for his mom to come pick me up. I stayed with him and his mother for a few days before finally going home. When I got home my mother had a garage sale set up with everything I owned. My entire room was sitting in her garage for sale. She emptied everything from my clothes to jewelry, even teddy bears I had had as a child. This was toward the end October.

The cops were involved in my life now that I had broken out and ran away from the runaway home. I had to go to court and I was placed on probation. My probation officer asked me if I wanted to go home and I said, "No." I was then placed in my first foster home. I started a new high school and tried to start a new life in a completely different town in the Thumb of Michigan.

My first foster mother was a sweet older woman who took very good care of herself. She was really big into the Catholic religion and tried to help me face the battles that I had been going through. This was the first woman that actually sat and listened to me. The nightmares of what happened to me as a child haunted me every single night. I couldn't get rid of the tormenting visuals in my head. It wasn't so much of what Joe had done, but the nightmares of being in my bedroom, my Uncle's finger inside of me and the shame that haunted me. My foster mother actually comforted me and even convinced me to turn my Uncle Carl into the police.

When we went to the police station I made a report, but nothing happened after that. I don't know if that had to do with my mother covering for her brother or not. Now that I am older I wonder if my mom told the police that I was a liar and all the usual things she tried to tell anyone who would listen. Perhaps that is why nothing was ever done with my report. Many years later I found out that during the year of 1991 my Uncle Carl's daughter was taking him to court for rape. It is my understanding she had the dates wrong and our family had pulled together to protect Carl. My cousin was only 12 years old when this was going on. With the dramatic events that she claims happened to her it is no wonder that remembering the specific dates was difficult. My cousin had no one to stand up for her as the events that occurred were at my grandparents' home which is where Carl lived at the time. Our family chose to protect Carl. In the end it is my understanding that, due to our family's testimony, he was found not guilty.

I had no idea about the horrible things Carl had done to his own daughter until I began writing this book and I finally contacted my cousin. Come to find out, she had felt as alone as I did all because our family, which was supposed to protect and support us, chose to hide their dirty secrets. Although I didn't have my aunt next to me, I can't express how thankful I am that my cousin did. She was the only aunt we had and she was always so loving. Our aunt was the only person in our family that believed in the truth of what happened to us. My cousin and I were the only girls in our family that were consistently around growing up. What is sad is every woman in my family has been attacked by sexual demons that have haunted our family for many generations.

It has taken a lot of forgiving my mother when it comes to this because a part of me feels like, had she allowed me to have a voice when Carl did what he did to me, perhaps it would have never happened to my cousin. Although we can't change our past we can give support and love to one another now. My cousin struggles daily and now suffers from Bipolar disorder, Multiple Personality disorder, Night Terrors and many other health issues. That, however, is her story to tell not mine. Even though the years separated us the Lord has brought us back together and I encourage her to know that she is not a victim, she is a survivor.

After filing the report at the police station with my foster mother by my side I ended up calling my grandmother. I just needed someone, anyone, to stand up with me, for me. After I told my grandmother what I had done at the police station she told me she wished I was dead. She called me a liar and just tore me down. I sat on the phone listening, crying and believing I was completely alone in this world. I was so hurt and the words my grandmother said to me that day tore me apart. It all made me come to this crazy conclusion that all I had was myself. I knew my mother hated me, but now my grandmother hated me too. It blows my mind now to think about the fact that these women hid the truth. They tore down the only two girls in their family when they should have been lifting us up. They should have been lifting us up for being honest. My mother and grandmother were more concerned about what others would think when the truth came out about the abuse that was in our family.

Honestly, I loved being in my first foster home. I enjoyed the other girls and got along with most of them. My foster mom spent time with me talking about God and reassuring me that everything would work out. She even nicknamed me Charlie. She said I reminded her of one of the Charlie's Angels. I have no idea which one, but I liked the name change and even went by it at my new school.

Unfortunately, my first foster mom's biological son and I had a serious personality clash. We couldn't get along at all so, after a couple of months, I had to be moved to another home and another school. I cried because I really loved the support from my first foster mom and I didn't really want to leave; however, there was no other way nor any other choice for me. I was then placed with another family who was located in another small town in the Thumb of Michigan. It was a very small town and the kids were very accepting. I couldn't believe how everyone would say hello to me even though they didn't know who I was. This town still has that kind of hospitality. I loved the high school I attended and the foster family was okay, at first.

My foster dad and foster mom argued a lot in front of us. It was a lot easier to deal with because I loved having my new foster sister. We connected quickly and it was nice to have a girl close to my age to talk to. She was only a year or two older than me and we had a lot in common. My foster sister had a boyfriend. They seemed to fight on and off but, for the most part, it appeared like normal teenage couple arguments. One night when my foster sister and her boyfriend got into one of their normal fights everything changed.

My foster sister's boyfriend ended up going back to his home for the night. It was there that he shot and killed himself. It was horrific and my foster sister blamed herself. The entire school felt and mourned the loss of him. I was told later that my foster sister ended up losing it and taking a shotgun to the school. I wasn't there that day. I had an appointment with my mother, so I was absent when it happened. No one was hurt, but it was scary and the school was shaken. Truth is, I never did see my foster sister again after that.

The holidays came quickly and, before I knew it, we were bringing in the start of 1994.

Chapter FIVE

1994: The kids at my new high school were awesome and I fit in well. It was a town that had people who didn't judge you and they embraced friendship. You can tell when you're in a town where the parents raise their children with morals. This is the kind of town if a random kid picks on a handicapped kid then that random kid better watch out because that handicapped kid will have backup whether they know it or not. I loved going to school there even if it was only for a short time. Honestly, it was and is one of my most favorite high schools that I attended.

Even though I was sneaking out and smoking pot with the stoners behind the trees near our school, I still fit in with each group. When I was a kid it was just the stoners, jocks, nerds and the preps. I'll never forget this one guy that needed a date for the Junior/Senior Prom and he ended up asking me to go with him as a friend. I agreed to go only as friends and I thought it might be fun. We ended up hanging out at the house of one of his friends that was in a different town the night of the Prom. His friend was a very fine young man.

I wasn't interested in the guy I went to the dance with. I was very point blank about that when I agreed to go with him. His friend, however, was fair game and I was all about that boy. He was my age, but he went to a different school than we did which was the kind of guys I liked. Back then I always liked the boys that I wouldn't run into again after having sex. He was just another one for my list. Even though the guy I went to the prom with was only a friend, I know and understand now that I had to have really hurt that guy by having sex with his friend. I can only ask for forgiveness now. It was done and

63

none of us can change the past even if we wish we could.

My foster parents continued to fight a lot in front of me. It was mainly my foster dad accusing my foster mom of cheating on him. It wasn't a healthy home for anyone, not even the foster parents. Not long after Prom night I came home from school to find the driveway full of cops. With everything that had already occurred with my foster sister, I knew there was no telling what was going on. When I walked in the house my counselor at the time was there. The same counselor that now lived next door to my mother, which was no help. I was told to pack my things up quickly. Come to find out, my foster dad tried to kill my foster mom by chasing her around with a butcher knife.

I was then taken to a temporary foster home where there was a very sweet older couple. It took me some time to get used to moving around so much, but I adjusted. I continued to look at each move as a new adventure, even a new start. It wasn't long and school was finally out for the summer. I was then placed with a strange couple who had two other foster girls. The foster mom was really large and we girls were there to simply clean her house and cook all the time. When I say large, I mean that her thigh was about three times the size of my head. The foster mom was very obese and very mean. She is the only woman who ever threw ice water on me to wake me up in order to clean.

The younger foster girl and I shared a room and she was so sweet. The couple was actually in the process of adopting her. We both became very close friends. The husband was just a strange submissive guy who sat back and watched everything and everyone. It was a bit creepy in all honesty. While I was staying there someone in their family was getting married in Branson, Missouri, and I was allowed to go with them. It was a great trip with the beauty of the area and hilly roads. It would simply amaze you if you haven't been there yet. Ironically, the depth of the roads reminded me of living in New Mexico. It took me back to the 'pit' where I used to meet to fight. There were all kinds of tourist attractions there and we did end up going to a drive-thru zoo. The animals would walk right up to your vehicle and you could throw food out if you wanted. That was a lot of fun. What truly amazed me was how nice my foster mom was around all of that family yet, back at home, her demons ran the show. Evil disguises itself well and in many forms when it wants to.

My opinion of my older foster sister was pretty negative. She was very rude. Truth be told, I thought she was a bitch. I now realize she had her own battles she was dealing with. She was dating this really large guy and one time they had sex in the swimming pool while I was swimming. I had no respect for her in any way; however, since all of us girls shared the same hate for our foster mom, we had a connection that no one else could touch.

My younger foster sister was about three years younger than me and knew that I wanted to get out of there. I continued to constantly beg my probation officer and counselor to get me away from that foster mom. My younger foster sister tried begging me to stay with her, but all I felt was hate from my foster mom daily. The day I left was sad because I knew that I would never see my little foster sister again. I still have the letter that she wrote me the day I left. It was so sweet and she tried begging me not to leave her. My probation officer ended up having me move back into the temporary home with the sweet older couple I had been with previously.

My mother had visitation of me at this time and I was able to go to her house on weekends. On one visit my mother and I somehow ended up in a town I had not been to yet, but it was still located in the Thumb of Michigan. We ended up at a small pizza joint. That place not only had the best Willy bread and waffle fries, but that's also where I met Brandon. The moment we saw one another we had a connection that would last a lifetime. We talked and played pool together all while both flirting with one another. He was a logger and worked with his family in the woods. Brandon lived in what looked like a box. It was one of the smallest houses I've ever been in. I know because the next day I ended up borrowing my mother's car and picking Brandon up.

As we continued to talk and get to know one another we discovered that the both of us were keeping count on how many people we had had sex with. We both kept a list and found it funny that we were both number 19 on each of our lists. Brandon became a strong shoulder to lean on for me during some of the roughest times in my life. He also had an older half-brother named Cory that I got along with. After my weekend visit was over, I ended up back at my foster home. After that, every visit that was supposed to be at my mom's house was spent with Brandon. I loved visiting with Brandon, but I had to return back to my foster home at the end of each weekend visit.

The one thing that bothered me most about each of the foster homes I lived in was the fact they would take me to all of my counseling meetings, but getting to an orthodontist seemed impossible. I still had my braces on, but my foster parents weren't getting me in for checkups. By this time I had been moved around five times in less than a year. I ended up having a piece of wire on my braces that started poking me pretty bad in the back of my mouth and it kept making my mouth bleed. I ended up just getting so frustrated I took a pair of nail clippers and removed all of my braces myself. I will never forget how angry my mother was but, again, I didn't care how she felt.

I was becoming miserable in the foster system and being moved around so much was ridiculous. I knew home was not an option with the way my mother and I were. One of the times I was on a weekend visit at my mother's house my Uncle Frank came around. He was going through a divorce and asked me if I wanted to come hang out for a weekend. I have no idea why I said yes or why my mother actually went through my probation officer to get permission for the visit. My mother only has two brothers and one sister. I was close to my aunt in my youth, but she disappeared to Florida after 1991. Come to find out it was because, when she stood by my cousin during the rape trial, she was actually cut off from the entire family for almost two years. Blackballed, if you will. Even though I hadn't hung out with my Uncle Frank much I was excited about going for the visit.

My Uncle Frank wanted me to be really excited and said we would do something really fun. I was thinking go-carts or something like that, something I hadn't done in a while. When the weekend came my Uncle Frank picked me up and off to Southern Michigan we went. When we arrived in the city my Uncle Frank took me straight to a liquor store and asked me what I wanted. With me being 15 years old I didn't hesitate to put my request in. The only thing he said was that I couldn't tell my mom about it. The events that occurred over the next eight months took me years to overcome.

"You cannot have victory without conflict." -T.D. Jakes

As soon as I finished off my liquor bottle I laid down on the couch to crash. As I was just about to fall asleep I started to feel my legs being touched. Next thing I knew, all of a sudden my Uncle Frank picked me up and carried me into his bedroom. We had sex. As I had done many times before with others, I just closed my eyes and allowed it. I didn't say no to him when I knew I should have. When I woke up the next day I left his bedroom and laid very still on his couch. I felt so disgusted at myself, but I was angrier at him.

I was shaking and too scared to speak much at all. He came out of his bedroom and sat across from me. He began to tell me about how much he enjoyed me. I could feel my stomach turning as he continued to talk. He began offering to help me get out of the foster care system and to take care of me. My Uncle Frank asked me not to tell anyone and I reassured him that I wouldn't. He also told me to take a few days to think about his offer of 'helping me' and to let him know as soon as I decided. I explained that I better get back because mom would be worried, but he laughed at that. He said I didn't have to be afraid and, after some time had passed, he ended up taking me back up north.

I was still staying with the sweet older couple that I had grown close to and eventually called mom and dad. Even on weekends I was staying at my mother's it wasn't rare for me to stop by my foster home and see both of them. One day, when I had Dakota with me, I went to get something from my foster home. My foster dad was in the garage doing something as he usually was. I asked Dakota to just wait in the car while I ran in because I was only going to grab something real quick. I went in the garage to talk to the man I called dad. I don't know what came over him, but he ended up grabbing me and shoving his tongue in my mouth. For some reason it was as if I had some sexual aura surrounding me that men couldn't control themselves around me. I began thinking something was seriously wrong with me. I didn't even know what to say to him. I just walked out crying and never returned. Dakota kept asking me what was wrong, but I just couldn't bring myself to tell him.

After thinking about what Frank said I ended up calling him and telling him I wanted to go there. So Frank and I set up this plan for me to run away while I was with him. We took it so far as to make sure I was caught on a camera at the gas station when I supposedly ran away from him so there was evidence if needed. The truth is I walked away from the gas station and Frank drove down the road where I was and picked me up. This was at the end of August. Frank truly had an elaborate plan.

I spent the next three weeks at Frank's friend's house hiding in their bomb shelter. That was how I celebrated my 16th birthday, in a bomb shelter. After three weeks I called my mother and had her meet me at Frank's house. We convinced my mother that I had been staying out of state and had just got back into town. I told her I wanted to live with Frank and that I was going to get a job in order to take care of myself. I begged her to get me out of the foster system and she didn't really argue with me at all. She ended up signing power of attorney of me over to Frank. It was then that I began living with my uncle as if I was his wife.

It didn't take long for the true colors of Frank to come out. He was very controlling and I realized quickly that I was to keep the house clean. Crazy things like we both smoked cigarettes and if he would come home from work with an ash in the ashtray he would hit me. I wasn't allowed to talk to anyone unless he approved. He was continually coming up with reasons to beat on me. I was so lost and hated life so much. After years of praying to be attractive and accepted by others I really began hating being attractive. I did get a job and worked hard to take care of myself. I set everything up to get my license even though I had already been driving everywhere on my own. I even drove to meet up with my driver's training teacher, illegally of course. All I did was jump from my car to his, handed him cash, we went for a ride and I was approved for my license. I was making money working as a hostess and Frank was a mechanic.

I never reached out to my mother nor did I tell her what was going on. I knew she hated me and blamed me for everything. I convinced myself that there was no point in reaching out to her. On rare occasions Frank and I would still go around our family and just behave as if everything was normal. At least what should have been a normal uncle and niece relationship. I was affectionate to Frank, but only in the privacy of his home. Truth is, I was young and the power he had over me was extremely scary. Frank would tell me to do something and I would jump. I was so afraid of him that I didn't question him. I was his housekeeper, sex slave and punching bag. I was missing Dakota so much and didn't get to see him as often as I had before.

I promised Dakota I would always have his back and I did. On one occasion when I did get a chance to go see him this older boy had been picking on him pretty bad. They were play fighting in the backyard and this 13 year old started really hurting Dakota, who was only eight years old at the time. From my brother's memory of this event our mother had went to the kid's house and got cussed out by the kid's mother. So my mother told Dakota to come get me. For some reason my mother always left me to handle the things she couldn't. I always tried to handle things as they were my responsibility, especially when it came to Dakota.

When Dakota came to get me he explained everything that had happened with the bully. I made him instantly jump in my car and I drove around until we found the kid riding around on his bicycle. I ended up driving my car into someone's yard in order to pin the boy's bicycle in between my car and a tree. The kid did jump off his bike in time so he wasn't hurt, but I grabbed him by the neck and shoved him against the tree. I didn't beat him, but I did make him sincerely apologize to Dakota and then I let him go. After that Dakota wasn't picked on often in school. In a small town events like that tend to spread around quickly.

Due to all the events I had endured I was changed, including the way I dressed. My style had changed a lot and my clothes weren't sagging off my butt anymore. I still wore really baggy clothes even though I was built for spandex. I was uncomfortable with my body and myself. When you live with a man beating you, you feel like a prisoner. Your entire being is stripped away and you conform to do what helps keep you from the next beating. At least you try, but the next beating always comes sooner or later. One thing that usually would happen is Frank would always give me gifts after he would beat and bruise me. One time he bought me tickets to a Boyz II Men, BabyFace and Tevin Campbell concert. It was December 29, 1994 at the Auburn Hills Palace. I loved every one of the entertainer's music and was so excited. Frank permitted me to go with his neighbor's wife. I didn't care who I went with, I was just happy I was going.

It was such a great concert and I really enjoyed the time away from the house. I cried when Baby Face was on stage because he brought someone from the audience up there. As he sang his song he kept placing money in the girl's hand. I remember thinking I would have given anything to be that girl. Boyz II Men were incredible also. They had a walkway set up above the stage and they were walking above the audience at times. I loved the concert and was so thankful to go. I think that it made Frank mad when I got home because I was in such a good mood. Even though he purchased the tickets as an apology for beating me for some reason he was still upset that I went. There was no pleasing him.

Every day was a challenge living under those circumstances. I loved going to work, but I hated coming home. Frank was unpredictable and I never knew what mood he would be in when he got home. Some days were good while others were like living in hell. On New Year's Eve Frank and I went three doors down to a neighbor's house to celebrate. I was sitting right by the walkway and this guy I didn't even know walked past me. As he did I happened to turn my head. According to Frank I turned my head and stared at the guy's ass, however, I hadn't. I never saw it coming. The next thing I knew I was being picked up by my hair. Frank literally dragged me across three front yards by my hair. Not one of our neighbors stepped in or did anything to help me. Once home he proceeded to beat me, badly. That night was different though. He actually grabbed his shotgun and pointed it at me. He said he would kill me and then himself if I ever fucked around on him or left him. I was scared and had no idea what I was going to do. I started thinking that there was no place for me, that somehow I was worthless to this world and had no purpose.

Most of us who have survived and gotten free from an abusive relationship at one point in our lives were the same women that said firmly, "I will NEVER be that woman. I would beat a man's ass if he ever hit me. Women that stay in those relationships are just weak." Here's truth, some of the women stuck in those relationships, for whatever reason, are stronger than the women that say judgmental things exactly like that. I know personally that it is not easy to get out of an abusive relationship. If you are in the same situation and you feel trapped let me reach out to you now and say; "YOU ARE NOT ALONE!" Keep faith and know that you have a purpose and being a punching bag is NOT it.

Most towns and cities have a women's shelter. Nowadays there is also remarkable information and help found online. There are hotlines, other women in the same situation struggling, there are answers and there is help. Even Dr. Phil's wife, Robin McGraw, has founded a website dedicated to helping with abusive relationships, escaping from one, strategies and so much more. It also focuses on survivors of sexual assault. You do not have to be a victim if you only rise and stand up for yourself. You are worthy! You can leave quietly like a thief in the night if it has to come to that. Only you can make the decision to take back your life. If you're interested in help, a plan to escape the abuse, or just want to see some of your options, one place you can turn is Mrs. McGraw's website and it can be found at; www.whengeorgiasmiled.org.

Chapter SIX

1995: It wasn't long after New Year's Eve that I found myself sitting at home alone covered in bruises. I couldn't believe my life was like this. I was only 16 years old. By this time I was completely convinced there was nothing left for me on this earth. As each day passed, all of my bruises faded but I was empty and felt completely hopeless. When Frank was at work one day I decided I was done with everything. I ended up eating a handful of sleeping pills and laid down. When I woke up Frank was sitting on the bed shaking me. I began hitting and slapping him. Due to the amount of pills I had taken I was hallucinating and I saw spiders everywhere.

I cried out to him and told him I was sick. I told him that I needed help and began convincing him that he needed to take me to a psychiatric hospital. At that point I didn't know what to do or where else to go. The psychiatric hospital was the only place I could think of to get away. I remembered that only because of when my mother tried to have me admitted into St. John's. I knew that I could convince them to take me as an in-patient. I kept telling Frank that I wouldn't expose the fact that he was my uncle and we were having sex. That seemed to be his only concern. I had to say all I could to comfort Frank and promise him that I wouldn't reveal anything about us. I told him that it wasn't "Us" that was my problem. I convinced him that we were fine by telling him that it was my past, the nightmares of what Carl had done was what was tearing me apart. He finally agreed to take me.

So Frank and I loaded up and headed to a psychiatric hospital. After my evaluation I was admitted to the hospital as an in-patient. I couldn't believe how many kids were there. It was crazy the way many of them were kept on heavy narcotics. I noticed as I looked around that half of the kids were sitting there drooling on themselves in the recreation room. That was something that happened every day I stayed there. Most of the kids couldn't even hold their heads up without it wobbling around, unbalanced and unable to control it, due to the effects of the heavy medication they were under.

The doctors were only as helpful as I allowed them. I told them I tried to kill myself because of what my Uncle Carl and Joe had done to me. The doctor kept encouraging me to take medicine and I continued to refuse it. I just wanted the safety the walls there provided, I wasn't interested in being put on drugs. Besides, I didn't want to be the one sitting there drooling on myself. I couldn't tell them the truth about my uncle, the beatings and the sex. I was honestly ashamed. I thought I was somehow to blame for where I was in my life. The people I met in the hospital were as lost as I was, but there were several interesting kids that I talked with.

I connected with one specific girl and we became friends quickly. I was only there for a couple of weeks, but Frank came for a few visits. He was making promises of happiness. He continued to promise he would never hit me again. As I mentioned before, after he would beat me he was always good at bringing roses, gifts and apologies. I would always believe him when he said he wouldn't do it again. We convince ourselves of the craziest things when we just want to be loved and accepted, that's why it's so important to understand that no one can complete you except you. It is **YOU** that has to realize that when you depend on someone else to complete you they will always disappoint you. Words with power, such as *acceptance*, *love*, *unconditional* and *forgiveness*, these words represent purpose for you, words you need to say to yourself. You have to find peace within you and not be reliant on another person to provide it for you.

The weeks seemed to go way too fast. Before I knew it, I was back in Frank's home. Soon after my release the girl I had connected with in the psychiatric hospital invited me out. She told me we were going to her boyfriend's to hang out. My thoughts were, "Frank's at work so why not." We ended up at this large house in Detroit somewhere. From what I saw when we walked in, there were about eight or nine people inside the house, not counting those outside. I saw drugs, guns and it was complete madness. Once we were in the house a few of the men quickly separated us and the girl just told me not to worry, she would be right back. I ended up in a room that had a blanket on the window, which made it pretty dark. This man sat there talking to me while we smoked a joint together. Soon after, we were having sex. I don't even know or remember how it happened so quickly.

Once he was done I rushed to get dressed, fighting to gather my thoughts. Thinking on it now, I believe that the joint he smoked with me was laced with something because I was so disorientated. After he quickly left the room another guy came in. I kept saying no as he kept touching me, but he was not taking no for an answer. He started talking to me and it actually calmed me down quickly. He had this extremely deep voice, similar to Michael McCary from Boyz II Men.

The man was at least 6'4" tall. I started to find myself turned on by his voice and height. In a strange way he seemed to soothe me in the midst of the craziness. I don't recall what he said or how he managed, but he also had sex with me. As we were having sex I convinced myself I wanted it because it felt so good. He continued to talk to me in my ear the entire time and it really turned me on. After he left the room a third guy tried to come in. I began crying and telling him I wanted to leave. Even though my mind was cloudy, I finally realized they were trying to run a train on me.

After I was fully dressed, all the while still crying, I kept trying to leave the room but the guy wouldn't let me. I started asking for my friend and where she was, if she was okay. The guy just kept talking to me and told me he wouldn't touch me. He promised he would take me to her soon. He sat there and talked to me for what felt like hours. He never touched me or forced me to do anything with him. Finally, the girl I thought was my friend showed up and acted like everything was fine. I had pulled myself together by that time and left with no tears running down my face.

I, too, acted as if everything was fine. I never talked to or seen that girl again. I couldn't even tell you her name now.

Once I got home I showered, changed my clothes and, of course, made sure the house was spotless for when Frank got there. I never mentioned a word about that day or the events that occurred to anyone until now. The night was pretty normal, but when we went to bed I had a wild dream, okay it was more of a fantasy, and I woke up physically acting it out. I was dreaming that I was with the man from earlier in the day that had the voice of Michael McCary. I didn't even realize that I wasn't until I woke up on top of Frank. I quickly closed my eyes and continued to picture the other man. The man that was able to calm me, even turn me on by simply talking to me, which was something that had never happened to me before.

Frank ended up coming to me the next day after he got home from work and he said he wanted me to, "Fuck like that more often." I felt nauseous when he said it. I decided right then and there that I couldn't take it anymore. I knew I didn't want to be there anymore and I had to take a stand, had to get away from him no matter the cost. In early April I finally called my mother and begged her to please come and get me. She agreed she would and I began packing my things. Unfortunately, it was just my luck Frank had gotten off work early that day and he ended up walking in on me while I was packing.

My mother didn't show up until a few hours later. I told Frank my mother was on her way, hoping and praying it would stop him from hurting me again. He ended up putting all of my things outside, grabbed his shotgun and just kept saying some of the meanest and cruelest things to me. He was telling me about how he was going to kill himself and, if I heard the shot while pulling away, I needed to know it was all my fault. I sat in silence almost the entire time just waiting for my mother. I did everything possible not to provoke him. At one point he even shoved the shotgun to his head and tried to make me pull the trigger by grabbing my hand. He kept telling me to just kill him because I was killing him anyway. He was really scaring me and I just kept praying for my mom to hurry up.

When my mother finally showed up, Frank made me go outside and he locked the door behind me. My mom thought it was funny that her little brother didn't want to face her, but she had no idea of what was going on. At least she claimed she didn't. On the way home I began telling my mom the truth as to what had been happening. I explained to her that Frank and I were having sex and living as if we were married. I told her the story of the first night he took me to the liquor store and about all the beatings.

After I was done telling my mother about the past seven months of my life, my mother just looked at me and said, "It's not my fault Zara. You can't blame me. You didn't give me a choice. You wanted to live there!" I just told her I agreed with her and that I thought it was my fault too. I can't express how alone and ashamed I felt. Truth is, I just needed someone to care enough to see what was happening to me. My mother was surprised when I told her about the psych ward. She had no idea I was even admitted to one. I prayed often, but never felt the love that the Lord had for me was real. Demons are good at hiding the light from us. As we walk around in the dark we tend to feel like being lost is meant to be our way. I assure you it is not.

Once I was back home it didn't take long until I couldn't stand living with my mother again. We fought all of the time and I refused to be under the rules a child should be. I ended up finding Brandon and we spent a lot of time together catching up. I always shared everything with Brandon and he never judged me for any of what I had been thru. He became my best friend and he was one of the few guys in my life that was always there for me. I began staying with Brandon and Cory at the end of April. We lived with their parents in a really small, two-bedroom house. The Box House I like to call it.

Brandon and Cory's parents worked all the time. I don't even think they realized I was there as much as I was at first. Even though Brandon's dad didn't care for most people, he did end up taking a liking to me. So he ignored that I was staying there even though he didn't like company at the house. Brandon and I always had something to talk about. We understood one another and related to events in our lives like no one I had ever known up to that point. Brandon and I picked up quickly where we left off. He reassured me often that, no matter what happened in life, I would always have a safe place with him.

During the next few months Brandon's brother never crossed the line with me, nor I with him. Cory became a dear friend to me and, although we disagreed a lot, we made our friendship work. My and Brandon's favorite spot was by this pond where we would go and park. We would look at the stars, drink Boone's Farm Strawberry Hill and have sex; all while we jammed to Nirvana. We spent a lot of time talking and listening to one another. We also spent a lot of time exploring each other physically and emotionally. It was awesome to share the stories of our crazy lives with each other. It seemed like we found a certain peace when we were together.

In time Brandon and I felt in love, but I had no clue what love even was and he didn't either. Brandon would have sex with other girls and I would have sex with other guys. It really wasn't too big of a deal to either of us because we slept next to one another at night. The love we felt was something powerful and jealousy wasn't a problem for either of us. It wasn't about sex with us, although sex was never bad, but it was a connection that built our friendship. We had both been thru so much craziness that somehow, when we were together, neither of our pasts mattered. We brought comfort to one another at all times.

We both refused to commit to one another because we just wanted to enjoy the moments we were sharing, no strings attached. I knew that, no matter what, I never wanted to lose the friendship I had with him. On days the boys didn't work, Brandon, Cory and I would wake up with our objectives being to have fun, find cigarettes, score some weed and find alcohol. Life was simple for a moment for me because I could just be me with Brandon. We were honest and open from the first time we met.

I was no longer answering to any adult. I had no rules except those of my own, and I was enjoying the freedom of it all. One day Brandon took me over to this place where some hippies lived on a bus. The bus had been gutted and converted into a home with a bedroom, kitchen and the whole works. The place was in the middle of nowhere and there was an orchard and garden. It was so peaceful. When Brandon decided to leave, I wasn't ready and was offered to stay for a few days. I decided I wanted to stay and explore the whole free-love experience. The person that owned the land was very welcoming and a younger hippie guy who talked about peace and love. It was something I had never experienced before; I wasn't being hit on and there was always a lot of people there to get to know and hang out with.

I learned about Rainbow Gatherings, (I will explain more on that later). I watched grown adults playing dungeons and dragons. We smoked a lot of weed and we laughed a lot. There were always deep conversations about life and love. It was a great place to walk around barefoot and just enjoy being me. There were many travelers from far away and locals from close by that came on and off the land at all hours. I never felt threatened. I did have great sex with one or two very good looking men that had stopped in for a night's stay. It was a place that was very distracting from the real world and it felt like an escape. It was a place where peace-loving people came and there were very few arguments. If there was a disagreement, it became a discussion and not some huge fight. I enjoyed my time there and met some very interesting people.

Although there were several opportunities for me to do free drugs, I still turned them down. I would smoke pot all day but, if you offered me a line of cocaine, a pill, acid or anything else other than a drink, I would say no. While I was hanging out at the -- let's call it the hippie orchard -- I ended up meeting this female with blond hair that had a car and she ended up telling me she was a virgin. I was missing Brandon and thought I would take this girl over to meet Cory plus get some quality time with Brandon. When we arrived things didn't go as I had planned at all. Once Brandon found out she was a virgin he was fascinated with her. He ended up pursuing her the entire night. The two of them ended up sneaking off and having sex that night. I didn't understand why, but for some reason it ended up hurting me really bad inside. I wanted Brandon's time and I wanted him to want mine. I went to see him and it tore me up when he disappeared most of the night with that girl.

Once the girl left I decided to stay with Brandon and Cory, but it was only for a short time. I was still angry at Brandon and one day I crossed the line with Cory. Although I cared about Cory, I wasn't really ever interested in him sexually, I just wanted Brandon to feel the hurt and pain that I had felt. Cory and I got a great buzz together in late June and ended up climbing to the rooftop of the pizza place we all hung out at, the same place where Brandon and I had first met. We had sex and ended up covered in black tar from head to toe. Of course, when we climbed down there was no denying what we had been doing up there.

Brandon was angry at me. Although he may not admit it, I think he was a bit hurt too. Perhaps not the same as I was by him; but, either way, it was the main reason we ended up going our separate ways. We weren't angry at each other when I left. We still swore we would always remain friends and have stuck to that promise. After I left Brandon's I ended up moving in with a friend that lived in the same town as my mother.

It was early July and the carnival was in town. Brandon meet Sadie at this same fair and they began dating. To this day they are together, married and have three children. As for me, I was really drop-dead gorgeous with flowing red hair and a body most would give anything to have. I was like a radiant light and many people were drawn to me. I was beginning to see and realize it more than I ever had before. I knew that physically I was beautiful, but the power it gave me over men was new to me.

At the fair I was walking around with no shoes, a rope as my belt and a flannel shirt. I was so confident about myself that I walked up to this man that was very good looking. I simply looked him up and down then proceeded to ask him if I could take him home with me. It wasn't a surprise to me that he said yes. My confidence was high and I felt superior.   I found another man that looked like Sam Elliott from when he played in the movie 'Roadhouse'. As soon as I saw him I just had to have him. At 16 years old I was messing with grown men, picking and choosing between them. I was determined that I would use who I wanted and no one would use me ever again.

I was starting to feel like I had power over my life and my body. I only pursued who I wanted and was finally able to say NO to what and who I didn't want. I wasn't afraid to look a man in his eyes and spit on him. I had no fear of anything and, because of that, I thought I was in control. I convinced myself that, if I didn't fear anything, there wasn't anything or anyone that could hurt me anymore. Truth is, I had a blast walking around the fair and checking everyone out.

Something about walking around the carnival made me desire to understand how it all worked. I wanted to be a part of the traveling, the operation and the family unit that each carnie seemed to have. Little did I know that fair would change my entire life. One night, as I was walking around, I saw this man working and I couldn't help but feel drawn to him. His name was Paul and he was 32 years old. He was bald and a little chunky, but he had the fullest lips I had ever seen. His eyes seemed so caring and he was very intelligent. After talking that night, each day I went back I would go straight to him. I was beyond intrigued with Paul and began pursuing him. I was so attracted to what he had, the strongest relationship with Jesus Christ I had ever witnessed. He wasn't afraid to talk about God in any situation. He also had custody of two of his three children. Both of the kids that he had custody of were girls who were under the age of 13 years old and I connected with them quickly. In all reality, after everything I had already been thru in my life, my intelligence and maturity was far beyond my age.

Once I began pursuing Paul he didn't want much to do with me at first, at least not the way I was pursuing him, because he knew I was young. I ended up lying to him and told him I was turning 18 years old in September, when truth is I was turning 17. I did get a job in the game next to one of Paul's games. See, he actually owned and operated six of his own games and he also had a sideshow that was in storage. The first game I worked was a water toss where you throw the ping pong ball and try to get it into a small glass that is filled with water. It was similar to the game you can win goldfish at, but this one wasn't as easy and my prizes weren't just goldfish. I actually had iguanas and a python named Monty. I thought it was funny to wear Monty around my neck like a tie. It would take a minute for people to realize he was there, but when they did most people would jump back. It would always make me smile.

I loved the carnival life and adjusted quickly. It was a lifestyle I was able to embrace and enjoy. I was accepted by almost everyone. Honestly, I felt safe there. It wasn't long before I knew most everyone working the show and I was actually protected by many of the carnies. At first, while I was still pursuing Paul, he and I would just spend our days talking. At night, however, after Paul and I would say our goodbyes, I was off to the bar with all my new carnie friends. Although I was only 16 years old, I looked well over 21. I had long, flowing red hair and, by this time, I wore a 36DDD bra size and was built like a brick shithouse (whatever that statement really means). I was never asked for an I.D. and had so much fun playing pool and drinking. Even though I was making my own money, I never spent a dime when I would go to the bar because drinks were always being sent my way.

Paul had his two girls and his best friend with him and, after about three weeks, we were all inseparable. It took pursuing Paul for about three weeks before he ever even agreed to try a relationship with me. Eventually I did end up admitting to him that I was turning 17 years old in September and not 18. At first he was upset and it really bothered him, but he had already met my mother and he knew a lot about my past. He couldn't believe I was so young, but agreed to stick with me after I asked him to just give me a chance. Even with my advances toward Paul he refused to have sex with me. He kept saying that we needed to take time to get to know one another, "Relationships aren't built on sex," he told me. He was the first man to treat me with so much respect. For the first time in my life I felt happiness. I loved Paul's children, Paul and even Dakota was a part of my life on a constant basis.

Dakota came out for several spots we worked. I would take care of him for a week or two then send him back to our mother. Paul, the kids and I read the Bible every day and prayed constantly. I had never truly felt Jesus Christ until I truly accepted and asked him into my life shortly after I turned 17 years old. Paul became my best friend and the girls and I loved one another deeply. Although we didn't see Paul's son, Dean, as often as we would have liked to, he was just as important to all of us. When Dean would come out on the road with us we always had so much fun with all the kids. We were a family together and things just seemed to fall into place. Paul wasn't much of a drinker or big on bars, parties, or anything like that so my life became family-oriented and Christ-centered for the first time ever.

It seemed like God was truly blessing us daily. Paul's son, Dean, was named after Paul's best friend who traveled and worked for us. As I mentioned, Paul owned and operated six carnival games, so when we took on the commitment of being together that included me becoming his business partner. I quit working for the other game and took on a business. I felt honored and blessed to become an influence to the children more than anything. I was so happy to have all of them in my life. Paul and I committed to one another in the moonlight with God as our witness. It's funny because, as I write about it, it really all happened so quickly. Paul and I prayed, laughed and lived together. I had never felt closer to anyone in my life and, to this day, I have never felt the way with anyone else like I did with Paul.

We usually moved to a new location every week with the fair. You can ask any carnie, the truth is when you're working in the carnival a week actually feels like five years. I can't begin to explain how good it felt to have my own family that loved me unconditionally. I was still admired by a lot of men, but I wasn't being pursued as much and I wasn't pursuing anyone. I would get whistles from the guys setting up rides and the marks (people who come to the fair, but don't work at it) would hit on me, but everyone knew I was with Paul so they didn't mess with me much. I loved my life and I loved Paul, so it was easy for me to simply turn others down when they would hit on me. I must admit the carnival lifestyle was unlike any other. I worked with and was trained by some of the best hustlers in the United States.

The game I was broke into, taught and trained to work, was called the Circle of Science. It's not even allowed on most midways nowadays. You may have seen or played it at a local fair. It is a larger red circle and then you have five smaller circles. The objective of the game is to cover the large red circle with the smaller ones. You have as much time as you need, but each of the smaller circles have to be dropped from an inch high and you can't move them once you drop them. It was the best game on any midway in my opinion. You can call it favoritism I suppose.

Although it is extremely tough to win, there being only a quarter inch space to play with, it is possible. It's built like a jigsaw puzzle without the lines. It could be turned into a game you cannot win, but I never ran my game like that. I still have several sets of boards and plates that I pull out once in a while and play with. They really bring back some memories the moment I touch them. I was continually traveling all over the United States and I loved the life. My mother was even keeping a huge map on her wall at her house for Dakota and he was marking all the places I would travel to. I tried to call Dakota as often as possible so he always knew where I was and we would talk a lot.

It was crazy. I joined the carnival in July and by September I had already been to Florida, Georgia and several other states. We owned a 32-foot travel trailer and had many adventures throughout our travels. I had so much fun working the game when I would jump in and actually go to work. There were many perks to being an owner and not just an employee. I will never forget the way some people would react to the Circle of Science. Some would walk past and wave their arms claiming it was impossible to win, others would claim there were magnets in the board. I assure you there are no magnets in the game at all; however, with my experience, looks and training, I was able to get many people to at least try the game once. During the times my employees and I would get bored we would superglue quarters in front of our game. It made many people stop and try to pick them up. It was so much easier to get people to come close to check your game out if they were already stopped in front of you.

One time when I was in Tallahassee, Florida this little boy about 12 years old came up to me and had a handful of money. He was determined to win and he was willing to spend whatever it took. At a certain point I wanted to ask him to stop because some parents would have thought I was robbing the poor kid. I had seen too many parents walk away from my game angry because they couldn't win and, in turn, they would tell their children they too couldn't win the game either. Being a survivor, and growing up as fast as I had, it would make me sad to hear that as often as I did. Whenever I heard a parent doubt their child's abilities I would always think to myself, "What if your child can do something you can't?" This little boy spent over two hours with me. I even ended up giving him a stool to stand on because it does help to look over the board. He spent a good $80 and said he was going to get more money. To my surprise he did just that. After spending over a hundred dollars with me I tried to help the kid out and cheat for him, but he actually got mad at me. His parents finally came up to my game and started asking about it. They stood out to me and I learned a huge lesson in that moment. The mother and father of this child started encouraging him. They weren't mad at him and they didn't tell him he couldn't win even knowing how much he had spent on the game. They stood there and told him they remembered that they both had tried it before, but couldn't get it. Yet both of them told the boy they believed in him and even gave him more money to play. It was the most amazing thing I had seen, parents supporting and encouraging their child like that. It was beautiful to me and I held that dear to my heart. Truth is, all I wanted and dreamed of was becoming a mother and wife. I grew up on all of the Disney movies and wanted my Prince Charming. This was a lesson I held close for when I was to become a mother.

I felt like I had found my Prince Charming with Paul. I was making great money and lived as if I owned the entire show. When I would walk on the Midway it was almost as if all attention was on me, but I learned to be humble. I was so thankful for all God was doing in my life. Everyday started positive with our family. Of course the girls had their normal sister disagreements, but we were a happy family together. I loved everything that was happening, especially the schedule I had for work. See, Paul took care of our business most of the time and my main job was taking care of the kids.

I was always a prima-donna when it came to the business. I was part owner, so I could show up when the money was there and then go home. I became so good that I could go the entire day just doing what I wanted, then in the evening I would jump in the game and make more money than everyone that had worked the entire day. I was making good enough money that the kids and I went in together and paid to have Paul's trailer airbrushed with our business logo as a surprise for him. Everything seemed to be going so good. Paul and I discussed homeschooling the girls and decided to make our decision once we got to the Oklahoma State Fair.

Unfortunately, our happiness only lasted for a short time. Paul had been through a custody battle with his ex-wife before he had ever met me and he was granted custody from the State of Michigan. When we went to the Oklahoma State Fair, everything changed. We had decided to go ahead with the homeschooling and, after researching several, had ordered and received a great program for the girl. The girls had just started school and I was their teacher. It was very descriptive and laid out easily so I didn't have any trouble understanding any of it. The morning was warm, the girls and I decided to head to the laundromat while Paul went to take care of opening all of our games. By this time we also had our sideshow out of storage and set up and the local paper even ran an article on it.

While at the laundromat, the girls and I had a blast as we always did. I recall the girls dressing up in my dresses and the three of us dancing around, singing and just being silly. As soon as the girls and I returned we unloaded the van. All of a sudden there was a knock at the door. To my surprise when I opened the door, there were at least four police officers and a few people dressed in suits standing there. They had a court order stating they were to take the girls. At the time the girls were 12 years old and nine years old. This was at the end of September and I had just turned 17.

Panicked and unsure of what to do, I allowed them to take the girls and began to run to the Midway. Our games were set up over half a mile away from where our trailer was. I ran as fast as I could. I remember I had a hard time getting the words out to Paul when I had finally reached him. Paul instantly panicked. Once we got back to the trailer he grabbed his briefcase, his small handgun and ran out of the trailer. There was some bad history with him and his ex, so he wasn't letting the girls go without a fight.

By the time he made it to the police station the girls had already been turned over to their mother and it was too late. The kids were gone and Paul was never really the same after that. He had court documents that showed Michigan had power and he had custody. The court documents even stated that another state had no right to interfere. Even though Paul did everything he could from where we were, his hands were tied. The girls were on their way to Alabama with their mother and there was nothing Paul or I could do.

Having two states involved in a custody case does not make things any easier, especially since the girls were now in their mother's physical custody. Paul and I decided that, after finishing a few more spots we had already booked, we would head to Alabama and stay until we could win the girls back.

In October we were finishing up our season at one of our last spots, which was located in South Carolina. Dean, Paul's best friend, was always a person to bring a smile to your face. He was a tall, good looking man that could light the darkest room. He was always a positive person and we all loved to talk about God in every situation. Dean could make you laugh, even on your worst day. One evening Paul and I were in our trailer reading our bible when Dean came to our door and said he wanted to be the first to wish Paul happy birthday. This was the 19th of October, 1995. Paul's birthday was on the 20th. After Dean left, Paul and I spent the night talking about life and how much we missed the girls. Paul was so hurt and just kept wanting things back to normal. He felt that because he was the man it was his responsibility to make sure we were all happy. He was convinced that unless we were all together we couldn't ever be happy again.

`As I write and reflect on all these memories, it simply amazes me that Paul and I were only together for three months during these events. The way we connected and the life we lived, it truly felt like we were together for years by this time. On October 20, 1995, Paul and I woke up to a missed phone call. We couldn't even begin to wrap our minds around the words that were left on our voicemail. The voice mail left was from the local coroner calling in regard to a body found that had our business card within the person's belongings. Paul called the number back and we were asked to come down to the morgue to identify our friend Dean's body. He was shot the night before in what the police explained to us was a drug deal gone bad. I can't explain the feeling of complete emptiness in the morgue. Unless you have gone into a morgue, I am not sure words can express the emotions I felt when I went in. The person working there tried to prepare us because the autopsy had already been started. He explained that Dean wouldn't look like we were used to. I had never identified a body before and, with Dean being such a dear friend, I was beyond nervous about the whole thing. Paul and I held one another tightly as the person moved the sheet away from Dean's head to rest it on his chest. His brain had already been removed, so his forehead was sunk in and it looked so strange. I will never forget the way he looked just lying there with no life inside of him. Dean was always full of life and laughter. I couldn't believe it was him lying there. I was just joking around and teasing this man the night before. Paul and I held one another as we cried. With complete dismay, Paul and I confirmed that it was our friend Dean.

It was one of the saddest days Paul and I shared. Truth is, Paul went crazy when we got back to the lot (Midway). He began asking everyone questions. We heard stories that Dean had volunteered to collect some of the carnies' money and go to town to score drugs for them. He was making a cut, some money for himself, out of the deal. Supposedly, that's why he offered to go. The person involved in the shooting was found, but later found not guilty due to police not handling the investigation and evidence legally. Unfortunately, due to our lifestyle, Paul and I were gone within a few days. It didn't feel right leaving without

Dean and things never seemed quite right after that.

By the beginning of November, Paul and I were living in our trailer on the top of a small mountain in Alabama. After all that we had been through Paul and I began to grow distant from one another. He was so lost after losing his children and then his best friend. I was so young and had no clue how to be of any comfort to him. He spent a lot of his time worried that he would lose me if he didn't fix everything and, in the end, it was only pushing me away. Simple things set him off. One time I accidentally locked the keys in our trailer and Paul was so upset he started yelling at me. He had never yelled at me like that before.

He wasn't talking to me like he used to. Even though our daily prayers and Bible study continued, Paul was consumed with anger and fear. It was a very tough winter trying to make sure we had enough money for food and basic survival. We had also hired an attorney, so the fight began to get the girls back. To make money we would set up side stands with all of our inventory (teddy bears) and sell them to try and make enough just for dinner some days.

This one time Paul got so frustrated that we weren't making enough money, I ended up making him wait in the truck and took one of our largest teddy bears into a small waffle restaurant. I explained what our situation was and asked if anyone would be interested in buying it. The manager ended up having me bring Paul inside. We sat down with a full meal paid for and the stock sold. It was moments like these that I would try to reach out to Paul and show him that God was still with us and everything was going to be okay.

It always amazed me when things like that would happen and it was often. I thought it was because I was some good saleswoman; but, it had nothing to do with how smooth or good of a saleswoman I was, I believe that God was the one who was making sure that we ended up in front of the right people. It seemed like God was using some of the most unusual people to make huge impacts on Paul and me.

Times continued to get tough on us and we decided to pawn our truck to help with money. On our way to pawn the truck, Paul was freaking out. He worried that we wouldn't get to the place on time and I kept telling him to have faith. The truck wasn't running good and we ended up having to pull over just a few blocks from the pawn shop. We only had about 18 minutes to get there before it closed. Paul was so aggravated and couldn't seem to figure out why the truck wouldn't start. Out of nowhere this very dirty and very bad smelling man ended up coming over to Paul. It took this man less than a minute and he had our truck running. It was hard to see Paul so torn, he had been such a solid rock for everyone else and there was nothing I could do. I, myself, was still learning and growing. It seemed; however, like God always provided what we needed. We did make it to the pawn store and everything turned out okay that day.

As the year was coming to an end, Paul and I were not doing well. When Paul would get upset he would usually walk away from the situation and pray. During this time in our lives he had so much hurt, confusion and loss built up within him, I truly don't believe he had control over his anger. He was getting so upset at me and taking his frustrations out on me. I didn't know how to react to his behavior. He was truly trying to save our family, but all the while pushing our love aside. He didn't feel like we could ever be happy and things couldn't be right without the children with us. He continually told me that he was convinced if he, "Could just get the kids back everything would be okay and our family would be happy again."

As we struggled to support one another emotionally, I knew deep down there was nothing I could do to comfort the loss of Paul's children and now his best friend. As hard as we tried, we just couldn't seem to pull together and see eye to eye on many things. I had no idea what he needed from me but, what made me feel worse was, I didn't know if there was anything I could do. We began fighting more often and over the stupidest things. During this time Paul was quick to anger. Most of the time he was also quick to apologize. We prayed every day and tried hard to stay focused on keeping our faith. We both believed the Lord had a plan even if we didn't understand it and the year finally came to an end.

Chapter SEVEN

1996: The winter took its toll on Paul and me. He was one person I knew I could always rely on and he was struggling with life, as we all do at some point. As time went on I began to feel alone and unable to provide the support he needed, regardless of my attempts. In March I ended up leaving Paul. I found myself on a Midway about four hours away in Georgia. I ran into a few friends that told me they had heard there was a Rainbow Gathering going on not too far from the spot where we were at. Ever since the time I spent in Michigan at the Hippie Orchard, I had always wanted to check out a Rainbow Gathering.

So I left the fair and ended up at a hotel close to the Alabama border headed to the Rainbow Gathering. If you have never heard of a Rainbow Gathering, one definition is: "The Rainbow Family is one of the largest non-organization of non-members in the world. There are no leaders, and no organization. The family here have been drawn to the community building, caretaking of mother earth, nonviolence and living a compassionate and loving life," http://rainbowgatherings.org/.

To me, a Rainbow Gathering was a bunch of hippies spread out and set up in different campsites in the forest. They united together. You didn't starve there and everyone was welcome. From what I was told at the Hippie Orchard, it was filled with music, love and peace. As I sat in my hotel room looking through my maps, I didn't know that Paul had been driving all day and was trying to find me. I called him after I received the many voicemails he had left on our 888 number for the business. The 888 number was always our way of communicating back and forth and we used that number for almost 16 years. I ended up telling him where

I was when I talked to him and he showed up within a couple of hours. Paul ended up proposing to me that night and I said yes. We agreed to go to the Rainbow Gathering and then figure out how to handle court and everything else we were up against.

The Rainbow Gathering was an experience I will never forget. It was in a National Forest and, when we pulled up, there were a couple of news vans and many people in the parking lot. We had to push through a crowd of people panhandling. Some were asking for cigarettes, others were holding out empty bowls (marijuana pipes) and asking for weed. I had truly never seen anything like it. Once we were able to push through the crowd we were one pack of cigarettes down from handing them out, but that is when it became an extremely amazing adventure.

There were campsites set up for miles through the woods. Paul and I walked around in amazement. We ran into a few friends and it just made me realize what a small world it truly is. Some of the campsites had fires going and people gathered around the fire playing instruments and singing. Some people were walking around naked, others dancing around the campfires. There were also soup kitchens set up throughout the woods where they served dinner, breakfast, etc.

There was one man out there that, if you collected two handfuls of cigarette butts and brought them to him, he would give you a hit of acid. He did it because that meant you were caring for the earth by cleaning up the butts. There was also what they called an 'A camp', which was near the entrance to the entire forest where we had pushed through the crowd to enter. That is where most of the people who drank stayed. They were loud and caused problems so they were kept at a distance from everyone else. Most of the time Paul and I spent there we talked about God with a lot of people. We were amazed how open everyone was, even a person running around naked in the forest can love God. In my opinion, it seems easier to stop judging and just love one another. Even in the midst of chaos we all have a need to hear echoes of love.

On our way home, Paul and I shared our feelings about the Rainbow Gathering and the events occurring in our lives. We both felt amazed and lifted by the whole experience. The new season was starting and it was time to get back to work. Paul and I packed everything up and left the small mountain we had spent our winter on. We had already been to court and I had already testified on Paul's behalf. There wasn't much more we could do for the girls except wait for the Court's decision. We worked in Florida for a little while at first. At one of the spots in Florida, I was at our campground trying to get everything packed up and ready for the next jump. After getting everything gathered up I headed into the small laundromat that was provided to finish our laundry. As I was switching the laundry this large man came into the small-built room. I knew something was wrong with him, he just didn't seem right. Have you ever experienced being in a bad situation just by someone's presence? It felt just like that. I was uncomfortable instantly.

The man started to talk to me, but I didn't look into his eyes. I've learned with some people, the moment you make eye contact with them they instantly think it's some kind of "go" sign. To my shock, and completely out of the blue, he jumped me and shoved me against the washing machine. He was holding my breasts while pushing me back and thrusting his midsection on me. I dropped down with all my weight and was able to push him away, enough that I was able to break free and run to the office. The police were called but, being a carnie with no in-state address leaving the next day, there wasn't much that could be done. The officer went and talked to the guy who, of course, denied it.

In the end, the officer said they really couldn't do anything unless I was willing to press charges and be there to testify. He told me he couldn't even file the report unless I was willing to, "Follow through with it." I told the officer I couldn't commit to that and asked him if he could at least escort me to collect my laundry, the officer agreed. When I opened up the washer to get my clothes, I found a pair of men's underwear thrown in on the top. They were not ours. The officer just threw them away. I quickly collected the laundry, packed everything right then and left. After I told

Paul about the incident he was upset. At that point there was nothing else that could be done except put it behind us and move on.

Paul and I ended up in Michigan to visit all of our family. We were able to visit with Paul's son, Dean. It was always a blessing to see Dean, he was such a great kid. He truly loved his dad and his dad loved him. Paul and Dean's mother were always great friends and remained that way after they separated. I am not saying they didn't have their disagreements, just as father and son had, but they worked it out every time. As for me, I always got along with Dean's mother. She was and is a blessing to have as a friend. I love Dean with all my heart and, to this day, we stay in touch and I am very proud to call him my son (stepson, but it's the same thing to me).

Dean always accepted me as his stepmom throughout the years. I'm honored to say that he still does. He recently got engaged to his best friend and she is a wonderful woman. Unfortunately, I only see him once or twice a year. It's been that way since he was four, yet we have an unbreakable bond. During this visit we also visited my family. Paul and I spent Easter with my mother, father and Dakota. It was pretty funny because Paul was Jewish and didn't celebrate Easter, Christmas or any of the holidays I was raised to celebrate. That year, however, Paul searched for his Easter basket just like the rest of us.

It was during this visit home that I also saw my brother, Derek, for the first time in a very long time. To me, Derek seemed different and withdrawn. I knew he and my mother had gone through some things, but I didn't understand why things were different with me. I tried to tell him about the years and what had happened with Frank, but he really acted like he didn't believe me. At least that's how I felt every time, from that moment on and even to this day, when I would try to talk to him and he would say, "I don't want to talk about that," or "I don't want to hear about that." It broke my heart and changed the way I looked at Derek for a very long time.

After Easter was over, Paul and I found ourselves working in South Carolina again. I told Paul that I really needed to get away and spend some time to think about everything. As I pondered where to go, I decided that New Mexico would be perfect. I wanted to visit everyone and it sounded like a great place to go for a visit. Truth is, it sounded like a great place to get away and think about life for a little bit. My car wasn't in the best of shape, but it ran. The only thing wrong with it was that it had to be physically pushed to start it. So I made sure, the entire way to New Mexico, any time I had to stop to get gas or go potty I stopped at a well-lit, large truck stop.

I never had any problems finding a couple guys to push the car for me once I got gas. I had a CB in my car so it made me feel safer in case of an emergency and Paul also made sure to buy me a zapper with many volts in it before I left. I never did get the chance to zap anyone with that thing. There was one trucker who talked to me for about six hours straight. I was actually behind him and we were flying down the highway together. He ended up inviting me to stop and grab some food with him and I agreed. He was actually a Christian and turned out to be a very nice guy. We ended up talking about God throughout dinner and he gave me a shower coupon, plus covered the meal. He was heading in the opposite direction when we said our goodbyes, but he did help me get the car started by pushing it for me. He was an absolute blessing and I appreciated his help. As I reflect on it now, I was truly lucky that I didn't get kidnapped or worse.

Once I made it to New Mexico I was able to get my car fixed. I was a little disappointed because my Butterfield friends had moved and we lost touch, so I ended up going over to visit with Ivy and Ashley. I wasn't sure if they were still in their old house and they were the only other friends I could think of. It didn't take long to find them and, to my surprise, every-one acted happy to see me. Ivy and Ashley were definitely different. We had all grown so much in the few years we hadn't seen one another. Ivy, the girl who used to bully me and make me cry often, had a boyfriend at the military base in Arizona and wanted to know if I would take her. She really wanted to go and begged me to give her a ride there and she would find her way back.

Even though I was reluctant to take her due to the way she had treated me in the past and the lack of money either of us had, in the end I said I would. I looked through my Amusement Business magazine (a magazine that provided all dates and places where you could find a fair), and found a small carnival show that wouldn't be too far off course. I needed more money, so I told her I would take her but we had to work for a few days. She was fine with that agreement and so we loaded up. Ivy and I were headed to Arizona the next day. The carnival show we were headed too was off of Highway 191 in Arizona.

Being around Ivy was different than I expected. I felt like I was just waiting for her to bully me. My plan was to punch her in the face because I wasn't a little punk anymore. However, it didn't go at all the way I kept picturing it in my head. I was actually enjoying Ivy's company. She too, had been through a lot in life and it had changed her just as much as it had me. Neither of us was looking at one another through young immature eyes, we both had a respect for one another. Together we had one crazy adventure driving up that mountain, and I learned a great lesson - You could literally only go 5 mph around corners because, if you went any faster, you would have rolled off the mountainside.

We ended up getting a flat tire; but, as if we were in a movie, two cowboys showed up out of nowhere and changed the flat for us. As we started back on our journey, we laughed about how crazy it was two cowboys just showed up in the middle of a mountain then disappeared. We tried but couldn't seem to catch up to them, or perhaps they turned off. All of a sudden it happened again and the spare tire blew. The only sign either of us had seen or noticed was the one that had said there was a lodge up the road about four miles. After we talked, I looked at Ivy and told her it looked like we were walking.

It was dark already but the stars and moon were shining. I personally didn't think it was that dark out. Ivy and I started walking and she kept saying she was, "Scared to walk." I thought she was joking at first because she kept saying she was afraid that something was going to jump out and eat us. She was right about there being no sign of human life close by. We were in the middle of a mountain in Arizona and I thought it was awesome. I loved the rush of new adventures. After we walked about half a mile, I realized she was genuinely scared. She actually began crying and that is when I started to really feel bad.

See, I was teasing her about being afraid. I thought it was some kind of a joke, so I started to make comments like, "How can you be scared? You used to bully me all of the time. You scared me and now your acting scared?" This woman, who pretty much tortured me, who was one of my worst bullies and always known as a badass, how can she be afraid? At one point I did look at her and told her to stop acting like a baby. Honestly, I really thought she was messing with me. This was a girl that caused me to have bad dreams from her making fun of me only a few years prior. When I finally realized, by the tears and look in her eyes, that she was really, purely and honestly scared, I decided we would turn around and go back to the car.

Once we got back to the car we had a chance to talk about everything. She admitted that she was afraid as a kid, too. I realized in that moment, although I was afraid of Ivy in my youth, she was battling her own demons and experienced fears also. Different fears, but still fears. I learned that she felt pressured in her youth to be the bully. She confessed that the older kids in school used to encourage her to bully. It was as if she felt like the older kids thought she was cooler when she bullied other kids. It made me realize that even she needed people to want to be her friend. I learned that she was just as afraid as all of us who were bullied by her. We judge others so much that we forget they have their own problems that everybody is going through something. If we cared more about others we might actually be able to lift someone who is down rather than just look down on them.

I may not be able to explain how God works, but I do know that he does things to and for us when we least expect it. Since it was obvious we weren't walking anywhere, I decided to take the chance and drive on my flat spare tire. We slowly made it and I can't express how thankful I was that they were still open. Someday I pray I have an opportunity to return to that place if it is still there. It was a gorgeous lodge/hotel in the middle of the mountain.

The room rates were around, $258 a night; way out of our price range. After Ivy and I spoke with the manager, he ended up giving us a room with double beds. Let me just say, the room was as beautiful as the rest of the Lodge. He didn't charge us anything, plus he offered to take us to town the next morning and ended up covering all the expenses for my tire. He really had eyes for Ivy, but she had her man and it was all kept as a friendly gesture on the manager's part. It turned out that the spot we were trying to reach wasn't too far away so once the car was fixed we headed to the carnival. The show was very small and there wasn't any work for either of us so I ended up calling Paul. He sent me some money and told me he missed me. After talking with Paul, I decided to just take Ivy to the Army base and I headed back to South Carolina.

As I drove across the country I took the time to reflect on everything and how much I had learned hanging out with Ivy. Even the people we think are the toughest people have their insecurities and weaknesses. I thought about Paul and me, how far we had grown apart, and I took the time to reflect on my life. When I got back to Paul, I thought the best thing for us was to go our separate ways. I loved him with all my heart, but I was just learning who I was. After I told him we should break up, he tried to serenade me with a guitar. He even put my hand on his pocket and said, "I have over $3,000 in my pocket right now. What do you want to do? I'll do anything you want." I just couldn't stay with him. Throughout time I was also convinced that we could never be happy because things were never going to be the same. It was as Paul had continued to say to me.

There were many times throughout the years I regretted my decision. I felt like I should have just married him and worked through everything, but that is not the path I took. Serenading me was one of the many sweet things Paul did and, with every attempt he made, I just pushed him farther away. We broke up and agreed: No matter what happened, we would always remain friends and we would always remain partners in our business. Paul truly was the only person that was there for me no matter what I needed. He remained my best friend for 17 years; but, truth is, he never wanted me to be, "Just a friend." The business, however, was something we had both worked for and knew, without one another, we would have lost everything. We almost lost all of our games during the winter months, but together we were able to hold onto them. Paul felt that meant I should always be a part of the business and made it clear he would never take that away from me. He never did.

Owning, operating and working as a carnie was one of the best jobs I have ever had. I loved meeting new people, whether they worked with the show or were just there to enjoy it. One time our game was set up directly across from a sideshow. It was called the Gorilla Woman. It's the show where the woman turns into a gorilla and then the gorilla breaks down the cage and jumps all over the stage. It's an illusion, but you wouldn't believe how many women would take their kids who were in strollers inside the tent and then run out screaming. The crazy thing was, they would leave their babies in the tent stuck in their strollers also screaming. One woman refused to go back in and made someone else go get her kid. I know it seems bad, but I'll admit it was absolutely hilarious to watch.

In September I turned 18 years old and spent it at a bar in some town I was working in. By October I had met a young carnie named Ned. Now, Ned worked a 'balloon store'. It's a game carnies call a, "Run 'em up" game. In other words, you're going to win and get what you want, but you pay as you play. Ned was a taller, good looking guy. We were around the same age and he was very sweet. I loved his hazel green eyes, they were so different, and I found them very attractive. It wasn't long after we met that Ned and I decided to spend the winter together and see where things went. Once the work season was over, the first place that I knew I wanted to go was to Michigan. I wanted to go visit with Dakota and my father and Ned had no problem with that.

When we finally arrived at my mother's house, my father was in pretty bad shape. The biggest thing I noticed while visiting was that his memory was fading. During this time, I spent every minute I could playing cards and talking to my dad. Mom soon sat Dakota and I down and explained that our father was suffering from Alzheimer's. She said that because I wouldn't stay, she had to put him in a home. I never intended to ever live with my mother again, but she enjoyed putting blame on me at all times. She explained that she couldn't take care of him and Dakota both on her own. Personally, it felt like she was trying to make Dakota believe that it was somehow my fault she was taking our dad to a home.

I was there the day my mother took my father to the Veteran's Home. When she put his suitcase in the trunk of her car, it instantly took me back to St. John's when she pulled my suitcase out of the trunk. My father hugged me while we both cried. He was so confused and had no idea what was going on. It was an extremely emotional moment for me. I asked my dad if he realized that mom was taking him to a new home and he reacted as if he had no clue. My father just continued to tell me he didn't want to go. I had no control over my mom placing my father in her car and driving off. In that moment, I was beyond angry at my mother. At that time I didn't understand what it took to deal with an older person suffering from Alzheimer's, plus taking care of a nine-year-old son. No, at that moment it just felt like my mother was trying to get rid of my father.

I left my mother's soon after that and headed over to visit with Brandon and Sadie. Cory just happened to be there visiting too. Cory was miserable where he was and really wanted to make some changes in his life. After thinking about it, I realized Cory might do really well on the road. I figured it would be a great new start for him and he could make money while doing it. As the day went on, Ned and I convinced Cory into going on the road with us. Although we were done working for the winter, I still managed to talk Cory into coming with us. I figured it could just be a good break for Cory until it was time to go back to work. So there we were; Cory, Ned and me, all loaded up and headed on the road to Wisconsin.

That is where Ned was from, Wisconsin. We were all headed to Ned's parents' house. Words to describe Ned's parents would have to include words such as awesome, beautiful, hardcore bikers, loving and welcoming people. Honestly, Ned's entire family was full of very cool people. His stepdad owned a mechanics shop set up right next door to their house. Ned was also a mechanic, along with his stepfather, and they were very good at the work they did. Needless to say, Ned had a job ready for him as soon as we pulled into town.

In my relationship with Ned, one of the downfalls was he was very addicted to marijuana, ganja, 420, the good green. If you have ever done any research on marijuana, you know that only a small amount of users actually become addicted. Ned was one of the few people I had ever met that actually fell into that category. He was a real jerk if he ever ran out of smoke, which didn't happen often. It wasn't long after we arrived in Wisconsin that I was able to find work at a local call center. Cory ended up heading back to Michigan after a short time. He wanted us to come get him when we were heading back on the road to go to work instead of spending the holidays with people he didn't know. I completely understood why he wanted to go and, after we said our goodbyes, he was on his way back to Michigan.

Around Christmastime, someone in the family ran across some acid and picked all of us up a hit. I had never tripped on acid before. In all reality, hard drugs pretty much scared me. After talking to everyone for a while about how to handle it and the environment being safe for a 'good trip', I decided I would give it a try. We kept it in the refrigerator and picked a specific day we would all take it together. The plan was Ned and I and Ned's parents would all do it together. I was nervous, but I was also excited to try it. I had seen Brandon 'trip' on acid one time and it was hilarious. He seemed to really enjoy the buzz it gave him.

The day quickly approached and, before I realized it, it was time to try my first hit of acid. I hate to admit it, but that first time was actually really fun. I enjoyed myself and the body buzz was amazing. It was unlike anything I had ever felt before. I was in a safe environment and no one was messing with me. All of us enjoyed ourselves enough that our cheeks actually became sore from laughing so much. I'll never forget the colorful dancing mice I saw on the wall as we all jammed loudly to Pink Floyd. I always felt safe at Ned's parents' home. I think what I enjoyed the most was the friendship I grew and built with his sister. She was a great person and still is. We ended up becoming dear friends and I loved being a part of her children's lives as well. I didn't feel like an outcast at any time during my stay with Ned and his parents.

This was also the house I saw my very first upside-down Christmas tree. Yes, upside down. It was so cool to look at and I instantly had to know what the meaning of it was. After asking Ned's mom, she told me she just liked the way it looked. I sat and stared at this tree for long amounts of time. To me, I felt it was a great way to express that Christmas isn't about the biggest tree or the most presents. To me, an upside-down tree represented that it's not about what society has turned the holiday into, it's about the birth of our Savior. It isn't about presents, decorations or a tree at all. Ned's mom still put up a regular Christmas tree, but I knew that her idea had sparked up something inside of me that I would treasure forever. Since that Christmas, and every one after, my Christmas trees have been hung upside down and decorated. To this day, I feel that was one of the coolest Christmas trees I had ever seen. I also enjoy and love the way that everyone is amazed when they would walk into my home and see our tree each year.

Now, I always kept my Bible close to me even if I didn't feel close to God. During my winter in Wisconsin, I continued to read my Bible but my relationship with Jesus Christ was a struggle. I knew he existed, I just had a hard time with understanding what he wanted from me. I couldn't figure out how or why all the things I had been through could have been for nothing. What was the purpose and was there a point to all of it? I was really taking more of my time to look at the world around me and not spending enough time searching within me.

Physically, I was still looking good. I literally stopped traffic just walking to the gas station across the street from the house where I stayed. One time there was almost an accident from someone staring at me rather than paying attention to the traffic light. I came to realize that beauty attracts all types, good and bad. I think to actually be famous would be a serious pain in the ass. I was no one special and people looked at me as if I have something they wanted. I was pursued by men and women all the time. I used to wish I could get attention; but, once I was getting the attention, it wasn't all that I thought it would be. My beauty made me question who was really there for me and who was using me. I admit that the time I spent with Ned's family was a great experience. They were all very welcoming and seemed to care deeply for me.

Truth is, the year ended well and I really enjoyed being a part of Ned's family. All of us got along most of the time and it was a pretty peaceful home. I truly enjoyed the friendship I had built with his mother also. She was an older, classy biker woman and I admired her because of the way she carried herself. I was also thankful for the time and all of the great advice she would give me. I recall her talking to me one time and telling me that she had never met anyone like me. She said it was impossible that I was a mix of gypsy, hippie, carnie and biker. I thought it was funny because she was right, I was a mix of everything and couldn't be placed into just one category. We never got into my past too much, but I appreciated the acceptance she always showed me.

The New Year was spent enjoying my new friends and people I considered my new family. We all laughed and got pretty drunk as we brought in 1997.

Chapter EIGHT

1997: As the New Year began, I was still suffering from nightmares of what I endured throughout my childhood; however, I was very thankful that the nightmares only came once a week and sometimes less. By mid-January, Ned and I were both anxious to get back on the road. Even though we enjoyed being around our friends and family, we both had an itch that staying put could never scratch. Ned and I both loved living on the road and going to new places all of the time. As we were planning our trip to pick up Cory and head out to work, Ned received some very sad news. His biological father had passed away from cancer. Instantly our plans were set aside. With no hesitation, we were headed to Wyoming where Ned's biological father and family lived.

It was my first time in Wyoming and the land was beautiful. I enjoyed the breathtaking visuals as we drove through the state. Ned's grandmother was the most beautiful, God-fearing woman I have ever had the chance to sit down and talk to. She owned this huge farm in the middle of nowhere. If I recall correctly, her son or daughter owned the farm across the street. The family was large and it amazed me how they all pulled together to help their grandmother with everything. She did lose one of her children, which is something I am thankful that I cannot relate to. I found it so incredible how everyone rejoiced in the life of Ned's father and, yet, grieved their loss at the same time.

Let me tell you, if you have never had a grandma from Wyoming's cooking, well, you are truly missing out. I had never seen such a large family, not only pull together during a hard time, but boy, could they eat together. Grandma was always cooking and I dare you to tell her you're not hungry. That was an unacceptable excuse to Grandma. She would say, "Everyone needs to eat." That visit was a huge stepping stone for me. I recall sitting back and just admiring the team work and the pure love this family shared with facing such a hard moment in life.

It wasn't just one or two people helping, either, it was several generations growing and loving purely with Jesus Christ as their leader. I couldn't help but admire it. I had hopes that once I had children I could raise them in the same environment. I felt welcome by everyone and no one let me sit out. I was welcomed as part of the family from the moment my foot hit their property. 'Grandma' and I especially had a truly awesome connection and we spent quite a bit of time talking one on one. She talked to me about life, and I remember her saying that she could see I was much older than I should be. She prayed with me and continued to tell me that if I ever needed any help, anything at all, not to forget that I could always call on her. 'Grandma' also called me a beautiful child of God. She told me, "Don't give up on him, he will never give up on you!" She truly made me feel so loved during the time I was in her gracious presence.

The comfort and love that woman showed me was beyond appreciated. During this trip to Wyoming I also had an opportunity to ride a horse for the first time. I thought I would act like I was some professional and had rode a horse before, but I hadn't. I just figured I had seen enough movies to know how to ride. As I was trotting along, I began to feel comfortable enough to have the horse go faster. It was fun until the horse jumped a small ditch that I didn't even see. I was a trooper and held on very tightly, as if I was holding on for dear life. I pulled through the small jump and, once I got back to everyone, the family clapped and acted like I knew what I was doing. They cheered me on saying things like, "Good pull through, it shows you have rode before." I don't know if they were trying to make me feel good or not because I had no clue what I was doing. I suppose I just pretended well. Unfortunately, the next day came and I could barely walk. Every muscle in my body was tender from the ride. I begged Ned not to tell anyone how sore I was, but everyone could tell I was having a hard time moving. Even though I experienced serious physical pain from horseback riding, I still wouldn't have changed a moment of it. After leaving Wyoming, Ned and I headed to Michigan to see Dakota and my mother and, of course, pick up Cory.

Once we got to Michigan our plan was to get Cory and hit the road, but Cory was nervous about going on the road. Cory ended up talking his friend into going with us. Cory's friend wasn't ready to go and we ended up having to wait a few days for him before we could hit the road. While we were waiting on Cory's friend, Ned and I stayed at my mother's house. You must understand that my mother has always been a bit of a freak. She is a sexual person and is not afraid to talk about sex in any way or with anyone. I believe it does have a lot to do with her past; whether she admits it or not. The internet was just starting to get big and mom was having fun with online dating sites. She was making dates and meeting men here and there. Dawn was also living there and was helping my mother with Dakota.

One of the nights while we were there my mother left to spend time with one of her new guy friends. Mom asked me if I would stay at the house and keep an eye on my little brother and I had no problem with that. I was there to visit with Dakota anyway. Later that same night, Dawn and this guy she was seeing got extremely drunk. I believe that Dawn and her boyfriend ended up having sex in my mother's room, but I wasn't babysitting Dawn. I looked at it as she lived there, not me, so she would have to answer for her actions. What was worse is, by the end of the night, the guy she was seeing ended up so drunk he pissed all over my mother's couch.

The next day when my mother returned from her date night she noticed that things were not right with the house. Ned and I had left before she got there, so I had no idea how Dawn was going to explain everything. When I returned to my mom's, she acted angry toward me and said that Dawn ended up telling her how everything happened, including the piss on the couch. My mom explained that Dawn told her that the house was a wreck because of me and that Dawn had nothing to do with it. I exploded in anger and kept asking my mother if she really believed that. When I saw Dawn walking in from the living room, I didn't ask any questions or for any explanations. I allowed my anger to take the best of me and I didn't hesitate; I instantly shoved Dawn into the staircase by her neck. My mother literally caught my fist in midair, giving Dawn the chance to duck down and run out of the house. I didn't see or speak to Dawn again until 2003.

Even with everything that had happened between Paul and me, we did stay in touch. Paul had went back and rented a home in Alabama. He was still fighting for custody of the girls. I ended up making a quick trip down to see Paul and the kids. Ned just went to work on another show when I made the trip. While I was visiting, Paul and I discussed a business deal in regard to putting me, Cory and Ned to work. I was definitely good with being put manager over two games and the split (pay) was a great offer. I headed back to Michigan to meet up with Ned and soon after Paul came up. We set up our games and went to work. What a crew we had with Ned, Me, Cory, Paul and the rest of us. At one point we ended up heading south for work. I even had a pimped-out, double-room tent. We would set our tent up at each spot we worked. I had one of those awesome kid recliners and a two burner gas stove top in order to cook our food. It looked great with a tiny living room and a tiny bedroom. Yes, a pimped out tent.

The carnival life may not be exactly what you picture if you have never lived it. One of the carnival shows we worked on was so big it actually had a homeschooling program and a Church. You have no idea how amazing it was on Sundays before we opened, watching all the carnies gathered and worshiping. When you think of a carnie, do you think about the dirty looking guy whose teeth aren't all that pretty? That dirty old guy probably fought in a war, wife passed away or was simply left alone in life. Perhaps you're one of those people that believe different jobs or social stature puts all of us 100% on different levels. Truth is, we don't truly know what one another are going through or have been through. We aren't on different levels because of some social stature, we are all equal. Judging others does not provide one of the most important necessities of life, which is love.

Love is the key. When we get hurt we abandon that truth. Usually, we then blame God for not protecting us from the hurt that our own decisions probably took us to. Embrace love even when you feel so far away from it, even when you think you'll never understand or have love. We are here, living this life in order to lift one another. Spend one day constantly making yourself think about others and how to lift them. If it is a simple compliment, paying for the person behind you in any line, whatever. Take notice of the waitress or the upset cashier and try to make them smile. If they don't, just walk away with love and prayer for that person. Do it for one day and you will feel a difference within yourself.

> *"If you want to lift yourself up, lift someone else"*
> *-Booker T. Washington, 1856*

I enjoyed the love that was shared on most of the carnival shows I worked. It was like having a huge family that always had one another's backs. Although I truly did like the agreement Paul and I had with the games we set up, we weren't making very much money. Ned and I decided to leave and work on another Midway for a short time to try to make more money. Cory decided to stay with Paul and work. Paul wasn't happy with the show he was on either. In the end, Paul also changed carnival shows. He was now playing a spot in Philadelphia. In May, I took my first train ride to meet back up with Paul from Chicago to Philadelphia. I couldn't believe that there was even a bar on the train and where I was at most of the ride. I may have only been 19 years old, but I had no problems getting into bars. From the moment I joined the carnival I really had no problem getting into any place I wanted to.

I loved the experience I had in downtown Philly. I walked around alone and looked through all the stores. The people were very friendly and the entire city was so beautiful. The city was full of different cultures from all over the world. I'm not a lover of big cities as far as living in them, but I love to visit and go shopping. I may be many things, but please don't forget that I am all woman. Travel and shopping is what I call a good day.

Working in Philly was adventurous. People walked around smoking blunts and then a cop would walk past like he didn't notice anything. It was crazy how the people were so carefree and didn't worry about the officers walking around in the same area. The money was great too. If you have ever played my game at the carnival with me, let me take this moment to say thank you. I hope you had a good experience and I at least made you smile. I think that was what I loved most about the carnival, making others smile. You get to meet so many different people and learn so much about how different we all are yet how we truly are the same.

Paul also had the girls in Philly with him. They ended up coming out for his visitation. He proposed to me again, even though I was dating Ned. I knew I wasn't in love with Ned because I still thought about Ezra --- someone special I will introduce later ---- but I was still in a relationship even if it wasn't wholehearted. Paul knew everything about me and he was my best friend for many years. He just loved me differently than I loved him. Not long after I arrived in Philadelphia, Ned ended up driving out to Philadelphia to work with us. Even though I knew I was breaking Paul's heart, I just couldn't agree to marry him and spend my life with him. I ended up telling Paul no.

I didn't look at Paul the same way after we broke up. I only saw him as my best friend and business partner. We traveled with Paul for a short time, but Ned and I ended up leaving for Kentucky to play with another show. Cory had fallen for a girl at the show Paul was working and decided to stay there and begin his life adventure. I have only seen and spoken to Cory once since then. By August, Ned and I had broken up and went our separate ways. By then, Paul was back in Michigan so I headed up to where he was set up and working. He made another deal with me and I was once again in charge of a couple of our games. The truth is, I had nowhere else to go. Since I was in Michigan I, of course, stopped in to see Dakota.

My brother Derek and his girlfriend, Ina, were living with my mom and Dakota. Dawn had moved out and was no longer living there. Derek and I still remained at a distance in our relationship, but he was and always will be my big brother. When I found out Derek was actually hanging out with and helping Frank and Carl, it just made me angry at him. I always looked up to my brother, and he didn't let any guys mess with me so I thought he should be hurting those men not helping them. But that was not what happened. He never wanted to hear about any of the things that happened, so I just stopped trying to understand why or explain what I had been through. I decided it was more important to have Derek in my life than worry about what he should or should not do about what happened to me.

Derek and Ina were really cool to hang out with and they came to the fair I was working at on my 20th birthday. There was a large beer tent with a cover band that was playing called 'Disturbed'. As we walked into this large, crowded tent it was almost like a dream. Derek and Ina were behind me as we walked in. It was insane the way people just started to separate, leaving me a path as if I was some superstar. I kept my eyes straight ahead and on both sides of me people just started turning, looking at me, then clearing a path. I literally walked us straight up to the front of the stage. Ina and Derek both called it out and I just acted like it was nothing. The truth is, that had never happened to me before. I was used to a lot of attention when I entered a room, but that was incredible. As I reflect on it now, I know I reacted like it was 'no big deal', because I was just trying to impress my big brother, but, honestly, I thought it was awesome and I still do.

While I was still in Michigan I stopped in to visit with Brandon. Sadie was at work when I made it to their apartment, so she and I didn't get a chance to see one another. It was funny, you would have thought that I had never left the way Brandon and I talked to one another. Sadie and I weren't real close in school, but I could see how much Brandon loved her and how happy he was. Sadie really changed Brandon and they truly brought the good out in one another. It didn't matter how I felt about Sadie in school, at this point in life I accepted her as she was because I loved Brandon and was happy for him. After our visit I needed to decide what I was going to do and where I was going to go. I felt like being around Paul was misleading him. The winter months were right around the corner which meant it was time to settle down till the next season for carnival work. At this time I was single and wasn't sure what or where I was going in life. I decided to head back to Wisconsin for the winter months. I had a job anytime I needed one at the local call center, and I had made several friends while I was there the previous winter. Even though it was where Ned grew up, I felt welcome there and thought I could get through the winter safely. Once I got set up with my own apartment, I asked one of my friends if she wanted to be roommates. I thought it would help me with bills and I wouldn't be alone. She was a beautiful, long-haired blond, really sweet young lady. I believe we were the same age and we got along really well.

We did party a little too much and one night it happened. We both had drank too much and realized that neither of us had experimented with a woman. We were both clean, beautiful and our curiosity got the best of us. I can say I thought it was fun and different, but it didn't do much for me as far as sexual satisfaction. I had never explored a woman's body, but I have always believed that women are beautiful, just as men are beautiful (or handsome, for you men that think being called beautiful is offensive). We were just two women exploring our sexuality. The experience didn't change anything between us and our friendship remained good.

During this winter I also had the pleasure of meeting Ezra. This man was like no other I had ever met, and I had met thousands of men by this time. Ezra was on leave from the military and was visiting his family for the holidays. Although he knew Ned, a mutual friend had introduced us. He was in the Army and was stationed in Georgia. From the moment I met Ezra I felt something in my heart that I had never felt before. He took my breath away and he wasn't after sex, he was a gentleman. He was close to my age and an Army man. I had never felt such strong feelings for someone so fast. Ezra gave me 'butterflies'.

We spent some time getting to know one another and talking about life. We connected on so many levels, from music to food. He was also an awesome skateboarder and he really seemed like he could be the one to change everything for me. See, I spent a lot of my life trying to find a man to complete me. You know, the one we dream about as a little girl, or boy (vice versa). Like in the movies, the ones that don't exist yet, we enjoy torturing ourselves believing that somehow, someone can complete us. Only one person can complete you and that person is you. No other man or woman can fulfill that emptiness we all feel at times in life. You have to forgive yourself and move forward. Learn to be happy with yourself, but don't spend all of your life focused on yourself. Lifting others can in turn lift you. Meeting Ezra made me feel like I had a chance at being happy, but there was so much from my past that I had yet to face or deal with.

Ezra and I ended up making a business agreement on a 1978 Chevy Camaro. It was the most beautiful car I have ever owned. It had a high Edelbrock intake, Holley double pumpers, and a dual exhaust. It was my pride and joy! I'll be honest, I've never actually known what any of that stuff means, but I know what kind of power that car had and all of those things contributed to that power.

The Camaro was deep purple and had a pearl glitter coating on the top. The color was called Hawaiian Orchid. I was a badass woman already, but now I also had a badass car. I would get challenged at stoplights all the time, and I had no fear of pushing on the gas. I was never beat when racing in that car. It seemed like life was coming together: I had a beautiful car and I only had interest in one person. I truly didn't want anyone except Ezra. I was sad when Ezra had to head back to Georgia, but we agreed to stay in touch.

It didn't take long before we began writing letters back and forth all the time. Ezra and I also began talking on the phone, and I admit I loved that man's voice. He was incredible and I quickly fell madly in love with him. I was and am a huge fan of Janis Joplin, The Doors and a lot of older music, and Ezra loved all of it too. I also loved that he introduced me to bands and music that I had never heard of before. We continued to write through the entire winter. The holidays were good and Dakota came to spend a couple weeks with me. He had the biggest crush on my roommate when he stayed with us, which was no shocker because she was beautiful. The year had finally come to a close, and I was positive 1998 would be the best year of my life because I planned to spend every moment I could with Ezra.

Chapter NINE

1998: After the New Year, Ezra ended up getting another leave and came to spend a weekend with me. It was so magical and every moment of it felt so right. I had never given myself as completely as I did to Ezra. It felt surreal to me. Making love to him was like being in another world. His visit was even better than I had dreamed it would be and we were on a path of commitment in a way I had never thought possible for me. I wanted him to know all of me, and I wanted to know all of him. I knew he was the man I wanted to spend my life with.

After Ezra left I started having problems with Ned. He had also come back to Wisconsin for the winter and he was acting like a stalker. He was threatening me and even threatened to cause damage to my car. The man was a great mechanic and I knew he could easily do something to destroy my car. I ended up putting it in hiding at my roommate's friend's house. It was my poor roommate that ended up having her tires slashed.

I didn't have a lot of money, had nowhere to turn, and so I called Ned's grandma in Wyoming. After I explained to her everything that was going on, she ended up sending me $500 to get out of there. I loaded up my car and hit the road. I was not sure what I was going to do, but I knew I was headed to the Army base in Georgia. I remember the closer I got the more my tummy was fluttering. When I would stop to get gas I would look up at the stars and think to myself, "We aren't that far from one another." Ezra and I were under the same sky and that alone brought me comfort. I didn't tell him I was heading his way, I just wanted to surprise him.

I couldn't stay away from Ezra. It was almost like I was drawn to him and he to me. Our conversations and the way we looked into one another's eyes was intense. I shared with him some of my past, but I was afraid to tell anyone the whole truth of everything. The shame held me down. Once I arrived, I spent all my time at the barracks with Ezra and with all of his Army buddies. We had a blast and I got along with all of his friends. I found that I wasn't attracted to any other man on the entire Army base. The only man I wanted was Ezra and, when one of the guys would hit on me, I wasn't shy to let it be known that I belonged fully to Ezra.

I will never forget the nights we would all load up and head to downtown Savannah, Georgia. It is so beautiful at night and the life that flows through the streets is breathtaking. Ezra, myself and usually at least two other guys would spend our nights playing pool and wandering in and out of the pubs and coffee shops. The boys would bring their skateboards and do some of the coolest tricks I had ever seen. Yes, I knew who Tony Hawk was then and who he is now. I mean it when I say these guys really had some talent, including Ezra.

Ezra was so good to me and he was just a good man altogether. For Valentine's he bought me a tattoo; which, if you know me at all, was the best Valentine's present ever. One night that stands out the most to me is St. Patrick's Day (I remember because of all the green beer). Ezra and I were walking and holding one another close when we came upon a man sitting on the ground outside of a small pub with his guitar in hand and the case open in front of him for tips. Ezra asked the man if he knew 'Time in a Bottle' by Jim Croce. The man, with his broken teeth, smiled up at Ezra and began playing his guitar. I fell more in love with not only Ezra, but fell in love with that song. I have it on my playlist even to this day. Those moments with Ezra were so dear to me. We had some funny moments, also, like when the boys' Sergeant came in for a surprise room inspection. I wasn't allowed to be there, so I had to hide underneath one of the beds. I have no idea how, but I didn't get caught. It was so crazy, but we all laughed about it once the inspection was over. The guys and I lived on Hot Pockets and video games: It was the life.

After some time I needed to get to work and start making some money. I referred back to my Amusement Business magazine and found a show that was about two hours away. When I said goodbye to Ezra it crushed me, but he knew that I had to get to work. I drove off and cried like a baby the entire time. When I finally made it to the lot, I turned my car off and just sat there staring at the carnival workers setting up the rides. I kept asking myself why I couldn't just settle down and get a regular, normal job. What was stopping me from being a productive member of society except myself? I kept thinking that I did it in the winter months and the carnival wasn't even as much fun as it used to be. I actually sat there for over an hour praying, crying and just unsure of what move to make for myself. Hours later I found myself sitting on Ezra's lap with tears rolling down my cheeks. I asked him if he would like to try and build a life with me. I told him I loved him and just wanted to be with him.

Ezra said he felt the same way about me and, the next thing I knew, we were apartment searching. We found our own place off base. It was perfect, and I was ready for a fresh, clean start with the man I was madly in love with. I felt ready to commit my life to being settled down and just being happy with Ezra. Ezra's mother lived in South Carolina, which wasn't far from where we were located. We ended up going to her house because Ezra's things were there. I knew from the first moment I met her that she didn't feel I was worthy of her son.

After we arrived I told Ezra several times that I felt underdressed. Here I was, this hippie, gypsy, biker and as unique as they come. When we were at his extremely wealthy mother's home, I was wearing a pair of corduroys and a half-cut belly shirt with a baggy flannel shirt over top. Now, I can fit into any crowd with the right clothes, and I was even taught good manners. I knew how to act like an upper class lady; however, I will never forget it because Ezra didn't think that the clothes I was wearing mattered. I knew they were inappropriate for meeting his mother and the first impression she had on me was an epic fail.

We rented a U-Haul and loaded up all of Ezra's things, which filled our apartment up. All I owned at the time was my car and what I could fit into it. We were in the apartment for two or three days when Ezra finally had time to go to town and have our utilities turned on. Ezra and I woke up and he took the car to handle our utilities as I began unpacking everything. It seemed like he was gone forever, but it was about six hours. I ended up getting everything unpacked and laying down to take a nap.

When Ezra walked in he was dressed in his uniform and had this pale look on his face. He said he was being deployed the next day and had to go back to the base as soon as possible. He told me that we didn't have much time and he needed me to take him back. The emptiness and heartache I felt was so strong I thought I was going to die. Why couldn't I just catch a break? Why did everything have to be crazy all the time? I wasn't prepared for Ezra to be deployed and I had no idea how to handle it.

Ezra made arrangements with his mom and asked me to go live with her until he came home. He told me he needed me to be strong for him, and I truly tried to be, but I wasn't strong at all. Truth is, inside I felt like my heart was going to explode from the pain. When I got home I just dropped to my knees and cried. I didn't know how to handle my love being sent to another country to fight a war that didn't even make sense to me. I don't know why, because I knew she didn't like me, but I did agree to go stay with his mother. The next day Ezra left. His mother, stepfather and I loaded everything back up in another U-Haul and headed to their home in South Carolina.

Ezra's parents' home was absolutely beautiful and in a very wealthy neighborhood. This was by far one of the most expensive homes I had been in at my age. The back yard was so big and the room that his mother gave me was downstairs. It was extremely large and could have been two living rooms easy. His mom acted friendly, yet she was politely rude to me. I knew she didn't want me there by the way she treated me. His mother thought that I was just out to use Ezra. In her eyes, I was beneath the girls that were already beneath her standards. I never cared about Ezra having money. I actually had no idea that he was from a wealthy family until I met his mother. I was madly in love with who he was and just wanted to be with him.

One day we went to the mall and his mom offered to buy me bras. I really did need some and I didn't want to seem rude. I felt like the biggest idiot that day because, as I tried on the bras, I realized they were 40 and 50 bucks a piece. She was all nonchalant about paying that much for several of them, but I couldn't accept that. I felt that was way too expensive and even offered to go somewhere cheaper. She insisted on buying them and it brought me to tears. It wasn't just that she wanted to spend that much money on me, it was because in that moment I was so thankful that she was willing. I ended up refusing the offer. I explained to her that was just too much for bras. When I refused her offer, I believe she took offense to it and it truly offended her which was far from my intention.

I believe that when she saw my tears she just thought I was ridiculous. It was like she looked at me as if I was a street urchin because after that everything changed. Ezra called in the middle of the night and she would tell me about it in the morning. She said she didn't want to wake me. I was crying all the time, and I felt like my world would never be right. She wasn't very nice to me, and I could feel her dislike toward me at all times. I tried so hard to make her happy and help around the house, but it didn't change anything. Daily she made me feel like I was unworthy to be there.

I knew I needed some support from people who knew me and accepted me as I was. I asked her if I could clean the house for a little gas money until I was able to get a job. I explained that I wanted to go to the base and hang out with the guys. She took that so wrong and it just made her think less of me, but she agreed to it. It was soon after she agreed to pay me for cleaning that Ezra's mother and I went to some fancy horse riding place and she actually introduced me as her live in maid.

I didn't know how to react and there was no way I was going to say anything rude to this woman because I loved Ezra. I just went home and did what I had been doing for weeks, I cried. Eventually, I was able to get a break and head down to see the guys at the base in Georgia. I just hung out with our friends and didn't disrespect my man in any way. One of the guys really tried hard to get with me, but I was 100% dedicated to

Ezra so it wasn't happening. It was a great weekend and it was nice to be around the people that lifted me and didn't judge me.

After my visit with our friends, I made it safely back to South Carolina. As I pulled into Ezra's mother's driveway the feeling was so heavy because I knew I would never be good enough for her. She sat me down the day after I got back and said that her and her husband were going to be leaving for Arizona and she didn't want to leave me in their home alone. It hurt my feelings so much, and I knew it was her way of getting rid of me. Ironically, years later I learned that the girl they had hired to housesit while they were gone actually ended up robbing them.

After packing my things into my car I left Ezra's mother's crying and completely lost. The only place I thought to go so that I could wait for Ezra to come home was back to Wisconsin, so that is where I headed. I talked to my old landlord, who had been going through a divorce from his wife, and his Army buddy, who was discharged and now living with him. My old upstairs apartment was still available and he was willing to rent it out to me again. During this time, the letters I wrote to Ezra were so depressing. I was the worst support for a man fighting for our country.

I was broken and felt like I would never have peace or happiness. I cried all the time and couldn't write about happiness and joy, which is what he desperately needed. As time went on, my landlord's friend ended up coming up to my apartment one night and brought a fifth of Southern Comfort. I was crying about Ezra and ended up getting really drunk. I don't remember too much of the evening other than telling the guy, "No" a few times.   That apparently wasn't enough. When I woke up, I went off on that man so bad he was crying when he left my house. I lived in a smaller town and had a small group of friends. Everyone seemed to know everyone else, so the news of me having sex with that guy spread quickly. It wasn't news of me being taken advantage of; nope, it was of me cheating on the man of my dreams, Ezra.

I knew I couldn't stay there any longer. Lost and alone, I packed up my car with no plan and drove until I was almost out of gas. I had very little money left and had only made it to Peru, Indiana. I pulled into a campground and asked for a place to set up my tent, but the people said it was too cold for a tent. I argued with them. I explained I had heaters, I just needed somewhere to stay for a week or two. I had no clue what or where I was supposed to go. By God's good grace the folks had an empty camper and agreed to rent it to me for the week.

I stayed in that small camper for days, not even paying attention to the sunlight that tried to shine through the windows. I spent my time crying, praying and reading my bible. I also read a book by Pastor Kenneth Copeland called *"Honor: Walking in Honesty, Truth & Integrity."* By the time I came out of that camper I felt just as lost as I had when I walked into it. I thought I would have some miraculous recovery and know all God had planned for me, but I didn't. I knew I had to get to work, that I couldn't just stay locked in that trailer forever. The folks that rented the trailer to me told me about a small carnival nearby. I decided to check it out.

As I walked the small Midway, I ran into an awesome couple who owned and operated a few of the games. We talked for a while and they offered me a position plus my own housing in the back of the game. I'll never forget when I realized how God had taken me out of that small trailer and actually placed me somewhere that I could work. I took a mental note that no matter what, even if I have nothing, not even a plan, God can always provide.

It's amazing how we can realize some of the brightest things in our darkest places. This couple, whom I came to love, said they would work on getting permission from the show owner to build a Circle of Science game for me. I was insanely consumed by thoughts of Ezra. I constantly thought about what I should have done different: How I could have stopped that guy. How everything would have been different if I hadn't drank with him. I knew he had a thing for me, but I thought I was stronger.

I was always calling friends back in Wisconsin checking to see if anyone had heard from Ezra yet. One day it happened and I found myself on the phone with Ezra. By then, the word went around that I was a slut who slept around. I think by this time someone even told Ezra I had some STD (sexually transmitted disease). I will never forget how hard my heart sunk when Ezra said, "I just wish you could have kept your legs together!" After we hung up I simply sat in a puddle of tears for hours. I ended up getting a fifth of Jägermeister, sometimes two, every day after that phone call.

I was drinking heavily and fell into a deep depression. Ezra was all I could think about. I convinced myself that I could never love another the way I would always love him. Now, being an independent owner on a carnival show simply means the show doesn't own your games or inventory, you're paying rent to put your games up with their rides and games. The show I was on was a smaller carnival and the owners were not the friendliest people. My bosses, however, were independent owners which meant I was their employee, not the shows. They continued to reassure me that, if I stayed, they would get my joint (game) built. I knew I could make good money with my game so I stayed.

I couldn't get Ezra out of my head. I convinced myself that drinking was helping numb the pain, but it never did. One night I was extremely drunk and I ended up calling Paul. I asked him to come get me. I told him I would marry him and that I was over everything. As I cried I told him I just wanted him to take care of me. In the time it took me to speak the words, Paul was in his truck and on his way to Indiana.

The very next day I was still really drunk and I ended up hanging out with one of the ride jocks (man/woman that run and operate the rides). His name was Chad. Chad was over 6'1" and about eight years older than me. He was a good looking man even though his teeth were very messed up. Something about him made me feel comfort. His eyes were kind and he talked sweetly, as if he just wanted to learn all he could about me. I told him about what happened with Ezra and how I was hurting. Chad was a big biker-looking man - Tattoos, long hair, love for Harley Davidsons and all of that, yet he was the most passive man. He seemed to genuinely care about my pain. Of course, it could have been the alcohol. Chad and I continued drinking even more after work. As the night went on, Chad and I ended up having sex. I just closed my eyes and pictured Ezra the entire time. I had been talking to Chad on and off for a few weeks by that time, but I compared every man I spoke to with Ezra. In my eyes, Chad didn't compare and had no chance with me. For some reason, when Satan would pop up and say, "Hey girl, come party, you're hurting too much," I didn't hesitate. The next day I worked and drank, as usual. Even though Paul was on his way, I was too drunk to even realize it. Chad ended up staying the night with me and we woke up to Paul banging on my door.

There are no words for how horrible I felt. Chad was pissed and wanted to kick Paul's ass, but I put him in his place quick. I told him that Paul was a dear friend and would always be a part of my life. I also told Chad that it was my fault Paul was there so he better just keep his mouth shut. I tried to alibi to Paul that I was extremely intoxicated when I asked him to come. I never meant to mislead Paul, he was the only person in my entire life that was always there when I needed a friend.

I tried not to call Paul often because I knew he wanted me as a wife and not a friend. I also knew that if I needed someone to talk to he would always answer my call despite that truth. Even if it was to just talk about the Bible or God, he would answer and talk to me. He promised he would always be there for me when we met and he always kept his word. Paul and I spent the night together at a hotel just talking about everything, how angry he was at me for having him come all that way and the fact that I was sleeping with Chad.

He wanted me to leave with him, but I didn't want to. I told him that I could never love him fully because I loved Ezra, the man that didn't want me. He was hurt by my words, but he told me he could see I truly loved Ezra and he understood. When he left he told me that he would always be there if I needed him, but he couldn't be just my friend. Paul explained that when I got over Ezra and was ready to come 'home' then I could call him. The next morning Paul and I said our goodbyes and he was back on the road.

123

After Paul left I continued drinking at least a fifth a day. Most of the time it was more. It became normal for me to wake up and go straight to a fifth of Jägermeister every morning. It didn't matter if it was piss warm, I didn't care. I just didn't want to feel anything.

I will never forget playing this one spot in Indiana. There was a small local bar right behind my game. I was in and out of that place the entire spot. There was an old veteran that hung out there all the time. Every time I went in, he and I would talk about how crazy life can be. He and I became friends quickly and he would always say that, when he was there, I would never pay for any of my drinks and I never did. One specific night he bought me 32 shots of Jägermeister and Butterscotch Schnapps. I only know that because the next day the bartender told me she had counted.

Everyone, especially Chad, was worried that I was going to end up with alcohol poisoning that night. Honestly, I am not sure how I didn't or end up even worse. During this time in my life I would often wake up in a pile of puke, not even remembering getting sick. I was a train wreck. I just drank and worked. I fought tears and misery with alcohol. My game, the Circle of Science, was finally permitted to be built and I started rocking. My pockets started growing with money now that I was able to work the game I was trained for, the game that I love.

Chad hated me drinking as soon as I woke up and we fought about it a lot. He ran and operated a ride so he couldn't drink until we were closed. I, however, could drink when I woke up and made way more money than Chad. I tried to tell him that he had people's lives in his hands, I only dealt with their money. I am not sure how I even functioned on some days, but I always managed to get through them. Chad drank heavily at night and I just drank all the time. I was consumed with nothing but the pain of how I messed everything up with Ezra.

Chad knew that my heart belonged to Ezra. I was honest about that from day one. As I got to know more about Chad, I found out he was into pills and was educated with experimenting in more drugs than I was. He was actually facing charges at the time and hadn't gone to court yet. He did let me know there was a chance he would have to go to jail eventually. He promised not to mess around with pills and hard drugs when we discussed being together. I really didn't care, because I had no intention of staying with anyone for very long. I hated life and myself. I blamed myself for everything that had happened to me. Everything was because of choices I made.

I was consumed with 'what if'. What if Ezra had never deployed? What if I hadn't left for the base when I stayed at his mom's? What if I would have said no louder to that guy? 'What if' became my taunting misery for years. I couldn't even tell you how many nights I cried myself to sleep. I even cried while having sex with Chad. He never noticed, which just hurt me more. Even though the show owners were related to Chad, they didn't seem to like him very much, especially when he started hanging out with me. They felt like I was distracting him from his work.

Chad was not the type of man I would have normally gone for, but I was so lost and very intoxicated all the time I ended up just staying with him. At one point, Chad's sister and mother came out to one of our spots. The first time I met Chad's sister she almost made me cry. She was one of the coldest people I'd ever met. I never really enjoyed nor liked being around her, she is very different. I tried talking to her and even gave her a free prize, but she didn't care and made it clear. She's one of those people who don't care about anyone unless it personally affects her. She was a very cold-hearted person.

Although I was still drinking heavily I finally stopped drinking daily. We ended up playing a spot near Chicago and Paul had the girls in Michigan. We still talked on the phone often and the girls were always in touch with me throughout the years. The girls wanted to see me as much as I did them, so Paul brought them to stay with me. They stayed with Chad and me for a weekend while Paul went to work on another show. After Paul and I had a deep conversation about it, we made a huge decision together. The girls had continued to become curious about marijuana and they asked if I could be the first to smoke with them. Paul and I always told the girls that if they ever wanted to try or do anything they needed to come to one of us first. Even after everything Paul and I had been through I tried hard to stay in all three of the kids' lives as much as possible.

I am not going to sit here and argue with you about whether smoking pot should be legal or not. Nor will I get into it with you with regard to if you can love God and still smoke pot. When it comes down to it, I am just sharing my story with you. My story, not my justifications. The girls both smoked their first joint with me and not with a stranger. The night was fun and the visit went all too quickly. Before I knew it, Paul was on his way to pick them up.

"There is one lawgiver, who is able to save and to destroy: who art thou that judgest another?" - James 4:12

Soon after Paul came and picked the kids up Chad did something to piss the show owner off, which really didn't take much. Chad was thrown off the show and asked me to give him a ride to his mom's, which was only an hour or so away. We loaded his things up and we were on our way to his mother's house. I remember I just kept thinking that once I dropped Chad off I was not going to see him ever again. This was the out I needed and wanted.

It wasn't something he had done, I was just ready to move on because he wasn't Ezra and never would be. As we drove down the highway, I happened to look in the rearview mirror and I saw lights flashing. I was being pulled over. Chad told me he had a pipe in his belongings and he couldn't take the fall because he was still facing charges. I was nervous and I think the cop could tell. That was the first time I had been pulled over or had anything to do with cops since turning 18 years old, but knowing Chad had a pipe in my car made me even more nervous.

The officer ended up running both of our I.D.s and, because of Chad's record, he requested to search my car. At that time I didn't realize how long his criminal record actually was until I obtained a copy years later. When the officer found the pipe and asked who it belonged to, Chad looked at me with those huge brown eyes and told the officer it wasn't his. The officer then turned to me and I admitted the stupid pipe was mine. Now, I smoked pot but that pipe didn't belong to me. But I covered for Chad and was placed under arrest for the very first time in my life. It took Chad three days to finally come and bail me out.

I had never been to jail before but, for some reason, I wasn't even scared. Don't get me wrong, I cried when the handcuffs were placed on me but, once we started going through booking, I was hard as a rock. I knew that no matter what happened I would handle myself. It was a trick of the trade and I could adjust to any surrounding and I knew that. Once through booking, nothing was as I thought or pictured, nor how the movies make it look.

Perhaps it was just me, but I compared a lot of what was supposed to be 'normal' to movies. After being placed in general population I was accepted by most of the women that were there. Most of the women were there for minor offenses and were just as nervous as I was. I ended up talking 'girl talk' and playing cards for three days. It really wasn't that bad. The food really sucked, but the company was actually enjoyable. Once Chad finally made it to bail me out, I felt obligated to stay with him. As soon as we left the jail, Chad and I went to his hometown and ended up going to a few bars.

At the bars Chad had no problem showing me off and introducing me to his friends. He was proud to have such a young, good looking woman on his arm. After an evening of drinking and having fun meeting new people, he took me to his mother and sister's house. Now, my first visit to his mother's house was rough. I may have lived in a tent at certain points in my life, but I had always kept my home clean.

I remember it vividly because, when I went to the bathroom, I refused to even sit on the toilet because it was so dirty. As I squatted to pee, I looked around, a little wobbly from the alcohol. I realized there was a pair of underwear with a dirty pad still stuck in them on the pile of dirty clothes right next to me. I almost puked I was so grossed out. We didn't stay there long, and I ended up talking Chad into moving to Wisconsin for the winter with me. After he bailed me out I just felt it wouldn't be right to leave him behind, and I wasn't staying there.

We moved to Wisconsin and stayed with a friend that I had worked at the call center with. She was a single mom and wanted to help us out. Both Chad and I were able to quickly find jobs and began saving money for our own place. By November, Chad and I were not clicking well. I was miserable with Chad and we agreed we should go our separate ways. The night before Chad was supposed to leave we ended up having break up sex. I knew the moment it happened; I was pregnant. Chad didn't end up leaving the next day. We worked through the fight and decided to keep trying in our relationship. Soon after, we were able to move into a small upstairs apartment.

It wasn't long after we got our apartment that it was confirmed, I was pregnant. Everything changed for me in that moment. I prayed and asked God to stop the demons that I knew existed in my family. I begged him to show me how to stop them from being passed to my child. I vowed to change the way I had been living and to always be a good mom. Even though my dreams were still filled with thoughts of Ezra, I felt that I had to try with Chad. He was the father of my child now. Although I wasn't in love with Chad, I wanted to make things work for our child's sake.

It was soon after finding out I was pregnant that I was going through a stoplight at 25 mph and I ended up hitting a bronco straight on. It totaled my Camaro and, I admit, I cried like a baby. Ezra had pretty much built that car inside and out. It was all I had left of him and, in that moment, I felt like I lost him all over again. I ended up with an older car and have never had anything as nice as that car since. I miss it to this day with all honesty.

Not long after wrecking my car, Dakota came to visit for a couple of weeks. He ended up stuck with us for longer than planned due to a heavy snow storm. Mom was off with whoever her guy friend was at that time. Mom was a huge swinger. Once dad was out of the picture, it all came out even more. Dakota was spoiled and he did as he pleased, but so did I when I lived with my mother. Our visit went great, as it always did.

Dakota and I never stayed out of touch for too long.

Spending time with Dakota was like spending time with Dean, my stepson. I always saw Dakota more like my son than my brother. He called me whenever he needed advice or help with anything. He has also always inspired me to be the best I can and even to write this book. The purpose of this book is not to hurt anyone, it is simply me being honest about where I am from and what I have overcome. I believe that each day has a purpose and meaning, it is how you choose to live it that can make a difference. It's choosing to rise above your past and your hardships with your head held high and with no fear of judgment because there is only one that has a right to judge me, there is only one I will have to answer to for my sins.

Take it one day at a time if you have to. Don't become your own worst enemy and allow stress and worry to consume you. When you feel negative thoughts coming on, give praise, help someone, focus on you children and take yourself away from yourself by focusing on someone else. You ask how is it you can help someone else in a moment you feel your weakest? Sounds like some crazy thing to do when all you want to do is cry, but pull it together and lift someone else and it will lift you in the end.

> *"One man cannot hold another man down in a ditch*
> *without remaining down in the ditch with him"*
> *- Booker T. Washington*

As the New Year approached, I took notice as to how well Chad and Dakota got along. I was trying my hardest to love Chad fully. I did love Chad for being the father of my child, but I was never in love with Chad. My heart belonged to Ezra and I couldn't give it to anyone else. Even though we got along most of the time and Chad did love me deeply, I believed there was always a part of me he could never reach nor have. I felt like Ezra would always hold my heart and my pure love. When the New Year came, I had no idea where I was headed. All I knew was that I was going to be the best mother I could be for my child.

Chapter TEN

1999: As soon as I found out I was pregnant, I quit drinking alcohol and started praying. I turned to my bible and started talking to God about everything. I was afraid that I would end up being a mom like my own and I refused to allow that to happen. I was also afraid of my child being sexually abused and I made a promise to God that stays between him and me to this day. I started purchasing every book you could find on pregnancy and being a parent. I was studying everything I could get my hands on.

Soon after January, Ina, Derek's girlfriend, also announced she was pregnant. I wish that she and I would have lived closer throughout our pregnancies, but we didn't and it wasn't meant to be that way. Chad and I also drove from Wisconsin to Indiana early in the year for my court date for the charge I was facing for possession of paraphernalia, Chad's pipe I went to jail for. When I met with the prosecutor he told me he was just going to dismiss all charges. I didn't argue with that at all.

While we were in Indiana, Chad and I stopped by to see his family. After the visit ended, we decided that things would be easier if we moved to Indiana where all of his family was. I swore my child would not be exposed to the horrific things my family had exposed me to. I wanted my child to understand the importance of family. I wasn't happy about the move, but I knew that Chad's family would unite and help us through the pregnancy.

We lived with his mother and sister at first and I spent much of my time cleaning. Once the house was clean, I stayed on top of keeping things picked up. Chad's family was different than others I had been around. They had a love and dedication to one another that may not have been the healthiest, but I felt that it was way better than my family. Chad wasn't close to his dad, but he was close to the rest of his family.

Chad would want to go drink on the weekends and I didn't want to make him feel like I was holding him back in any way. I would walk up to the bar and spend hours up there with him as he drank. I began doing what I could to please Chad. I didn't even want to be with Chad; yet, here I was - stuck, pregnant and feeling alone. I was still consumed with thoughts and dreams about Ezra. I didn't think I would ever get over that man.

A couple months after we moved to Indiana, Chad and I got into a huge fight and I decided I had enough. I loaded my car and headed down to Alabama where Paul was living. When I arrived, Paul was welcoming and the girls came often to visit. They still lived with their mother and Paul was still fighting to get them back. He was upset that I was pregnant because, he said, it should have been his child. He just wanted to be with me and build a family. He said he would love the child as his own if I chose to stay with him.

I loved being there because I felt safe, but Paul was so persistent and kept telling me how I would never be happy without him. He knew how I still felt about Ezra. He just kept calling out that I was still in love with Ezra and always would be. Chad and I ended up talking on the phone and he asked me to come back. Honestly, I didn't want to go back, but I couldn't support myself and Paul was putting too much pressure on me. Paul and I ended up in a huge fight about how unhappy I would be if I didn't make the right choice, so I ended up leaving. I felt like he was pressuring me to be with him rather than just being a supportive friend. I have no idea where things would have ended up if he would have just stopped lecturing me.

The trip back to Indiana was horrible. I was crying, confused and felt like God had abandoned me. On the state line of Tennessee and Kentucky, my piece of crap car broke down, but not before I was able to get pulled into a rest stop. I didn't know whether I was coming or going, so I asked God to just get me home safe and I would do my best to focus only on Chad and our baby.

I ended up walking around the rest area for a bit until I ran across a trucker who was actually headed to Indiana. I took the plates off my car, grabbed the few items I owned and jumped into the semi-truck. The trip home was interesting and the trucker was very nice. He was also a Christian and ended up talking to me about Jesus Christ. I really thought that I was meant to ride with that man. He ended up giving me a ride all the way to Chad's mom's driveway.

I got along with Chad's mom pretty well. She was definitely excited about becoming a grandma for the first time. I pretended not to know a lot around her because I thought it made her feel more involved with everything, especially with me. I would ask her questions about a lot of things I already knew the answers to, I just felt it made her feel special to be the one I turned to. I thought it would help build our relationship.

Chad's sister was another story. No matter how hard I tried to be friends with her, it wasn't happening. She was the most hateful, rude and bitter teen girl I had ever known. She was very good at making me feel like I was some piece of shit and meant nothing to her. It was tough with all of us living under one roof. I was constantly trying to please everyone and avoid fights. Half the time Chad and I were fine and the other half was hell. As much as I tried, I could never get thoughts and dreams of Ezra out of my head. Every single day he was who I thought of when I went to sleep and who I thought of when I woke up. I felt horrible about how much I thought about Ezra and, even when I would try not to, thoughts of him would overcome me.

I was so focused on making sure that I was doing everything right with my pregnancy, I was also catering to a grown man and his family. I sacrificed myself for their comfort, and I did it by my own choice. I just wanted to make sure our child had a family because I knew I would never allow my family around my child. My mother and brother, yes, but I didn't want anyone else in that family near my child. It was a choice I made to be submissive to Chad's family. I convinced myself that it was in the best interest of my child. I never really felt like I fit into Chad's family completely, but I did love being pregnant. I kept a record of every feeling and every time I was sick. I still have that little book I marked everything in. It was crazy how things got easier living with everyone the further along my pregnancy got.

Chad was still drinking, but all my nonsense stopped once I knew there was a life inside of me. I never realized how beautiful being pregnant could be. Although many of the books I was reading explained that most women suffer from postpartum depression, I was determined that I would not. I thought it was a matter of spirit over mind. Truth is, I never suffered one day of postpartum depression.

After getting settled down, Chad and I began job hunting. I was determined to make everything work and work was something I was not afraid of. I worked all the time, as often as possible. I worked in a plastic factory for a while and was even offered a second job. I finally broke down and told Chad I needed him to find something because I didn't want to have to work two jobs. It wasn't because of a lack of him trying to find a job, it was his criminal record that hurt him in all of his job searches.

I remember when Chad and I were looking through my bible searching for a name for our child. We had decided we didn't want to know the sex of the baby until the day it was born. We had boy names all ready, but no clue for a girl. Living in Chad's hometown was a very strange experience for me because everyone was friends from the time they were little. I was a bit of an outcast. Chad had many friends and I really got along with most of them. Many of them were just like Chad, bikers without bikes.

Chad was pretty popular with all the bad boys of the town and, when I say bad boys, I mean take no shit or they will hurt you. One of his dearest friends, Aaron, was born with a disability and was motorized by an awesome speed-racing wheelchair. I grew to really love his friends, but especially Aaron. He became a dear friend to me and still is. I thought it was funny how Chad hung out with such a tough crowd, yet he was nothing more than a huge, passive teddy bear.

I'll never forget one time I was sitting at the bar with Chad and he was drinking. I was about eight months pregnant and one of Chad's friends staggered up next to me. The boys exchanged words for a moment then, out of nowhere, his friend leaned down and bit my breast. In tears, I looked at Chad as he took a drink of his beer. I told him he better beat that man or I was going to. Chad looked at me and tried to calm me down because, supposedly, the guy was a badass in the town and Chad was intimidated by him.

Chad was a very tall, large man. He made at least three of me. I felt safe with him because I thought he would always protect me. I will be honest and say that he never laid a hand on me in anger. He was not physically abusive in any way. It didn't take me long to learn that Chad may have had this reputation as a towering, scary badass; but, come to find out, it was all just rumor. I learned that Chad had never been in a fistfight in his life. I'm not even sure if passive is the right word to describe him because it was obvious that I wore the pants in our relationship. He was just so tall and big that nobody messed with him. Most people were intimidated just by his appearance. Plus, he was known as and hung out with the rougher crowd which gave him a bad-boy reputation. I realized quickly that I had more balls than Chad did. Chad had no backbone and I eventually realized that he did pretty much what he was told.

Preparing for the baby's birth was fun for me. I had self-prepared by studying everything I could get my hands on and I kept all of my doctor appointments. I would walk in with a small list of questions and I tried to always be prepared. I scheduled a walk-thru at the hospital nursery and talked with the nurses on how everything would happen once my water broke. Although I hadn't taken a Lamaze class, I was confident in the videos and reading material I had watched. I also prepared my delivery bag, including a cassette tape player so that I could listen to Pink Floyd's "*Dark Side of the Moon*" to help sooth me during birth.

I wasn't going into this blind and made sure that I was as prepared as I could possibly be. Before delivery, I requested that I not be given any drugs during birth even if I asked for some. I had read the statistics on the epidural and, although rare, anything that was a risk wasn't worth it to me. I will admit that during my entire pregnancy Chad and I did smoke marijuana. Again, as stated earlier, I am not going to spend time arguing about the pros and cons of marijuana in this book.

Chad's mom and family ended up throwing me a baby shower, which I thought was very sweet. By this time I was actually starting to feel welcomed and loved by Chad's family. His grandma was a very sweet older woman and was always so nice. She was like my father in the way that she never cussed, but she wouldn't hesitate to say how she felt about things. Chad got a decent job and we ended up making a plan together; I was going to be a stay-at-home mom and take care of our child while he worked and provided for our family. Yet, lingering over our heads was the unknown court date, charges for possession and a few other things that Chad had yet to face from before we had gotten together.

A week before the baby was to be induced, Chad and I were invited to a Ted Nugent concert. I was scared to go because I was so close to delivery. Chad insisted he wanted to go, and I got tired of arguing, so we ended up going. It was an awesome concert and we had fun. Chad got pretty drunk, but that was normal for him when we went out. I was very aware of everything happening around me throughout the entire time I was pregnant, especially when I went to the bar with Chad on the weekends. I always remained belly cautious of everything around me to ensure the safety of my child. I realize that I shouldn't have even been in the bars to begin with, but I wanted Chad to feel like he could still enjoy himself. I tried hard to keep him happy and he loved going to the bar when he could. I didn't mind it too much because his friends were there and I didn't want to sit at home alone.

Being pregnant and preparing to be a mother made me feel as if I had a purpose. I knew I was now in charge of the safety and care of another life. It was time for me to step up and be an example for my child. Have you ever had your mom say that she hopes you grow up and have children just like you? My mom said that all the time while I was growing up. My response was always the same, "I hope so because I'm a good kid." I felt like I was doing all the right things to prepare myself. I was emotionally set to make sure that my child was safe and no predator would ever get to my child. At least that was my intention.

The very next week, on July 10, 1999, it was early in the morning and I was lying in bed. Chad and I were both sleeping when my water broke. I was excited and scared at the same time. I woke Chad up and told him it was time. He jumped up pretty quick. We were upstairs at his mom's and, when we finally made it downstairs, I just sat down while Chad gathered our bag and things. Off to the hospital we went.

I went through 17 hours of hard labor and, in the end, I still had to be induced. I was given no epidural, even though I was begging for drugs; but, due to my previous request, it wasn't happening. Since Bree wasn't born till July 11, my mother and Dakota also had time to get to the hospital. Dakota says all he remembers is sitting in the hallway and hearing me scream that I wanted drugs and many vulgar words. I am thankful that I refused the drugs before labor, but while in labor I wanted nothing but the pain to stop. I kept yelling at the nurses, "Please just give me drugs."

I remember while going through labor my mom tried to hold my hand. I yelled at her about something and it made her cry. I didn't mean to, but I still had a lot of anger towards her. The pain from the contractions was like nothing I had ever felt. I knew it was going to be tough and hurt, but I had no idea how much. Out of all the books I read and people I talked to, no one ever told me that when you are allowed to push that is when it actually gets easier. You would think as the baby came out it would be the worst part, but for me, when I was permitted to push, all I felt was relief.

Chad was a solid rock for me that day. He was quiet and made sure that Pink Floyd's *"Dark Side of the Moon"* was constantly playing for me. I kept passing out in between contractions; it was rough. Most of the time when I would have a contraction and Chad was the one holding my hand, I would look at him and tell him I loved him. Not one time did I blame him or yell at him as if what I was experiencing was his fault or a regret.

I was excited to be a mother and can't express how anxious I was to know if my baby was a girl or boy. I remember when going through contractions and was allowed to stand, I would have my back to Chad and his arms were like armrests of a chair for me. He held me up when the pain would get really bad, all 219 lbs. of me. I have pictures in our daughter's baby book of those contractions and, trust me when I say, Chad and I both looked terrible.

At 3:58 pm on July 11, 1999, our beautiful baby girl, Bree, was born. I thought I was supposed to have this most awesome connection and feel some magical bond with the baby when I looked in her eyes, but there were no stars nor was it a magical moment. Truth is, I was just glad it was over and all I wanted was food. I thought for several years that there was something wrong with me for not feeling some magical connection or bond so I never admitted it to anyone.

What's funny is, after talking with other women about it, I have come to learn that many women experience the absence of that feeling, that instant connection. I knew when I looked into Bree's eyes my life would never be the same and she would always be number one. I knew I would be the best mother I could be for her and I would do everything in my power to keep her safe. I never wanted Bree to go through anything like I did and I was willing to settle down so she could have a normal life.

Everyone came to the hospital to see Bree. It was wonderful to have the support and love surrounding us. I even had a pizza delivered to my room before I was even moved from the delivery room. I was starving!

By 9 pm Chad and I were able to talk the nurses into letting us sneak down for a cigarette. Here we stood in front of the hospital as new parents of a beautiful baby girl. We were so very blessed. Chad and I were so proud of one another that day. At least I know I was of him. The first few nights after having Bree home, I found myself waking up in the middle of the night several times just to make sure she was breathing. I just loved staring at her. I couldn't believe that someone so beautiful could come out of me.

About two weeks after Bree was born there was a big biker rally and Chad's best friend, Aaron, wanted to take Chad. I really didn't want him to go, but he went anyway. It broke my heart because we were new parents and I wanted him to stay with me. It made me feel like the biker rally was more important to him. Aaron tried to convince me it was okay, but I was really mad at him for even asking Chad to go. Off the boys went and I was left at home with my beautiful newborn for about four days.

By the time Chad got back I was pretty pissed off. Then the lovely pictures, which I still have, surfaced of Chad passed out in a lawn chair and a condom being held over him. I couldn't understand why he even left Bree and me for that, but drinking and partying was what Chad enjoyed. I was upset with Aaron for a while for taking him, but I love the man and could never stay mad at him for too long. I realized it was Chad's decision to go, not Aaron's.

At the end of August, Paul ended up bringing the girls to me and they stayed with Chad and me for a little while. Chad's mom, Tracy, was okay with the girls coming to stay for a short time. In September, Chad and I were heading to Essex Junction, Vermont, to take the girls back to Paul. I decided to work a little while we were there just to make some extra cash. The spot was awesome and I was making good money in the Circle of Science game that Paul had set up. Chad took care of Bree while I was working, which, of course, was only when the money was on the Midway so I only worked for a few hours each evening.

I ended up having a great experience in that game in that specific spot. Michelle Pfeiffer was actually in the area making a movie with Harrison Ford. I want to say it is called, "What Lies Beneath." Ms. Pfeiffer and her family had come to the fair that evening. I noticed that this woman had these huge glasses on and kept acting so weird when she walked up to the game with her family. Some of Ms. Pfeiffer's family played one or two games with the guy working next to me and I just watched her as she stood back and kept looking around.

I knew something with this woman wasn't right or had to be off with the way she was acting paranoid and I knew she looked really familiar. All of a sudden, I realized who she was and why she was looking around. I didn't say anything. After they walked away, I asked the guy if he even realized who that was. He said, no, he wasn't paying attention to her because she wasn't playing the game. I explained to him that it was, "Catwoman," Michelle Pfeiffer! That guy grabbed a big teddy bear, jumped the counter and was out of the game quick. When he came back he said she told him thank you for the teddy bear, but not to tell anyone she was there. He said something about how she was just trying to enjoy the fair with her family. I wonder if she remembers going to that fair? No reason she would remember me, but just that fair perhaps.

On September 5, 1999, I turned 21 years old. It wasn't a huge deal for me because I had already done so much already, more than most 42 year olds. Soon after Chad and I returned from Vermont, we ended up going out for an evening. Chad's mother, Tracy, offered to watch Bree. Although I wasn't drinking as I had before my baby girl, that night Chad and I drank a lot. I won't try to explain what began it or who started the argument, but we got into a huge fight. It even continued into the next day and Tracy got very involved.

She thought she was going to stop me from leaving Chad and taking Bree with me. I ended up at a family friend's with my daughter after having to get the police to help me get my daughter back from Tracy. The things she said to the officer to try and keep my child from me is exactly why I never lived with Tracy again. When I say Bree and I were at a family friend's, I actually mean Chad and his family's friend. After Bree was born, I started to feel like I was surrounded by people who were only there for Chad and Bree. It felt like I had no one on my side. At times I felt somewhat ganged up on. I reached out to one of my distant relatives on my father's side whom I had only spoken to and met once when I was very young. In my father's first marriage he had three daughters, all older than my mother. I only met each of them once or twice throughout my life. I don't recall exactly how it all worked out, me connecting with them, but Bree and I had a ride and a place to stay in Michigan. I want to say it was my half-sister's daughter, but I truly can't recall our relation to one another.

Chad came over to the house I was at while Bree and I were waiting for our ride. He was high as a kite and I remember that made me angry. I smoked pot, too, but had actually, for the first time in my life, wanted to live right for our daughter's sake. I really had no idea what that entailed or how to do it. I just knew that I wanted to be better for Bree, better than what we were living, and I was ready to commit to change. The conversation with Chad didn't go very well and I ended up asking him to leave.

Once my ride showed up, it wasn't long until Bree and I arrived in Michigan with my family. The family I stayed with had some issues of their own that were more than just bills. It took some adjusting on my part but, when you live with another family or someone else, it always does. I remember talking with my family member and her saying that her husband had a demon and that she had named it. I was so uncomfortable right away because I know demons exist and there was a thickness to the air in the home, but her naming the demon was a whole other level I wanted nothing to do with.

Her husband wasn't this horrible bad guy, but you could tell he was off. He never disrespected her or me, he never hit on me in any way and I never left anyone alone with my daughter. All through her life I have been very protective of who was around her or who held her as a baby.

The husband just made me feel uncomfortable if I looked at him. You know the people you can tell just by looking at them that they would have no problem stabbing you or going crazy in a split second, or the ones that you look at and realize you maybe shouldn't have made eye contact for so long? Yes, that was him.

I knew I didn't want to stay there due to the environment, so I ended up working things out with Chad over the phone. I told him as long as he got us our own place to come home to, I was willing to come back. I refused to ever live with his mother again. We also agreed to get married and really settle down for our daughter's sake. Chad loved me and I tried my best to love him. I was blessed and thankful for my estranged family's help, but the night Chad walked in the door to take Bree and me home I was relieved. It was during this time that I heard the news that Ina, Derek's girlfriend, had given birth to my first nephew, Luke.

I was so proud that Chad had kept his promise and, when we pulled into Indiana, we pulled up to our new apartment. It was a duplex, but it was all ours. I was really proud of Chad for stepping up and making sure we had our own home. Chad and I discussed getting married and we agreed that it was best for our daughter, not realizing that was the worst reason. On November 30, 1999, Chad and I went up to the courthouse and filled all the paperwork out. When we walked out of the Courthouse, we were officially married. Chad had finally found a good job and things were really looking up until we received the court date for the charges filed against Chad from his past.

In December, we went to Court and sentencing was done. Chad was sentenced to serve 18 months with nine months suspended. That meant he had to serve nine months in prison. He was also ordered to write a five-page letter to our daughter explaining the dangers of marijuana, as well as probation and fines. I found it to be the most ridiculous punishment, but I was a bit biased. I, of course, went to the library and did all the research on marijuana to help my husband out because he didn't spell or write well.

If you have ever done this kind of research, you know it is really hard to put together five pages of negatives about marijuana, at least five pages of negatives that are from accurate studies about marijuana, especially if you compare the information that was available in 1999 to now. Not to mention, most of the information obtainable was based on the author's opinions only. I completed the entire five pages and mailed it to Chad so he could copy it and turn it in as complete.

It was hard on me when Chad went to jail. Bree was only five months old and we were married less than a month. I was constantly talking to Bree and playing flashcards with her. Before she could even speak her first words I was doing all I could to educate her. There was not a night we didn't say bedtime prayers and read out of her children's bible that Paul had bought her. I went to visit with Chad as often as I was allowed, but I only took Bree up a few times. Neither of us were comfortable with our daughter going to the jail for visits. It was only for special occasions that I took Bree for visits and one was for Easter.

By this time Tracy and I had worked things out and she promised that she would never try to take my daughter away from me again. I would only allow Bree to stay with Chad's sister, Stacy, or his mom, Tracy, if I needed help or a babysitter. I knew they wouldn't hurt her and they loved her dearly. Chad and I wrote so many letters during this time; some arguments, some love letters, some sexy letters, etcetera. It is crazy looking through them now because the things we argued about and the love we shared was complete madness and very unhealthy. I still hold onto all of those letters to this day because I think someday Bree may want to read them or just have them.

Our daughter's first Christmas was the first of many 'firsts' Chad missed out on. I had to face everything alone as a first-time parent. I had many lonely nights, but they were usually spent crying over missing Ezra. Chad was gone, and a part of me missed him, but a huge part of me resented him for leaving us to begin with, as if something he had done before we even met could have been changed. Thoughts of Ezra continued to consume me. If I wasn't dreaming about times we shared, I was dreaming about finding some way to win him back. I truly did try to stay focused on the family I had, the husband I had married; but, no matter how hard I tried, Ezra was always the one I saw in my dreams.

This was when the whole Y2K New Year's Eve was going on. I never wanted to miss the first of anything with Bree, so I spent New Year's home with my baby. I kept thinking, if something was going to happen, I would be there for her no matter what. As my baby girl slept peacefully in her bed, the New Year came and went. As you know, the whole Y2K scare never happened.

Chapter ELEVEN

2000: Chad tried to get work release in the beginning of his incarceration, but he didn't pass the drug test. I had been telling him he needed to flush out the marijuana and prepare for that test, but he didn't listen to me. It made me so mad because now he wasn't allowed to work and I was left with all the responsibilities. Trying to figure out how to make money but keep my daughter from being put in a daycare was very stressful.

It was important to me that I be the one raising my child and not have to put her in a daycare for eight hours a day. I don't think anything is wrong with daycare, don't get me wrong, I just wanted to be the one with Bree through every step of her first year. I knew moving in with Tracy and Stacy was never going to be an option for me. I tried coming up with alternative ways to make money so I could stay home with my daughter and still pay the bills. I came up with several ideas, but one I knew would make me good money was baking. I started baking everything I could think of - fudge, pies, cookies, cakes and much more. I would spend hours baking and, when they were finished, wrapping all the goodies up. I would then load up all the goods, put Bree in her stroller and head out. Bree and I would walk all over town and sell everything I baked.

My favorite place to go, and where I made the most consistent money, was the same courthouse that ordered my husband to be locked up. Bree and I would take fudge in the courthouse and sell it at $5 to $10 a bag. Every week we would make good money selling to probation officers, jailers, etc. The other place would be our local Eagles Club where Chad's mom bartended. With the money I made from bake sales and from babysitting I was able to carry Bree and me. It was tight, but I was able to pay bills and make it work.

With as many books and videos, plus all the studying that I did, I was always doing something with Bree. I owned almost all of the kids' arts & crafts and how to help your child learn books, not to mention all the flashcards I could get my hands on. I even made some homemade flashcards for Bree. I had so many books on how to be a better parent and how to be a better spouse, I really could have built a small library.

Because of the way Joe used to hold me, I was very strict about who held Bree. If I thought you might do something to hurt her, you weren't going near her. Tracy and Chad's sister, Stacy, were there with me through everything, including Chad's trial. Even though Stacy was a complete bitch to me most of the time, she loved Bree and so did Tracy. On occasional weekends Tracy would offer to keep Bree and give me a little money and tell me to get out for the night.

I trusted Chad's mom and sister with Bree but, in the back of my mind, the things said to the cops previous months earlier always stayed with me. I really needed a break when Tracy offered so I don't think I ever said no. I would just go to the local bar and dance, talk with Chad's people and try to laugh as often as possible. I hung out with Aaron a lot during this time. I never cheated on Chad while he was locked up. I was so focused on being a good mom and wife, I decided the rest meant nothing to me. I also couldn't explain the desire I had for Ezra and what I felt I had destroyed with him. Where would we be? You know, the 'what ifs'. I just tried hard to make sure Bree was happy and build my own family that wasn't all fucked up.

When I would go out I was always given compliments but, if anyone did hit on me they were quickly ran off by someone nearby. I think that is in part why it was easier for me to not give in to temptation as I quickly realized everyone in that town would know. I wasn't constantly surrounded by temptation, either because of Chad's bad-boy reputation or everyone knew him. It didn't matter that I was the only one who knew Chad was a submissive man who had never been in a fight, I wasn't about to tell anyone else that. I knew I was in a safe town because I was Chad's wife. Bree and I ended up spending a lot of time with Aaron while Chad was locked up.

Aaron and Chad had actually been friends since they were four years old. Aaron had custody of his son, Stanley. He was so adorable and is still dear to me. Stanley was six years old at this time and a great kid. Another person that started hanging out with me was Bob. Bob was a brother to Chad's good friend Alan. These two were something else. I only hung out with Alan a few times, but his brother Bob was crazy fun. Bob became a true friend and would even crash on my couch on occasion when he needed a place to stay. Chad knew about it and said it didn't bother him if Bob stayed at our home. Chad knew I was waiting for him and he trusted me.

I couldn't help to feel like I was becoming a part of something. It was new for me to have friends, family and people who seemed to care about Bree and me. As soon as my daughter was born I actually started caring about my actions and myself more. I not only wanted to be a good mom, but I wanted to be a good example to Bree.

There was an uproar in our community not too long into the New Year when a dead body was discovered and the police were after Alan, Bob and a few others. I was involved in the murder trial, but only as an observer. Alan and I would write back and forth early in his incarceration and we actually became friends as we continued to get to know one another. Again, I asked Chad if it was okay to write his friend, Alan, and he said he didn't care. I didn't want Chad to doubt that I was waiting for him, so I always asked him what he thought when it came to his friends.

The murder trial was so interesting to me. The way it was all handled and the roar in the Courtroom when the verdict came in. It was intense and the fact I had met most of the people involved was crazy to me. I had a love for the Courtroom and the way that everything worked. When

I was in school I was told my top career choice would be an attorney. Long story short, Alan and some of his friends had a guy come up with a chunk of money from out of state for a drug deal. They ended up killing the guy and split the money between them. In the end, each of them took this guy's life for a few thousand dollars apiece and ended up with jail sentences that, in turn, took most of their lives.

"For the love of money is the root of all evil: which while some coveted after, they have erred from the faith, and pierced themselves through with many sorrows."
- 1 Timothy 6:10

It was during the trial that I also became close to Alan and Bob's parents. They were both very loving and they simply couldn't believe what was happening. The state tried to convict Bob for being involved in the murder somehow. I didn't think Bob was actually any part of it and the verdict for him came in not guilty and he was set free. Bob was the most energetic and fun person to be around. He would do whatever it took to make you laugh. Looking back, he was the definition of the 'class clown.' He went to a carnival with Dakota and I one time and Bob kept jumping around like an ape. It was amazing to watch how people would react to him. He lit the Midway up because people would go from looking at him like he was crazy to having a huge smile on their face. He lit their faces up and it was pretty cool to stand back and watch. I was convinced that between Bob and Aaron I had the best, best friends a girl could have.

While Chad was locked up, his mom invited Bree and I to go to Kentucky with her to visit a girlfriend she worked many years with. Bree and I were all for a road trip. Okay, Bree may have not known she was up for a road trip, but I sure was. We drove down and it was Tracy, Stacy, Bree and me. That was a great trip. Tracy's friend was so nice and lived on some beautiful land. They also had horses and I got to take Bree for a short, slow-paced ride. It was a very small town and I talked Stacy into going up to this hole-in-the-wall arcade place. I think we shot some pool and just talked about the trip.

As I mentioned earlier, Chad missed out on so much, including our daughter's first birthday, her first Easter, St. Patrick's Day, 4th of July. First steps <u>and</u> first words. He pretty much missed all of her firsts. Even though Chad missed so much, I tried to share everything with him through our letters and phone conversations. I took a lot of pictures so he could at least see how fast our daughter was growing.

I'll never forget Bree's first steps. Stacy was over practicing walking with Bree and I ended up grabbing my camera. I actually caught it in pictures when she took off walking. It was so exciting. Stacy and I threw Bree's coat on and headed up to the Eagles to show Grandma Tracy that Bree could walk. It was so awesome to celebrate such a great moment with her Grandma and Aunt. It was small moments like these that I felt like we would always have a family no matter what.

Our apartment was pretty small so for Bree's first birthday we decided to have it at Chad's moms. Tracy threw a barbeque and we had all the family there. Tracy's brother lived next door to her. The family had its problems, however, most of them were pretty close and stuck together. I admired their dedication to one another and how they embraced Bree and, eventually, me. I was committed to them also. Chad was the only man I had slept with in over two years. I felt like I was getting right with myself and with God.

Prayers were being fulfilled and I was able to be home with Bree without having to get a job. The bills were paid and we had food in the house. I have always been good with budgeting and, honestly, if I was ever short on anything, Tracy was there for us. Every day's a hustle for most of us and, when we are just barely getting by, we need to remain thankful. Even in the times you feel like you're not making it at all, keep your faith.

Paul also brought both girls to spend some time with Bree and me, which was awesome. I stayed involved with all three of Paul's kids and he made sure of it. I was thankful for Paul being in my life and I loved his children with all of my heart. Paul and the kids were my family and Paul made sure I never forgot that. I loved Paul so much, I just couldn't find it in me to ever settle down with him again.

I remember all the girls playing in my makeup with me and putting it all over our faces. We had so much fun when we were all together. Stacy was in a parade around this same time so the girls played in my clothes and dressed up. Chad and I had some great conversations and we were really committed to working things out. Although I was still thinking about Ezra daily, the thoughts didn't make me cry out of the blue as often. I convinced myself I would never find another man that could make me feel the way Ezra did. I dedicated to staying with the father of my child and felt that was more important for our daughter than anything else.

After my birthday in September, Chad got out of jail. It was the day we had talked about for nine months. I dressed up in a leather outfit and told everyone to stay far away from the house. I had Stacy and Tracy take Bree for a little while so Chad and I could get alone time. It was what he asked for in his letters and what we talked about on the phone. The afternoon went nothing as planned, but it was still nice to have him home.

I had built up this most awesome relationship in my head between Chad and I while he was gone. We were actually communicating and talked about dreams and goals we had when he was locked up.   Some of our letters to one another were intense. Throughout all the time Chad was gone I convinced myself I had fallen in love with him. The problem was I fell in love with the idea of Ezra somehow being tied in with Chad and that's who I pictured was coming home to me. It was so unfair to Chad that I thought and felt this way. Eventually I tried not to say Ezra's name to much around Chad because he knew that my heart belonged to him and it hurt Chad.

I began bartending not too long after Chad was released. I took a position on third shift so our daughter was always with either Chad or me. That gave Chad the opportunity to seek work while I was with Bree during the day. We actually worked well with one another as far as caring for Bree. Chad and I both loved her so very much and wanted the best for her at all times.

We had no problem with Stacy or Tracy babysitting Bree or her staying the night at their home so, on occasion, Chad and I would have our date nights. Some were a little crazier than others. We had some fun and wild nights with friends and some with just one another. It wasn't always a horrible marriage, however, our negatives outweighed our positives by far.

I found a new love in bartending. I was able to be in the atmosphere I enjoyed and not drown myself in drinking. Honestly, bartending and watching others act a fool was a fun and crazy job. It was the only job I have ever had where I could knock a man off his barstool and the next day he would come and apologize to me. Men had more conversations with my breasts than me at all times, which I found extremely annoying. I dealt well with all that comes from being a bartender and knew how to handle myself when it came to the men. I didn't put up with any bullshit from anyone.

I enjoyed the freedom of working, of getting enough sleep that I could be with Bree the entire day, being there for her bedtime story and prayers, then I would be off to work. I loved listening to everyone and the loud music, plus the tips were usually always good for me. My body bounced back fairly quickly after I had Bree and I was shining even brighter than I had before. I didn't mind the attention because I was married and had the power to say no. Even though I was miserable with my sex life and had many opportunities to fool around on Chad, I wanted to make my family work more than anything.

We spent the holidays with all of the family and some of our friends. It was so nice to be a part of a real family that didn't hurt one another physically or sexually. Even though we didn't always get along, we were family. Bree was the happiest baby I had ever been around. She could make you smile even if you didn't want to. She was very smart and never really talked baby talk, so her communication skills were above average. I have always been blessed to be that child's mother. We had a great Christmas and a good New Year with everyone.

Chapter TWELVE

2001: It wasn't long after taxes came in that we moved out of our apartment and into a house of our own. We found a nice two-bedroom, two-story house. I decided that I would never live next door to someone in a one-bedroom duplex again. That was one of the worst experiences I had as far as living arrangements. One day, when Chad was still locked up, Stacy came over to see Bree and we were sitting in the living room talking. All of a sudden, out of nowhere, we heard this 'dong' noise. I looked right at Stacy and said, "That sounded like a frying pan hitting someone."

It wasn't even 15 minutes later that my neighbor, a guy, showed up at my door and asked if he could borrow my phone. He went on to explain that his girlfriend had hit him over the head with a frying pan. I just looked at Stacy like, "See, I was right." While Chad was still incarcerated, my neighbors drove me crazy with late night fights, and I'm not talking about just yelling. Most of the fights were violent and abusive. It was the first time in my life I witnessed a woman actually being the abuser. Her boyfriend would get his ass kicked by her and it was usually with heavy objects or weapons. Bree actually slept through all of their fights, but I was at my wits end.

Needless to say I was beyond happy we were getting our own house and Bree would have her own bedroom. Two months after we moved into our first house Chad's dad started coming into our lives more often. His dad still owned the house Chad had grown up in and it had become available. We ended up making an agreement to move into that house and quickly left our two bedroom house behind. Our new home had three bedrooms, was out in the country and I was definitely okay with the move. Once we got settled, I began reading my Bible every day. I wanted to get right with God and I felt like, if I could do that, everything else would fall into place. For a long time I was persistent trying to get Chad involved in reading with me, but almost all of my studies were done by myself or with Bree listening to me read. On many occasions I would call Paul and we would talk about God. As I tried to be a better 'God girl', wife and mother, it felt like I was the only one who cared enough to try.

Even though Chad didn't care to read with me, I was determined to make our marriage work. I never felt happiness or love when I was with Chad. He was like having another kid around. With Chad I was left in charge of all bills, everything to do with our money and all responsibilities. He wouldn't even take the trash out without me asking. He wasn't active and, every time I wanted to talk, it just seemed like a one-sided conversation. One thing I hated most is he never had an opinion on anything. I would ask him, "What sounds good for dinner?" His reply would be, "Whatever sounds good to you." I would ask him what he would like to do for the day. His reply would be, "Whatever you want to do." I hated being with a man that had no opinion or desire to do anything.

I started going to a local Church praying it would help me to better understand my purpose, but it didn't last long. I felt like I was an outcast no matter where or what I did to get closer to God. I wanted to believe God was near me, but I couldn't seem to find peace within. Truth is, no matter how hard I tried to embrace the Lord, I felt more of the dark and loneliness that surrounded me. I fought to reflect positive every day in order to hide the pain and all the crazy emotions that went on inside me. I became really good at acting happy and portraying the look of a healthy marriage even though deep inside I was miserable. It was easy to pretend because we had the most wonderful daughter any parents could ask for. It was only about four months in our new home when Dakota came to live with us for a short time. My mother and her boyfriend decided they wanted to move to Florida and asked if Dakota could come stay until they got settled. Chad and I never had any issues with Dakota coming to stay with us and it made things easier for me.

Having Dakota around made me feel like I wasn't so alone. Bree loved having Dakota around at all times. That little girl would light our hearts up just by a simple smile. I prayed so much over Bree every single day. She was the one person that I knew what my role was, I was mom. Even though I went through what I did, I truly believed that Bree had a real chance to grow up without being under attack or hurt. As parents we are supposed to protect our children. If some attack occurs, then support and believe in our children. If your child tells you someone is hurting them, it's your job as a parent to help your child and find out the truth. Children are not ignorant because they are young. Most kids are wiser than most adults because they are open to learning and they are usually brutally honest. Chad and I were good with our daughter and agreed on how we wanted to raise her. Early on we promised one another that, no matter what happened between us, we would always work together as Bree's parents.

Our marriage had no problems when it came to our child. We both loved her unconditionally and wanted nothing but the absolute best for her. It was other areas of our marriage that took their toll on us. Finances were a huge problem for Chad and I. Due to his unreliable employment, it was in our toughest times that I grew resentment towards Chad. There were several times we were unable to pay our rent. With renting from Chad's father I felt that he should be the one to go to his dad and talk to him about our situation. But no, Chad refused to talk to his father and it forced me to go to my father-in-law and explain our financial situation. Again, I just felt like I was facing everything alone all the time.

Chad was a very laid back man, but his attitude and personality could flip within minutes. Our sex life also became a problem for me. Since he wouldn't initiate sex, and the repetition of what we were doing was numbing me, I wasn't sure what to do. I hadn't stayed with anyone as long as I had Chad, but I was already cheating on him all the time in my mind. No amount of prayers were helping me with my thoughts and I tried so hard to fight temptations.

When Bree was asleep it was rare that our adult time included much communication. Sitting in the middle of nowhere with a man that seemed content with being a lump on a recliner was not my idea of living. Don't get me wrong, Chad and I did have some good times and made some good memories. We hung out with friends and had our fun on the occasional weekends, we were trying to build a good life together, but Bree ended up becoming the only good thing about our marriage. Chad was an awesome dad. Bree was and is his only child so she was a bit spoiled as a little girl.

I truly believed that Chad would never hurt Bree and his love for her was genuine and pure. How my father loved me was how I saw Chad's love for Bree. I never doubted that Chad would be anything less than the most awesome dad he could be. Little things like sitting at our dining room table for dinner and Bree wouldn't eat her green beans, Chad started a silly game with her and, next thing you know, that kid loved green beans. We always tried to have dinner as a family and say prayers before our meals. I didn't know how to be the best example for Bree, but I was giving my all to try to be just that. Bree remembers her dad letting her drive when we would get about a half mile away from our home. He would pull over and Bree would climb in his lap and steer us the rest of the way. He would go real slow and, since it was in the country, there was never any other traffic. He was very loving and affectionate when it came to our daughter and that was the one thing that I loved most about Chad.

With parenting set aside, Chad and I began having severe up and downs. I was seeking a romantic partner who cared enough to talk to me and give me his attention. I just wanted to do things together and had this dream of being a 'normal' family that could just turn to God together, pray together and live in peace. Chad would be happy one minute and the next he would be withdrawn and seem upset at nothing. It was confusing me so much and caused many fights between us. At one point I asked Chad to please go in for an evaluation because his mood swings were becoming more extreme. We found a place nearby and Chad was psychologically evaluated. When the results returned, Chad was diagnosed with Bipolar disorder and given medication to help level him out. It didn't help, though, because Chad refused to take the medication as he was prescribed.

It was soon after when I decided I didn't want to have more children with Chad. I knew that Chad and I weren't the best for one another and I didn't want to bring more children into a marriage that seemed to have an end in sight. I made an appointment and convinced a doctor that it would be best for me to have my tubes tied. I went through with the surgery and felt relief when I came out of it. I knew Chad was a great father, but bringing more children into such a messed up relationship seemed unfair to not only a child, but to all of us. Chad wasn't happy with my decision and we continued to argue about finances. I just couldn't seem to make ends meet.

At certain points throughout our marriage Chad and I both worked. Chad had a hard time holding a job down for more than four months, but I continued to work every night I could in local bars. I discovered as I worked surrounding areas I was able to make my own friends that had no clue who Chad was. These were people that hadn't grown up with Chad and hadn't known him all of his life. It wasn't too long and Dakota headed to Florida to start his new life there with my mother and her boyfriend. For me it was easy during the day to be a mother to Bree, but at night it was as if I was living a double life. I still fantasized that Ezra would walk into my bar every night. I dreamed that we were going to somehow find one another and work everything out. Even though I knew it would never happen, I loved thinking about it. Living the double life was doable for a while. I was able to spend my days with Bree, put her to bed and, after bedtime prayers, I was off to bartend.

Working in the bars was never really a job to me because I enjoyed bartending so much. I think part of why I loved the atmosphere was because I received the attention I so desperately wanted from my husband. With Chad, I continued to feel more and more empty inside. I did end up having my first affair one night while I was closing down the bar. I had met someone that had all the right features and reminded me of Ezra. I knew it wasn't him and I knew it was wrong, but I just couldn't resist. I remember how bad I felt because I had never cheated on Chad before, not even the nine months he was incarcerated. I loved Chad as the father of my child, even as a friend by this time, but I was never in love with him. I don't think Chad ever found out about that affair and, since nothing was said, life simply went on.

Soon after my birthday on the 5th, my mother called and woke me up. Tt was September 11, 2001. I had worked the night before and was sleeping when she called. When I answered the phone she asked me if I had seen. I asked her, "Have I seen what?" My mother replied with, "We are under attack. Turn on your T.V. Zara." It was there I watched the horrific scenes of the planes crashing into the Twin Towers. My heart dropped that instant. It was about a month after that tragic attack on our Nation my mother called again and asked me if I could come down to Florida to help her with Dakota.

Unfortunately, my mother's boyfriend, Oscar, had been diagnosed with cancer. Oscar was a pretty cool guy. I didn't have much time to get to know him, but he was really close to Dakota. Dakota loved Oscar very much and still shares stories of support and love that he and Oscar shared. I am glad Dakota had a good man to talk to and get advice from. Oscar really seemed to love Dakota and my mother, so from the start I, too, loved Oscar.

I didn't hesitate when mom asked me to come to Florida. Chad and I talked about it and we decided that Bree and I would go help. I was going to help my mom and we were going to take time apart to think about things. I wanted to take the time to figure out if being with Chad was even the right thing to do for Bree and me. I knew she could feel the tension between us, even when we tried our hardest not to expose her to any of the arguments and fights we had.

Bree was always so smart and growing so fast. I wanted to do right by her at all times, even if I wasn't sure what was right. I just wanted to be where I was supposed to be and that seems to be the hardest thing in the world to figure out sometimes. Questioning where we are supposed to be is something many of us do throughout this life and at many moments in life. I wish the answer to that was easy. It may be hard to figure out where you are supposed to be in this life, but you simply can't give up. Each of us have a purpose and giving up won't get us there.

I knew being with Chad was not where I wanted to be and it never was. I kept trying to figure out if it was where I was supposed to be, regardless of my feelings. Within days of receiving my mother's call for help, I loaded up the car with all that I could and Bree and I said our goodbyes to Chad. We fully intended to keep in touch and did the entire time I was gone. When Bree and I finally arrived in Florida, I took a deep breath of fresh air and felt relieved. It was such a long drive and I was falling asleep, so I decided to get Bree and me to a hotel. By the time I found a hotel it was around one a.m.

I used the last of my money to cover our room. I just couldn't wait to lay down and stretch my body out. When we walked in the room and turned the light on, cockroaches scattered everywhere. I was not willing to stay there and I sure wasn't allowing my daughter to stay there either. When I went to ask for my money back and explain what happened, the receptionist refused to give me a refund. She got really rude and ended up calling the police on me. I just waited for them. I was certain they would help me get my money back and I could be on my way. Surely the officer would see I had my child with me and was just trying to find a safe place for us to stay the night. I was shocked when the officer didn't help in any way. He treated me as if I was just trying to get my money back and not for a legit reason. What a welcome to Florida that was. The officer asked me to leave and, at that point, I knew it would be best for me to be on my way. Due to giving the lady at the hotel the last of my money, Bree and I barely made it into my mother's driveway with the gas we had left, but we made it. When Bree and I arrived at my mother's house it was pretty late. We visited for a bit, but both Bree and I were worn out and headed to bed.

My mom and Oscar had to go to the cancer center to stay, which is why Bree and I were there for Dakota. They didn't have to leave right away and that gave them time to get their things together and prepare for their journey. I talked to my mom about the problems Chad and I were having. As always, my mother had some advice. She told me that I needed to go to the swingers club. She said at least at the swinger's club I can go get what I want and go home. She encouraged me by telling me that I didn't even have to know anyone's name and I could get in most of the clubs for free because I would be going as a single woman. My mother hooked me up with a bunch of really cute bra and underwear sets and encouraged me to create an account online. She guided me through the online dating sites and was open about her experiences at the swinger clubs, sharing all the details with me. She also educated me as to what a key party was. She told me it is when three or more couples get together and put all their car keys into a bowl. At the end of the evening, the women pick a set of keys out of the bowl and, the keys they grab are who they go home with. Now, I am a bit freaky but my mom was way beyond where I had ever been. I didn't and still don't judge her on it, nor anyone else: Who am I to judge another?

After a few days at my mom's it felt so nice having Dakota and Bree back together. Although I was happy to be with Dakota, he wasn't doing real well with his new surroundings. He was getting into a lot of trouble at school and hanging out with some pretty wild kids. Dakota's best friend was the son of one of the biggest Meth dealers in the area at the time. I hated the things Dakota was exposed to, but there wasn't anything I could do for him except be there when he needed me.

About a week after Bree and I arrived, mom and Oscar left for the cancer center and the house was all ours. Some of Dakota's friends were skateboarders and really cool kids. Not all of his friends were into dealing or getting into trouble, just most of them. Some of them smoked pot, but it surprised me that's all the boys were doing with the heavier drugs at their fingertips. That made me extremely proud of Dakota because he could have gotten into way more than he did. His best friend didn't do heavy drugs, either, even with his father's profession providing all the boys could have ever wanted.

I found comfort in the fact that Dakota and Bree always had an awesome bond. Those two were raised more as brother and sister then uncle and niece. It was funny because Bree was addicted to the Shrek Movie that had just come out. By addicted, I mean it is all she ever wanted to watch. It didn't matter if we had just finished watching it, she wanted to watch it again. Dakota, Bree and I would run around the house dancing and singing to all the songs. To this day, Dakota and I know almost every single word to Shrek. It was a lot of fun hanging out with him and I couldn't believe how fast both of the kids were growing.

Some of Dakota's older friends were a lot of fun and all of us got along pretty good. Once Bree was down for the night, I allowed Dakota to have a few fun parties. I remember one time when Dakota about knocked this kid out with our mother's two-headed dildo. It was hilarious. Mom had all kinds of sex toys and movies hidden in her room that Dakota knew about and, of course, showed me. I allowed Dakota to have friends over and do what they pretty much wanted in exchange for Dakota babysitting Bree on the occasional weekend so I could enjoy time out with adults.

I found two good bars that I enjoyed and stuck to both of them the entire time I stayed in Florida. One of them was a large biker bar always full of people and very loud most of the time. The other bar was an extremely small place outside of town in the middle of nowhere. I loved hanging out at the smaller bar. It was so much fun and became my favorite place to go when I was able to get my nights out. There was one pool table and barely enough room to play. I loved how random Harleys would pull in and the once empty bar would become full within minutes. The people were so friendly and I always had a good time while I was there.

I did end up getting a little wild and crazy on some of my nights out. I suppose you could say I took my mother's advice. Not attending swinger's clubs, but definitely exploring my options with sexual partners. I had sex with a couple random men I had met and, although it was fun, I always felt horrible and like a worthless wife because I was stepping out on my marriage. I never told Chad about my affairs, but I always felt guilty for having them. Truth be told, anytime I would feel like I was falling further away emotionally I would call Paul. He was always there to talk to me, whether about God, the kids or what I was going through.

As we had agreed, Chad and I kept in contact while Bree and I were at my mother's. We talked on the phone almost every other day. At one point we ended up agreeing he would come down for Christmas to spend the holidays with Bree, Dakota and me. Before the holidays came, Paul made a quick stop in to see us. He ended up taking me to dinner and we talked about life. One thing with Paul I loved so much was there was never a dull moment. He always wanted to talk about something and, if we ran into a quiet spell, he wouldn't hesitate to pull out a book. It was usually his Bible, but he would just start reading to me. I loved it. Paul always provided me with the feeling of unconditional love and peace. For some reason I felt like I was unworthy of Paul after everything I had done. Yet, to Paul, he always looked at me as if I was flawless.

Soon after Paul's visit, Chad made it safely down for Christmas and we made the best of our time together. Bree was happy to see her daddy and even got to wear her beautiful Christmas dress. Due to mom still being gone, we didn't pull out any Christmas decorations or even put a tree up in the house so Chad and I ended up making a Christmas tree out of the presents we had for Dakota and Bree. I must say, it did look pretty good.

The kids were happy and that was all that mattered to me. Chad and I talked and I agreed to come back home and work things out with him as soon as my mom and Oscar returned. I knew that I couldn't live with my mother ever again, and I didn't want to. I knew that Bree loved her daddy and I didn't want to raise her in a broken marriage. I didn't realize that was already what I was doing. We made all of our 'Merry Christmas' phone calls and Bree got to talk to Tracy and Stacy. I still have pictures of Bree in that beautiful Christmas dress on the phone with her Grandma Tracy. We also spoke with my mother and Oscar. They explained that things were going good at the cancer center and they would be home soon after the New Year. Christmas went by quickly and another year came to a closing.

Chapter THIRTEEN

2002: Soon after the New Year Oscar and mom made it home. Chad, Bree and I headed back to Indiana. I hated the way I felt when we pulled into the driveway because it caused me to feel this heavy weight on my shoulders. I knew I didn't want to be there, but there was nowhere else for me to go. Once again, I started digging into my Bible. I was trying to figure out the answers to why I'm here. Always fighting to understand what my purpose was. Why did I make the constant mistakes that I was making and how could Chad and I just find happiness? I dug deep into my Bible and called Paul often when I needed help understanding verses. I just wanted to find peace and to be content with my life.

I studied so much I think I drove Chad crazy with it sometimes. I tried to share with him, but not force anything on him. I just wanted a companion that also cared enough to better understand what God wanted and to grow with me in understanding, but Chad wasn't interested in seeking God out. Chad and I weren't fighting as much once we returned from Florida. I think it was because we were both pretty tired of arguing. I spent most of my time focused on just being a mother to Bree. With her it was easy to be happy. She made me smile all the time and I did my best to make sure she smiled just as much. Although I didn't know how to get close to God myself, I knew raising her to know God is real would make a difference in her life. Throughout Bree's entire childhood I always read the Bible to her and said prayers with her. When I wasn't there to do so, Chad had no problem doing the nightly routine with our daughter.

A few months after being home, my mother ended up calling me. This time she needed me to take Power of Attorney over my little brother because there were more surgeries needed for Oscar. Chad and I, again, had no problem with Dakota coming to live with us. We had a spare bedroom and even a small shed out back that we turned into a teen zone for him. Once he arrived, I got him settled and enrolled in school. Dakota and Bob hung out a lot during this time. Dakota really liked Bob and they got along as if they were best friends.

Dakota adjusted quickly, but he did have a few kids at school that were causing him problems at first. Chad and Bob really helped Dakota out with the kids because they both knew everyone in the town. The moment Dakota told Chad who the kids were, Chad instantly knew who their parents were. Bob helped Dakota out by showing him some fighting moves, but Chad told Dakota to tell the kids he was related to him. All Dakota had to do was explain he was Chad's brother-in-law and the kids backed down and stopped messing with him. It amazed me that Chad had such a bad boy reputation for a man that had never even been in a fist fight, but I was thankful it helped Dakota out.

We received great news in March. Although I didn't stay in touch with Ina and Derek, my mother always made sure she kept all of us updated on one another. It was in March that I heard about Ina having her second child with Derek. My big brother had another boy and they named him Jeremy. I felt the excitement of being an Aunt and I couldn't wait to meet both of the boys. I didn't realize I would be able to hold both of my nephews the very next month.

I will never forget standing in my kitchen when the call came in. It was my mother and she told me Oscar had passed away, but had been revived and was going to pull through. I didn't know what to say except I was sorry she was going through that. She then said she had received a phone call from my father's home and he had passed away. I was so confused. I asked her if she was serious and she explained that perhaps my father passing somehow helped Oscar to recover. I had no words for my mother. After I hung up with her, I just fell to my knees in tears. Why and how could a woman, a mother, tell me my father passed away the way she did? It made no sense to me. Later in life, she explained that she felt I would handle the news of my father's passing better if she claimed that Oscar had life. It didn't, with all honesty, it simply confused me. At first, I wasn't even sure whether to believe her or not.

I hadn't seen my father since the day my mother took him to the home and I only called him once while he was there. When I called, he didn't recognize my name or that I was his daughter, but he kept saying "I'm waiting for you." I somehow convinced myself that, if I didn't go see him, he would stay alive forever. I knew realistically that wasn't the case, but I just couldn't bring myself to go visit him. Mom and Dakota had gone a few times while he was there, but they both told me that our father didn't recognize them. I thought if I went he wouldn't recognize me, either, and that really scared me for some reason. I was devastated when I heard that my father passed away and feelings of complete guilt overtook me. My father, my hero, passed away alone and I felt like that was in some way my fault. I loved him so very much, yet I couldn't go see him. Why? I realized I had to pull it together because it was now my responsibility to go to Dakota and tell him our father was gone.

Dakota took the news pretty hard but, after we held one another and shed tears, we pulled together and began talking about how we were going to get to Michigan for the funeral. Chad was such a rock for me at this time. He held me as I cried and was okay with whatever we had to do to get to the funeral. Once Dakota and I settled down we called Derek and made arrangements to go straight to his house and all of us attend the funeral together. The very next day Chad, Dakota, Bree and I loaded up and were on our way to Derek and Ina's house. It was such a blessing to meet both of my nephews. They were so adorable and the love I have for them has been strong since the day they were born. I hated that our first time meeting was under the circumstances that it was, but we couldn't change what had happened. To be honest, it was comforting to be around all of the kids and my brothers. It eased the pain of losing my father and it helped me to get through it a little better.

Throughout the day Ina and I did arts and crafts with the kids and made a picture with all of their handprints. It is something I have treasured since the day we made it. My brother's and I spent time together visiting and sharing stories of our father and all the things he had done with us when we were little. Although Dakota didn't get to be a part of our father's active life, Derek and I told him the stories of going to Moon Lake and jumping off of our dad's shoulders, racing him, and all the fun things he used to do with us. We cried a lot and, once all of the kids were down for the night, we started to drink. All of us got a pretty good buzz on and ended up staying up way too late.

As I fell asleep that night I had dreams of when my father took me on a boat in Florida with some of his friends and we went to a house in the middle of the water that was built on stilts. It was one of the coolest houses I had ever seen. I dreamed about how fearless he was, how he was not afraid to walk in a gated yard that had several big dogs in it. I remember watching him do it and asking why he wasn't afraid. My dad said that the dogs could smell fear. He said, "If you're not afraid, you won't get bit. You have nothing to fear, Zara." My father was one of the bravest men I have ever known. He fought in World War II and, in my eyes that alone made him a hero. Once morning came, all of us felt the alcohol we drank the night before and had to get ready for the funeral.

The day of the funeral was a mess. We were all hungover and counting on Derek to get us there. I was sporting a lovely black trash can that I carried in the van with me while puking my guts up. Ina and I scrambled to get all the kids and everyone together. Derek seemed like he just didn't want to go. He continued to drag his ass and even mentioned that maybe we shouldn't go. Dakota and I were not accepting that and it made me mad that Derek even said it. I didn't understand why he was being the way he was, even if he had a hangover. To this day I am still not sure why Derek acted the way he did. When we all finally got loaded up, Derek stalled us and acted as if he had no clue where we were going. He really didn't want to go and it didn't matter to him that Dakota and I did. Derek stalled so long that I knew we weren't going to make it on time. I called the funeral home several times and left messages, but no one ever answered. By the time we got there our dad was already in the ground and I was broken into pieces that we missed the entire funeral. I was angry at Derek for that for a long time. One of my father's daughters from a previous marriage was the only one to attend my dad's funeral. That is something that took a long time for me to forgive myself for.

Our half-sister somehow knew we were coming and had waited for us to arrive. When we got there she presented Dakota with Dad's flag and me with the bullets from the gun salute given. We ended up finding our father's grave and of course it was covered with fresh dirt. I remember standing there so angry at myself for never coming to see him while he was still alive and for not being there for the funeral. It just didn't seem fair that I didn't get the chance to say goodbye and I blamed myself for that for a very long time. It was only later that I realized the body in that ground was just that, a body. I find comfort in knowing that someday I will see my father again.

After we returned to Derek and Ina's home, I explained to Chad about the promise I had made years earlier with Brice. Although there was no way for any of us to attend the funeral, I still wanted to keep my word and let Brice know that my father had passed away. Chad and I headed to the town that I once lived in. It was only about a 30 minute drive from where Ina and Derek were living. I didn't know where to start or how to find Brice so the first thing we did was stop in a store we used to hang out at. By some miracle a customer heard me asking if the clerk knew Brice or how to find him. The person behind me knew exactly who I was talking about. We were guided to a rehabilitation center where Brice was now employed. It was by God's good grace that Brice was actually working and that we even found him to begin with. When Brice walked out to meet me it was pretty funny. He had complete shock on his face when he saw me because it had been such a long time. I explained that my father passed away and the first thing Brice said was, "When is the funeral?" I told him that I didn't have a chance to come sooner and that the funeral was over, but I wanted to stick to our promise and let him at least know. He was thankful and told me he was sorry for my loss, and that was the last time I ever saw Brice.

After we stayed one more night with Ina and Derek, all of us loaded up and headed back home. I had a real hard time adjusting after my father passed away. I truly hurt so much inside. In May, Chad's sister Stacy was graduating and, for some reason, I was still trying to win her over. I thought if we threw her an awesome graduation party she would surely be more open to me. To this day, I am not sure why I fought so hard for her acceptance. She was several years younger than me, but she was my sister-in-law. I wanted a good relationship with her, but I didn't know how to overcome her coldness.

Chad and I began planning her party and had everything set up for her at our home. I wasn't keen on the idea of having minors drinking at my home, but it was something that Stacy wanted and none of the parents seemed to mind. Chad and I had spoken with all of the parents of the kids that were attending the party and made them aware that there would be alcohol at the house. They all agreed that, as long as the kids didn't leave our home, they didn't mind. I was also told as long as Chad and I supervised there wasn't a problem. I tried to stay focused on the party and making sure everything went as planned.

The night of the party Stacy was so excited. I don't think I had ever seen her get so excited about anything. Once Tracy dropped Stacy off and picked up Bree the party began. The evening was going so good and some of the kids' parents even stopped by to visit. Stacy was walking around everywhere and talking to all of her friends. The house was pretty full and it was all for her. Stacy was so happy and smiling so much. For a moment in time I truly felt like Stacy loved me. Sad it was because I had done something for her, rather than just being real. That truly isn't love at all.

As the evening went on there was a loud knock at our door. When I opened it, there stood a police officer. I knew the music wasn't too loud because we lived in the country, so I stepped outside to find out what was wrong. I thought we had spoken with all the parents; however, one of the kids were living with mom thru the week and with dad on the weekends. We had spoken with the kid's dad and all was good. The mom found out, and she was not happy. Looking back on it now, I would not have been happy either. The officer ended up writing me a ticket for serving minors alcohol. I didn't want to be the one to get the ticket, but Chad was still on probation and it left me the fall guy yet again.

Once the officer left the party died down quickly. The kids that had drank ended up staying the night as Chad and I had promised to their parents. The next morning the last of the last kids ended up leaving and Tracy brought Bree home. When Tracy and Stacy left, Stacy ended up saying thank you, which was rare for her. She is truly a tough person. She stays withdrawn, hard, cold, or whatever you call it. She truly has no care for anyone she deems unworthy, which is everyone but a select few. We tend to choose to love only those we want, but I think that if we love everyone without judgment we would feel the difference in our daily lives. I try to choose that every day and it has brought me to one of the most peaceful places I have ever known.

Soon after the graduation party, all of Oscar's surgeries were over and Dakota went back to my mother's. In June, she married Oscar and they had a small wedding. It wasn't long after their wedding that Paul ended up stopping in to visit Chad and me for a night. Even though Paul wanted me as his wife, he always respected Chad and the two of them got along well once they had a chance to get to know one another. Paul also loved Bree as if she was his own, as I did his children at all times. Paul brought all of his crew with him, which consisted of about five guys. I had known the guys since I had joined the carnival in 1995 and was happy to see everyone. It was a blast visiting and talking with everyone. All the guys kept trying to talk me into going back out on the road with them, but I didn't feel that it was the right thing to do at the time.

Once Paul and his crew left, Chad, Bree and I went back to our normal daily lives. Even though the guilt of the circumstances with my father's death pulled hard at my heart, I tried to stay focused on what was best for Bree and our family. Neither Chad nor I were working and I knew I had to do something to start bringing in money for our home. I ended up going right back to bartending. This time was different, though, because

I started drinking while I was at work. Back to the double life I went. Days with Bree and nights in the bar, but this time I was getting drunk almost every night.

I was trying to drown out so much pain with alcohol. It took a long time before I realized that alcohol was hurting me more than just facing what I was feeling. I began to get engulfed with my job and started taking on more hours. Any hours that needed to be filled, I was the one jumping up and volunteering to take them. My days were always good because I was with my daughter and that alone made me happy. However, my nights became a very unhealthy escape from my marriage, my past and my pain.

Once I started working again, it wasn't long that our car ended up breaking down and leaving me no way to get back and forth. A friend of mine, Lee, who lived in the town I worked, offered to allow me to stay with her. With no other options, Chad and I agreed that I would stay with Lee only until I could save enough money for us to get a new car. I looked at it more like a break and time to get my head straight. So off I went to stay with a girlfriend who had just received a large settlement for a house fire that had happened a few months prior in her home.

Reflecting back, I feel like it was crazy that I left my daughter. The truth is, I was only about 30 minutes away. Chad and I agreed that he would bring Bree over to me as often as he could and, when possible, I would come home. I was so lost and doing the best that I could, but I didn't understand why I always felt so alone. Most of all, I couldn't understand why everything was always a battle within me. I tried so hard to pray and get close to God, but I felt like he wasn't listening or just couldn't hear me. I did the same as I had so many times in the past, I gave up on my Bible.

Moving to my girlfriend's wasn't one of my best ideas. My friend, Lee, was crazy fun and hung out with the top of the top. She had a beautiful home and had a lot of construction going on because of the fire. She showed and took me places that I hadn't ever been before, which was tough to do for me.

Lee took me to the racetrack for the first time and watched the horses race. We made a small bet, but it was just so she could show me how it worked. We actually went there to cheer for her friend that was in the race. She kept saying that I needed to prepare if her friend won because we would be headed to the winner's circle. Unfortunately, her friend didn't win, but it was still a great experience.

While I was gone trying to earn money for our home, Chad brought Bree over to visit me several times. I was always calling and talking to her on the phone, at least every other day. Even though I was only gone for five weeks it felt like an eternity. I can't express how much I missed my daughter during this time. I hated that I was away from her, but I knew she was safe and I was making the right decision. I had to go through what I did in order to bring me to where I am. When we are going through our worst and we don't see light anywhere around us, too many of us just stand there in fear. You may not see the light from where you stand, but you will never see it if you simply keep standing in the same spot.

"There are three C's in life. Choices, Chances, Changes. You must make a choice to take a chance or your life will never change!" - Zig Ziglar

Even though I was missing Bree terribly I did have fun when I was living with Lee. She was dating the president of a biker club from a nearby town and we would go on bike runs all the time. It would be Lee with her man first, then somehow I always seemed to end up on the Harley Davidson second in line. I will never forget when the club was doing a run and made my bar one of their stops. I was prepared as best I could be. You could hear the roar of the motorcycles as they were coming into town. I was so excited because it was just me and the boss working the bar and they had over 50 motorcycles in the run. I loved the rush of having a huge crowd when I was working. Of course, Lee and her man came in first and I already had their drinks ready.

The rest followed and, before I knew it, the entire bar was overflowing. It was such a rush and my tips were killer. Lee and her man ended up presenting me with a plaque that day, which I have hanging on my wall even now. When it was time for them to leave, Lee looked at me. I looked at the boss and he just smiled and told me to get out of there.

It is incredible to ride with so many motorcycles all together. It felt like we were leading an army and we somewhat were. The roar of that many Harley Davidson's is something that you never forget and always appreciate once you experience it. The president of the club lived in this huge, beautiful, expensive home that had security cameras everywhere. I really enjoyed the time we spent just hanging out and talking about our lives and beliefs.

Even with all the fun things that Lee and I did, I was also living a secret. I didn't know much about cocaine because I was never interested in trying it. After the third week of being gone from Bree and 'home', one of my regular customers came into the bar. This customer was a woman who had a strong, independent, take no shit attitude and I loved it. She and I had spent many hours talking about everything, just sharing our opinions about life with one another. This particular night during our conversation she asked me if I did blow (cocaine) and I told her that I had never tried it. She in turn asked if I wanted to and, for some reason, I said, "Why not." I didn't really feel anything at first, but after the third line I felt the effects. I really liked the way it felt and I soon found myself doing it every day.

Once I started snorting cocaine it was like my eyes were opened to everything going on around me. I had no idea how many people in that town were actually involved with cocaine, until I, too, was captured by it. I had never realized how many people were doing cocaine in my bar, but once I was in the circle it didn't take long for my eyes to open.

While I was on cocaine I really enjoyed the effects it had on me. I was enjoying the high and energy it gave me. At the time I thought my only negative was that I had to force myself to eat. I only had a grilled tenderloin a day, and half the time it was a struggle just to eat half of it. I had a healthy, fit body, but it only took a couple of weeks until the cocaine began making me look sickly thin.

The small town I was bartending in had lost two brothers and both were young when they passed away. On the anniversary of one of their deaths, the bar was filled and there were many tears and shots that went around the entire night. I didn't ask too many questions about the brothers, but it was my understanding they both passed away from what everyone claimed was an accidental overdose within a short time of one another. There were many people in the town who mourned those two boys.

As I locked the bar down, after closing, I started to count the draw and get everything ready and prepped for the next day deposit. It was a really profitable night and I had an over $800 deposit, which was a lot for us on a weeknight. Once I had everything done with the money and was getting ready to clean, there was a knock at the door. It was one of my regulars that had been there most of the night. He was a younger, smaller guy and I didn't feel threatened by him at all. He begged me in tears to let him come in and just to take one last shot for the brothers. I felt really bad and, after being involved with everyone through the evening, I had learned that the guy at my door was actually one of the brothers' best friends. I felt sorry for him and it wasn't unusual for me to let a friend or two hang out with me after hours. I didn't really think it would hurt anything, so I went to unlock the door.

As I unlocked the door, he pushed past me and staggered to the bar. His pain and heartache seemed to follow him as if he carried his own rain cloud. I locked the door and headed behind the bar to pour him a shot and finish with cleaning. At the same time I turned around with his full shot glass in my hand, he sat a gun down on the bar. In that instant I knew this was a really bad position to be in. I hadn't had a gun pointed nor aimed at me since Frank and his shotgun.

I wasn't stupid and just acted casual as I placed his shot in front of him.

I started asking question after question to try and keep him talking until I could figure out what to do. I asked him about the brothers and anything else I could think of. I wasn't scared at all and almost felt challenged by his gesture of putting the gun on my bar. He started to tell me about all the trouble he was in with some dangerous people. He said that he owed money for drugs and swore up and down the people he owed were going to kill him. After about a half hour of small talk, he finally said the words I was praying he wouldn't. The guy said he was there to rob me. He said he was going to take the money whether I was willing to let him have it or not. Then he began trying to talk me into just giving the money to him and telling the police I didn't know who it was that robbed me. For some reason I sat there and argued with him. I told him he had two choices; he could shot me and take the money or he could walk out and we would never speak of it again.

As I was standing there saying the words, inside I was asking myself why I was saying them. I refused to let him rob me and I was determined to get him out of my bar with both of us alive. He was crying and emotionally delusional. Throughout what turned into a two-hour conversation, he would pick up his gun and wave it around. Even with the gun in the air, not at one moment did he ever point it at me. After a little over two hours, I finally talked him into putting his gun away and leaving the bar. I walked him to the door speaking words of encouragement and telling him things would work out for the best. Once the door was locked and I walked behind the bar, my legs gave out on me. I began shaking and crying thinking about how bad that could have really turned out. For some reason it was only as I sat in a ball on the floor crying that I actually felt any fear. My body was shaking and I couldn't move for over an hour. I finally got myself together and called my boss who lived above the bar. He came down and we talked for a while. We decided not to file a police report because there was no harm done and all the money was still there. That moment was one that stayed with me for a very long time. It made me rethink everything and I knew I wanted to be with my daughter and I knew I didn't want to be a drug addict and live my life always chasing a 'high'.

It had been about a month since I had been living with Lee and I was ready to leave. I knew that my cocaine use was out of hand and that wasn't the person I wanted to be. I missed my daughter so much and knew that I couldn't continue living the way I was. One of the last nights I worked was a very busy night. The bar was doing good and there was a large crowd of people. I was the only one working, which was normal. I kept getting complaints about the women's bathroom being locked. After I was able to get everything caught up, I walked to the back to find out what was going on in the bathroom. I banged on the door. I heard someone trying to answer, but it was more of a mumbled mess. I knocked again and got the same reaction. With concern, I stood back and kicked the door open. I couldn't believe what I saw. There was the same guy that tried to rob me just lying on the floor. He had his belt wrapped around his arm and a needle still sticking out of it. There was blood everywhere. It was a mess and I thought the guy was dead. After I yelled at him a few times he finally regained consciousness. I was able to get one of his friends to get him out of the bar and take the guy home.

The very next day I called Chad and told him I needed help. I asked him to please come get me and take me out of that town. I told him to take Bree to his mom's and to come get me right away. I didn't want to go home yet because my body was starting to withdraw from the cocaine. Once Chad arrived, we headed to a hotel room. Even though later in life Chad used this time against me, I can't describe how much it meant to me and how thankful I am to this day that he came and got me out of there.

I took the time to explain to Chad that I had been using cocaine and I didn't want to keep doing the drug. He acted so understanding and listened to every word I had to say. I apologized to him and he just kept telling me he forgave me. Chad tried to get me to eat, but my body was rejecting even water at the moment. He was there for me as my body kept shaking from withdrawal. It was beyond comforting the way he held me so tight. It was as if his embrace almost took the shaking away. That night I felt more love for Chad then I had our entire marriage.

As I cried to Chad, I just kept repeating to myself, "You know this isn't me." He cried with me and comforted me, he encouraged me and told me we would get through this. Chad kept saying he knew this wasn't who I was. The love he showed me by helping me through that moment in my life will never be forgotten. I am thankful to this very day. Once Chad and I got through that night, we headed home.

It wasn't long after we were home that I was finally starting to feel stronger and better. Being with Bree again helped me a lot. Things between Chad and I were a little better for a short time. About three weeks after being home Chad and I were talking and, for some ungodly reason, we decided to buy an eight ball of cocaine. It was something we both agreed to and I am not even sure why. Living in Chad's hometown, he had all the connections. It was a simple phone call and we had an eight ball in our hands. We held onto it and made arrangements for Bree to stay with Tracy and Stacy. Once Bree was gone, we broke down the cocaine and began snorting it. The effects came instantly. I talked like crazy when I snorted cocaine. I could barely stop talking. Chad and I ended up spending the night talking about a lot of things. I remember sitting in our living room and asking him if he thought my dad could see us and what we were doing.

I kept wondering if my dad would be really disappointed in me and, truth is, I knew he would be. We talked about Ezra and how he was still a part of my dreams. We talked about our relationship and how neither of us were very happy in our marriage. I told Chad I wished things could just be normal for us and he seemed to agree. The night was going really good and we were both opening up about how we felt. Although it was drug induced, Chad and I talked about everything, including how we would always remain friends for our daughter's sake. We agreed that no matter what happened between us, we would always be good to one another. It felt like our friendship grew that night.

After many hours of deep conversation, we ended up snorting the entire eight ball. Once it was gone we both decided we wanted more. Chad called his buddy back and, although we didn't have the money, Chad was able to get a front (got the cocaine on a loan). We really hit it hard that night. By the time the second eight ball was gone, the withdrawal effects began to take hold. I hated coming down from cocaine because my mind and body would try to convince me I needed more. My spirit, however, would be screaming at me about how worthless and horrible of a person I was. I told Chad I never wanted to do cocaine again. He didn't argue and we never did cocaine together again.

It seemed like Christmas came quickly this year and, needless to say, I wasn't in what most call the 'Christmas spirit'. By Christmas, Chad and I were able to purchase a very old, beat-up car. I quickly found another job bartending and planned to quit once our taxes came in. Once I got to work on Christmas Eve, I began drinking my sorrows away. I wanted my dad back just for a moment to tell him I loved him and to get the chance to say goodbye. I wanted to find happiness and stop being haunted by my past. I was having a huge pity party for myself and it was ridiculous. I drank way too much and knew I shouldn't have been driving, but I didn't hesitate to get behind the wheel. As I was driving, I saw the flashing lights and knew I was in trouble. It was this night that I was arrested for my first D.U.I (driving while under the influence).

I spent the night in a cold jail cell and woke up in the morning angry at myself for drinking and driving. I knew it was wrong. Once I was able to pass the breathalyzer I was released on my own recognizance and walked to the nearest phone to call Chad. I kept thinking to myself that I had to change. I needed to figure out what I was doing and where I was going in this life. I didn't want to continue living with so much anger and hurt inside of me, but I didn't know how not to. I constantly felt like there had to be more to life than just struggling to survive financially and emotionally. Now I was facing a 90-day license suspension and I was the only one working. My job was around 30 minutes from our home and I had no idea what I was going to do.

The few jobs that Chad did have while we were together caused more stress on me than anything. He was so immature about working. I would have to wake him up and then fight with him because he always wanted to call in. Chad constantly wanted to argue about going to work and I would have to explain that we had a family and bills to pay. It was like I mentioned earlier, I felt like I was raising another child. I was tired of being the only adult in the house.

The holidays were spent with Chad's family and, of course, another New Year began.

Chapter FOURTEEN

2003: After the New Year passed, my boss was being very patient with me because getting back and forth to work was really hard on me. There were nights I would end up getting a ride to work and have to wait till in the morning to get a ride home. I remember a few times I locked the bar down and tried to sleep on the pool table. I would never suggest it. It was freezing, even with my leather jacket. I was still suffering from nightmares. They seemed to be more frequent and I was angry because I thought God had forsaken me. I missed my dad, Ezra, and I just couldn't accept that pain and suffering was all there was.

When taxes came in we were able to catch up the bills and take care of a few things, but the money went quick as it always did. I did quit bartending and started working for Chad's dad's fiancé. She owned a small restaurant. I enjoyed the work, but I felt like I was treated more like a slave. They were not very nice to me and claimed that people said I was closing the 24-hour restaurant at night and going out drinking. I found this funny since most nights I had to bring Bree with me. I would load up a small T.V. and V.C.R, set Bree up in the back room with her blanket, pillow and favorite movie as I worked. The job didn't last long because of the way I was treated. I felt like I was a target for everything that went wrong in the restaurant.

In March, my 90-day license suspension was up. I left Bree with Chad and headed an hour south to see Bob. Bob and I stayed in touch all the time, but he lived far away and we didn't see one another often. Chad, Bob and I always had a blast when we all hung out. Aaron was also a constant part of our lives. Bob and I decided to go to a few bars and then he decided he wanted to come stay with Chad and me for a short time. On the way back to my house, I was pulled over and arrested for my second D.U.I (Driving Under the Influence). Due to my first D.U.I. still pending in the Courts, and this arrest being made in a different county, the charges didn't cross one another. I plead guilty and was placed on a year of unsupervised probation. I will honestly say that I am against drunk driving, and I am beyond thankful that my ignorance never caused injury to anyone while I did drive under the influence.

Bree was growing so fast and I knew I had to do something if I was ever going to provide her with any kind of normal life. I just wanted to be able to provide for Bree and not worry about bills all the time. Chad tried to pull close to me, but at that time I just didn't want anything to do with him. I kept Bree close and spent much of my time with her. We played all kinds of games and read books all the time together.

I knew we couldn't survive unless I found a job quickly, but I wasn't sure what my next move was going to be. I turned yet again to my Bible. I tried so hard for so long to connect to God, but deep down my shame wouldn't let me. The demons from my past clung tightly to me and convinced me that I was unworthy of love and forgiveness. I felt and thought that I was nothing and no one. I didn't realize that it was never and has never been about me, my wants or my feelings. God has a purpose for each of us. He can quickly take us out of the darkness most of us find ourselves in. The thing we have to realize is, once we ask Jesus Christ to be our Savior, we are no longer sinners that sin. My friend, we are Saints that sin. We are forgiven for even the sins we feel are unforgivable. The battle is realizing you are worth forgiveness even if others tell you that you are not. Even though I was thankful for the job at the restaurant, I felt the way I was treated wasn't worth continuing to work there. I didn't leave with bitter feelings and Chad's dad was still Chad's dad.

Soon after quitting the restaurant, Bob was back in town and hanging out a lot. He was a breath of fresh air for me. He always made me laugh and he seemed to give a shit about how I felt. I didn't talk to him much about the problems Chad and I had, but I felt comfortable with Bob. We had a lot in common. Plus Bob and I had never done anything sexually, which made me think that our friendship was real and beyond what anyone could touch. Bob was staying at our house most nights while he was in town. It wasn't long and Chad's birthday was creeping up on us.

For Chad's birthday I wanted to put together a huge hog roast for him. Bob was a lot of help getting everything together. We had the hog, the roaster, a tent with a band and a keg. I went around to everyone in our neighborhood to let them know there would be a band and it would stop playing at 10 p.m. Everyone was so friendly and thankful for letting them know, not one neighbor complained or argued about the band playing.

The day of Chad's birthday everything turned out perfect. We may not have had as many friends show up as we expected due to a storm that was moving in, but we still had a great time. The band showed up on time and when they started playing it was so surreal. We sat staring at the sky with the tent and band right in front of us. The storm passed by on both sides of us and the sun was shining on us the entire time. It was like a movie, okay. It was an incredible view.

It was so cool to see our neighbors coming out and standing on their porches enjoying the music with us. I think Chad had a really good day and I couldn't believe the amazing beauty we witnessed in the sky. That was in June. In August, Paul had come to visit and told us he could use some help to manage the games. He was heading to Michigan and offered me a good deal. After Paul left I debated if I should take him up on his offer. It didn't take too long to decide. Bob was interested in going to work on the road, also, so soon after Chad and I discussed it. We both agreed that I would leave one more time to see if the money would be any good. We agreed that I would go to work for Paul and try to make enough money for a fresh start for us. Next thing I knew, Bree, Bob and I were packed up and off to Michigan to work for Paul.

Paul had purchased a small travel trailer for Bree and me so that we had a safe place to stay at night. It was so sweet and unexpected. It was crazy, though, because Paul was angry that I brought Bob. I just thought he was being silly because Bob and I were just friends. I never planned nor saw what happened next, but Paul did. Bob and I were best friends for years at this time and we never crossed that boundary until we went to Michigan. I don't know what brought it out of us, but we began to have the most passionate and exciting affair.

At night, after Bree was asleep, things got wild between Bob and me. He was very energetic and spontaneous, which I was enjoying very much. We were having adventurous sex on picnic tables and many spots where we could have been caught at any time. He was my best friend and I actually gave a bit of my heart to him. I was happy and excited. I hadn't felt that way in a long time. Bob didn't make me feel like Ezra had. I honestly gave up on being able to love anyone that way, but I didn't think about Ezra so much when I was with Bob. Even though in the back of my mind I was comparing him to Ezra, the connection I felt with Bob was incredible on its own.

Money was tight the first spot we worked. Bree and I did spend some time visiting with Derek, Ina and the boys. Paul, Bree and I also went to see and spent some time with Dean. I couldn't believe how big that kid was getting. He was growing into such a handsome young man and did grow into one. Brandon and Sadie also made their way to the show I was working. They were married by this time and I can't express how happy I was to see them both.

Sadie was pregnant with their second child. Their first child, a son, and Bree played as if they had been friends for a long time the entire week I worked that spot. We even joked about how funny it would be if the two of them dated one another when they got older. You could feel the happiness from both Brandon and Sadie. They truly loved one another unconditionally and figured out how to make things work for them. To my surprise, Brandon asked me if we could go for a walk and talk about some things.

As Brandon and I walked, he began apologizing to me for ever hurting me. He explained to me that Sadie was the love of his life. He said that she taught him what love truly meant and that he knew he was going to spend his life with her. Brandon continued to express that I taught him how to feel love, but Sadie showed him how to live, express and accept love. I thought it was the most beautiful thing in the world I had ever heard. I loved Brandon and knew I always would. I was happy for him and the love he and Sadie shared. In a way, it gave me hope that some-day I could find the same. I convinced myself that was exactly what Bob and I were doing; we had the friendship down, now to see where the relationship went.

Then, of course, being the smart ass Brandon is, he said that he told Sadie if it was possible to have two wives he would have her and me. We both just started laughing and gave one another a hug. I could see how much Brandon loved Sadie and how much she loved him. Brandon told me that nothing would change the fact that Bree and I would always have a home and a safe place with him and Sadie. I can't explain how much that has always meant to me.

Bree was in heaven when we were in Michigan. She got to play and we did all kinds of fun things. Bob was so good with Bree and he was really big on staying active. He was far from a couch potato. Our days were never boring with Bob and we were always doing something together. Work and money wasn't as good as I had thought it would have been and there was never money to send home to Chad. Paul was also being real distant with me; which, looking back, makes complete sense. He was so upset about Bob being there and me being with him. Again, I didn't understand I was to Paul as Ezra was to me. I could have never been just a friend to Ezra even if he asked me to. That was exactly what I was doing to Paul.

One night Bree wanted to stay with Ina, Derek and the boys. Bob was doing his own thing that night so I went over to hang out with Brandon and Sadie at their house. Brandon and I had a blast talking about the past and some of the stupid things we used to do. All of us joked around and just enjoyed the evening together. Sadie and I were really just getting to know one another, but I knew that she was someone that I wanted in my life.

For some reason the things that happened with Dawn were eating me up. I looked her up online and discovered she wasn't far from me at all. The next morning Brandon ended up giving me a ride to see Dawn. Something inside of me made me feel the need to apologize to her. Truth is, I didn't know if what my mom had told me was true when I got mad at Dawn. If it wasn't, I wanted to make things right with her.

Dawn and I had a good talk on her porch. She had been through some really tough times. She had been through being a stripper to being with a man that had abused her. Dawn had two little girls and had gotten away from all of that and was trying to make a better life for her and her babies. I felt for her, but I also knew she was strong and would pull through. Come to find out, she didn't tell my mom that I was to blame for the wrecked house. We parted ways with a hug and never saw one another again. Years later we reconnected on Facebook just as if the years hadn't passed us by.

After about three weeks I realized the money wasn't going to be as good as Paul had told me and Bob thought he had a way to make some money down in Texas. Bob also had a half-brother that he recently reconnected with and was sure we would be able to stay at his house in Texas. Bob ended up making a couple calls and we decided to head south.

When I let Paul know what was going on he asked me to go for a walk with him. Off we went and on the walk Paul told me how much he wanted to be with me and that Bob was a joke. He said he understood me better than anyone. He knew that I would always love Ezra, but felt I could overcome that and love him if I would just give him a chance. Paul ended up down on one knee and pulled out a beautiful engagement ring. Paul proposed to me again.

At this point in my affair with Bob I couldn't help but wonder what was going to happen with him and I. Things between us were so exciting, fresh and new to me. What we were sharing wasn't something I could walk away from. I had to see where it was going. If I didn't give it a try I was afraid it would haunt me as the thoughts of Ezra did. I told Paul I loved him, but I just couldn't be with him as his wife. I told Paul I was sorry, but what I felt with Bob was too powerful to walk away from. I hated hurting Paul but, again, a part of me felt like I was unworthy of his love.

A few days after Paul's proposal, Bob, Bree and I were headed back to Indiana. When I got home I told Chad the plan to go to Texas and try to make some money. I told him I wouldn't be gone for more than a month and we agreed that he would take care of Bree until I got back. I think Chad tolerated my leaving so much because he loved me and was hoping I would get all of the wandering out of me. I'm not sure if he realized Bob and I were having an affair or not, but he never said anything. I was determined to believe Bob was the one for me and could bring me the happiness I had been praying for years to have. I ended up saying my goodbyes to Bree and told her I would call her every day that I could.

Bree wasn't too upset because she was happy to see her daddy after we were gone for about a month. Plus, Bree had all of Chad's family there and they were all close to her. Bob and I loaded the car up and drove the entire way to Texas. It was during this time that I witnessed the horrific nightmares that Bob was battling. Being next to Bob throughout the night was scary all by itself. He suffered from horrific, violent night terrors.

Once we finally arrived in Texas it was night time and I must admit I was taken off guard by the beauty of the city lights. It was simply breath-taking. The ocean was nearby and it made the air smell wonderful. When we first got there, Bob's brother and family were actually on vacation and not even home. That had me a little worried, but Bob reassured me that everything would be okay.

Bob worked things out with another one of his family members and we ended up with a key to his brother's home. We had the house to ourselves for almost a week before his brother and brother's family got back from their vacation. It was a beautiful home filled with top of the line name brand items, including a beautiful leather couch and all of the home interior. One thing I loved was that Bob was as sexually active as I was and he wasn't shy about it. I'll admit that running around the house naked did happen a couple times. I am not proud, either, but at the time it was a lot of fun.

Things between Bob and I were going really good, but I did notice small comments he was starting to make. It was simple things like one time when I dressed up in sexy lingerie and I approached him. I asked him what he thought and his reply was, "I've seen worse." That hurt really bad and I ended up walking away quietly crying to myself. I just changed my clothes and convinced myself he was just in a bad mood and didn't realize how much he had hurt me by his reaction. I approached him later about it and he apologized so I just let it go.

When Bob's brother and his family came home from their vacation it was strange and uncomfortable for me. His brother was very welcoming and happy that we were there. The wife, however, wasn't happy at all. She was never mean in any way, but you could tell she wasn't happy. When I think back on the situation and put myself in her shoes, I wouldn't have been at all happy either.

The plan didn't go exactly as we thought it would, but we both had jobs within a week. Bob ended up in a construction job and I ended up as a bartender/waitress. On my first day working it was Karaoke night and by the third song in I realized that something was off. The guys were singing Madonna, Material Girl and other very good, independent, strong female songs. As I actually started paying attention to the people around me, and not just focusing on what the boss was trying to tell me, I realized I was working in a gay bar.

Honestly, I enjoyed working in that bar because there was way less violence. The regulars were friendly and everybody always seemed to be happy in that place. I enjoyed my job and the people I worked with during that time. On my down time I truly loved being around Bob and how he always wanted to do something. We played basketball, went for walks and just enjoyed one another's company. I will never forget when we headed over to San Padre Island. We took the ferry and, while we were standing on the ferry, we watched the dolphins jump next to us as we went across the water. The people on the Island that we ran into were so friendly. I called Bree often and that day I loved talking to her about the dolphins and how much I wished she was there to be able to see them.

I also enjoyed and loved the fact that Bob talked to people. He was charismatic and wasn't afraid to strike up a conversation with a stranger. This particular day was an amazing and a very hot one. I think that was the only thing I didn't really like about Texas, it would get so hot during the day that I even put an egg on the sidewalk to see if it would cook. It didn't do as well as I thought it would, but it did turn pretty white.

As time went on I noticed that Bob was beginning to act strange. He continued to make small comments that would hurt my feelings, but I would hide how much it really hurt me. Bob also started to act a bit controlling of me. I didn't think much about it and just tried to act like it was just the circumstances we were in. I wanted Bob to be the man that I had been praying for so bad that I got caught up in the excitement of our relationship because he was such a good friend to me. I dismissed all the signs he was showing: The controlling, the mean comments. Simple mistakes, not big deals, no problem. We all have issues, this was something we could work through. Lord knows I am not like other women, so surely I could help him with his aggression issues, right?

It's amazing what we put ourselves through to convince ourselves we can make something work that isn't meant to work. I didn't care if Bob had problems to overcome. I felt like we had a connection that was unbreakable because we had been friends for so long. I was convinced that part of overcoming problems with someone was being willing to face them together. I felt like it meant nothing less than victory. I had never had a healthy, stable relationship and I thought since Bob was willing to try and I was too it meant I wasn't alone anymore. With Chad I felt like

I was alone. Bob made me feel like he was willing to grow and learn with one another.

Staying with Bob and his family became very uncomfortable because I could tell that Bob's brother was attracted to me. He had just purchased a brand new Harley Davidson and the motorcycle was gorgeous. His wife wasn't a rider at all and I think he was going through what we call a man's 'midlife crisis'. We had been there for a little less than four weeks when the night came that I needed a ride home from work.

Bob's brother offered to pick me up when I got off work and all of us agreed. He ended up at my bar a few hours before my shift was over. We began taking shots together for most of the evening. When we left the bar on his Harley, we somehow ended up at a small private beach, naked and in the water having sex. I admit that it was pretty intense, but I realized more than ever that Bob and I needed to get out of there. I had already been telling Bob I wanted to go and get Bree. I was missing her so much. Now, however, I felt ashamed and I didn't want to destroy a marriage nor what I thought Bob and I had together.

This was one affair that completely freaked me out. I hated the fact that I did what I did, but I knew I couldn't tell Bob about it. Somehow I was able to get myself and Bob back to Indiana within days after that night. It was freakishly easy for me to dismiss consensual unexpected sex. I was beyond ready to be back with Bree and to tell Chad the truth about Bob and me. I really felt like Chad would be okay knowing that I was with someone we both cared for. Bob and I talked about everything and coming clean about our love for one another. We came up with the plan that we would live with his parents for a short time, just until we could get our own place.

By that time I hadn't seen Bree in close to a month and I had been going crazy from being so far away from her. I couldn't believe how big she had gotten in such a short time. I didn't want to miss out on any more time with my baby girl ever again. I was so happy to see her and she was happy to see me too. We had talked on the phone almost daily, but it wasn't the same as being in front of her. I promised her right then and there that I would never leave her again and that was a promise I have always kept and will till the day the good Lord takes me.

When I got to the house, I sat down and talked to Chad about everything. I explained to him that I fell in love with Bob and that it was never my intention. Chad wasn't too hurt. Actually, he handled it well. Truth is, he was seeing someone while I was in Texas when Bree was with his mom, which was most of the time. I didn't ask him too many questions about his affair because I believed I had what was perfect for Bree, a family life that was built on friendship and on love. Once I was home, I was honestly shocked by how the house looked. It was a train wreck with carpeting ripped up because the dogs had pottied on the floor so much. The house smelled so bad and had this darkness to it. Blankets were hanging over the windows and just dark, literally.

I was happy that I was getting Bree out of there. Chad and Bree had been camping out in the living room while I was gone and she wasn't even sleeping in her own bed. I didn't realize how bad Chad was doing on his own with Bree. He never said anything about the carpets being ripped up, weeks of dishes not being done and how much he had been drinking. As Chad and I sat in front of one another, inside we both knew that our relationship was over. I had betrayed him, he too had stepped out on our marriage. Together we were no good for one another, but we were a wonderful little girl's parents. Chad and I didn't split up hating one another and fighting. It wasn't perfect, but we managed to come to an agreement. We had a love for one another as Bree's parents and we were both committed to do our best for her. Chad even left for a few days while I packed and tried to get all of mine and Bree's things together. Bob came to pick us up with his dad's truck while Chad stayed at his friends. Bree and I were on our way to a new life.

I was excited about the move because I knew both of Bob's parents and they were both so sweet. They were a bit older, but we got along well. We had all become very close during Alan's trial and we had stayed in touch throughout the years. In fact, I was still writing Alan when I would get the chance. Bree was excited, too, because she really enjoyed being around Bob and his parents. She had always been around all of them since she was a baby and, for some reason, I convinced myself that would make the transition for her easier.

Bob was always very active with Bree so they already had a good bond built between them. Bob was not a stranger in Bree's life in any way. I think that was what started attracting me to Bob. I would often watch how well he was with her throughout the years and then watching the connection they had was warming. I knew Bob already loved her and she loved him.

It wasn't long after we moved in with Bob that Chad called and wanted to know if he could take Bree to his new girlfriend's house in Tennessee. Something about it made me feel real uncomfortable. I am not even sure why or what it was. I questioned the way he had been taking care of Bree when I came back and how bad things were at the house. I told Chad I thought it would be better if I at least met the woman before our daughter left out of state with them. Chad wasn't very happy with my answer, but he acted like he understood and said he would talk to her about meeting me. This was in late August.

Although I did love Bob's mom, I have to admit that once we began living with her she did seem to be a bit strange in my opinion. She was very emotional and had a hard time coping with life in general. I will never forget all of her porcelain dolls that were spread out throughout the house. I am talking the ones that stand up to your hip. Some of the dolls were almost the same height as Bree, if not taller. I found it silly how she would talk about the dolls and how she felt they actually would move their eyes to follow her sometimes.

At first I thought she was joking, but later realized she wasn't which was just creepy. I also learned a lot about Bob during the time I spent with his mother. Things like how his mom rocked him in a rocking chair till he was about ten years old. It made me question how long he had suffered from night terrors and anger problems. A short time passed and I began asking myself, "What did I get myself into?" I couldn't believe the man I knew for a little over four years was turning out to be a man I didn't know at all. Bob had a job waiting for him when we got there and I was able to get to work quickly. We agreed to start saving for our own home and planned to move out of Bob's parents within the month.

Only a few nights after Bree and I had moved in something happened that I never saw coming. I had put Bree down for the night and, without missing a beat, it was bedtime bible story and prayers. She never gave me problems when it came to bedtime because she would go right to sleep. I raised Bree on a strict schedule no matter the circumstances she was exposed to. She could always count on her schedule and that was consistent. We can be a good mother and still be lost; it doesn't make you any less of a mother; fear not.

Once Bree was asleep and the night went on, Bob and I ended up in an argument about something and we went outside in the driveway so we didn't wake Bree. I don't even recall what the argument was about nor what I said, but Bob got so angry he ended up putting his hands around my neck and started strangling me. I think the shock of the situation is what prevented me from doing anything and, right as I was about to pass out, Bob's dad stepped in and Bob let go. I think Bob went in the back yard, but I am not even sure where he went. I ended up stumbling over to the neighbor's yard and dropped to the ground crying, trying to catch my breath. I knew in that moment there was no way I could stay with this man. What was I going to do?

There is no explanation for what happened next and to this day I swear it was God intervening. It was really dark out as I sat in the neighbor's yard crying and feeling hopeless. There was no light on me so I know there is no way someone could have seen me from the road, but when I finally looked up a truck had pulled in the front yard where I was sitting.

I recall an older man walking up to me and asking me if I was okay. I could barely breathe and my crying was just making it worse. I just shrugged my shoulders because I knew I wasn't okay, but questioned what in the world he could do to help? That gentleman knelt down and placed his hand on my shoulder and asked me if he could pray for me. I started crying more and shook my head to gesture yes. I still have no idea who that man was, but I can't express how grateful I was he took a moment to do that.

At this point I really wasn't sure what I was supposed to do. In tears, Bob apologized to me and his parents made me feel like I shouldn't judge him just because of the one incident. His mother convinced me that we had been friends for too long to allow that to hurt us. I convinced myself that because it wasn't in front of Bree it wasn't that big of a deal. I didn't really have many options at that point in my life, plus I was good at making excuses for Bob's behavior. It only took about a month and a half before we were able to get our own place. We were all so excited. Bree had her own room and we even had a yard. It was a decent two-bedroom house and Bree's daycare was actually only two blocks from our house.

I began to feel more comfortable with Bree going with Chad to visit. I was uncomfortable with her going out of state, but I didn't want to keep her away from Chad or his family. I trusted Chad and I thought he would die for our daughter before allowing anything to happen to her. By this time Chad had moved out of the house we once shared and moved to Tennessee with his girlfriend. After only a few visits down south Bree started to cry when it was time to go back. She complained that all dad and Jade did was fight. Chad and I were open and communication was really good between us so I asked him about it. He said that Jade would say something rude about me in front of Bree and they would end up in another room fighting for long periods of time. Chad said he was defending me and he wasn't going to allow Jade to disrespect me in front of our daughter. I have to admit I was pretty impressed and felt blessed that this was the father of my child. I was shocked that Chad was standing up for me, but I knew in my heart I would have done the same for him. To this day I don't like when anyone talks bad about Chad, including Bree, even after the hell Bree and I were put through.

During one of Bree's visits with her dad, Bob and I decided to take the opportunity to enjoy our evening. We both had been working really hard to get our home put together and needed a break. Bob was great when Bree was around, but when she would leave for a weekend visit it was as if Bob's personality would almost flip. This particular night Bob and I went out to a few bars and had some drinks with a few friends. The night went great and we had a lot of fun. As we were heading home I realized I had run out of cigarettes and asked Bob to stop so I could get some. Bob didn't smoke, but he had never threw a fit about me smoking. I have no idea what triggered him, but he started yelling at me and calling me names. I was so confused and tried to calmly get him to rationalize what he was saying. He ended up throwing the truck in park in the middle of the road. Then Bob took his seatbelt off and climbed on top of me. He started beating the shit out of me really bad. I don't know why or what made him act like that. All I could do was put my arms up to try and protect myself from his vicious punches. Some guy on a bicycle ended up stopping at the driver's side door and asked if everything was okay. Bob instantly got off of me and turned to the guy punching him hard and knocking him flat off his bicycle then put the truck in gear and sped off.

As soon as we came to a stop sign I jumped out and just started running. I could hear Bob yelling for me, but I wasn't looking back. I found myself at a nearby gas station covered in blood. I didn't let anyone see me, I just hid behind the building crying. I prayed to God and asked him why everything always had to turn out so messed up for me. I didn't understand what I had done to deserve all that was happening and had happened to me. I started to feel angry at God for just leaving me. I felt like I was going to have to go through this life always alone.

I waited until I knew Bob was asleep and ended up sneaking into our house. I just cried myself to sleep as I laid on the couch. The next morning I woke up to Bob sitting next to me crying and telling me he needed help. He swore he never wanted to hurt me again and he would do whatever it took. I told him if he didn't get help I was done. I explained that I never wanted my daughter to see anything like this and I refused to be an example to her that it was okay to be beat by a man.

He listened to everything I said and cried as I spoke to him. He admitted he needed help and promised to get it. A few hours later Bob's parents came and picked him up. They took him to a volunteer inpatient treatment program and he was admitted into the psychiatric hospital. To be honest with you, I didn't see that morning going the way it did at all. I ended up calling Chad and told him what happened. I had a fat lip, black eye and bruises all over my neck from where Bob tried strangling me again. Chad agreed to keep Bree for a week longer so that my bruises would heal before Bree saw me.

Bob didn't stay in the program long before he was back home. All seemed good for a very short period of time, but it didn't last long. It wasn't even a month after the last incident when Bree went to her father's for another visit and Bob attacked me again. This time I had drank enough alcohol that I thought I was ready for him. He swung his first punch and it connected, but it didn't faze me. I called him out and asked him if that was all he had. Then came the second punch and it also connected. Bob was strong, but I was built bigger than him and felt like I could kick his ass if I could just bring myself to fight back. For some reason we can be the baddest fighter in the world, but some of us will not and cannot fight back when the person we love is the one beating us. I was one of those women that thought if I stayed with a man that beat me then I was asking for it. Here I was now being beaten by the second man in my life and this time I was taking a stand. I was not going to allow my daughter to think it was okay to be beat. I refused to even allow her to see that kind of behavior.

Once the second punch landed I just started laughing at him and calling him a pussy. It was then that Bob threw me to the floor. As he had done several times before, Bob started strangling me. I couldn't bring myself to actually fight back for some reason. I just looked right at him started yelling, "Demon, you better kill me. Come on demon kill me. You can hurt my body Demon, but you can't hurt me." I wasn't even able to completely finish what I was saying before Bob simply let go of me. He sat back on the floor and started crying. I didn't care that he was crying nor that he was in his own spiritual war. All I knew was I was done and

194

he was not going to hurt me anymore. As I rubbed my neck, fighting to catch my breath, I stood up and called Bob a few choice names. I just simply walked upstairs, got my pajamas on and went to bed. The next morning when I went downstairs Bob was sleeping on the couch. Our ceiling fan was broken and, when I looked around, I realized that he had tried to hang himself from our ceiling fan with his belt. He was extremely unsuccessful and it was just a cry for help.

Within a day of this Bob ended up getting drunk and driving his dad's truck uptown. The police pulled him over and he lied about his identity, but the police didn't buy it. Come to find out he also had a warrant out for something else in another county. I can't explain the way I felt when I heard that Bob was going to be locked up for a long time. When the news came to me all I could do was drop to me knees and thank God.

I made sure Bob's parents got all his things and explained to them that Bob and I were done. I told them he would never be welcome at that home again. Bree was a bit heartbroken about Bob being gone, but she adjusted quickly. I never told her about what really happened with Bob until she was older.

I can't express how good it felt to have my job and to be supporting my daughter. For the first time I had my own place and could just focus on Bree and me. Truth be told, I felt like I had everything together and could provide for my daughter on my own. For the first time in a long time I was happy and it felt like there might be the slightest chance that things could just level out for me. Bree and I were doing really good. We had dinner together every day, we talked, we laughed and went to the park all the time. We were actually starting to enjoy our lives and things were finally peaceful, until the visits with Chad became more of a problem.

The day did come when Chad brought his girlfriend over to my house to introduce us. I admit I was surprised. She wasn't very attractive and dressed like she was stuck in the eighties. Her appearance wasn't really my issue, it was Jade's personality and attitude toward me that seemed very cold. Honestly, in some ways she reminded me of Chad's sister,

Stacy. She really seemed to have some kind of chip on her shoulder. This woman didn't know me and she seemed to hate me from the start.

Meeting Jade for the first time wasn't comfortable at all and she put no effort into making it comfortable. I offered her something to drink and tried for a friendly conversation, but it wasn't happening. I knew something was off with this woman, but I just couldn't put my finger on it. Chad wanted to get Bree for his Thanksgiving visit and we had already agreed on it. In November, Chad said he was going to take Bree to his family's for Thanksgiving and I was fine with that. He came to the house to pick Bree up and all was good. The day after Thanksgiving his mother called me asking where Chad and Bree were. I was unable to contact him and began worrying about Bree. I knew that Chad would never hurt Bree, but I didn't know anything about his hateful girlfriend. When Chad returned Bree he told me he took her to Jade's family Thanksgiving and I was livid. I was so angry that he lied to me, but even more angry at the fact that Bree didn't spend the holiday with her family, his family, as we had agreed. I told Chad that his mom was looking for him and that he could only visit Bree in Indiana. I explained Bree's behavior when she would return from their home and that it was getting worse. I then mentioned how he was now lying to me about where he was taking her. I expressed to him that this would be the new rule, at least till our divorce and a court order was in place.

There were several visits that Bree would come home and tell me about how Jade said mean things about me. Bree's biggest complaint was Chad and Jade's fighting. Their fights weren't in front of Bree often according to Chad, but she could hear the yelling from the other room. It pissed me off that, after everything I had gone through to ensure my daughter didn't see the negatives, now here she was exposed to nothing except hate when she was around Jade.

Jade was not happy with the fact that I didn't trust her with my child and that I limited Chad's visits to Indiana. Every time Chad and I were on the phone trying to make arrangements for a visit, Jade was continually in the background calling me bad names and saying really rude things.

There were a couple times that Chad told me he would call me later. With Jade's loud foul mouth in the background we couldn't even hear one another talking. By this point I was just angry because this woman was so hateful and we had spent a maximum of a half hour together. What the hell could Chad have told her that made her so angry at me?

During this time I had so much on my plate. Chad and I talked as often as we could. We weren't angry at one another so I didn't care what Jade thought or said, I had more important things going on in my life. I was focused on raising my little girl and fighting my own demons, not to mention I was trying to make sure that I had all my bills paid so we didn't lose our home. Regardless, I wasn't going to just stand idle if Jade was hurting my child. Chad was the only reason I was willing to allow Bree to go because he kept telling me he wouldn't allow anything to happen to her. He promised me he wouldn't allow Jade to say anything bad about me in front of our daughter, but I knew he couldn't stop it.

In early December I received the news that I was being laid off. I was through a temp service and the factory didn't need most of us for the winter months. Many of us were sent home. I started to panic and questioning how I could support Bree and pay bills without a job. I started job searching right away and found something promising, but I had to wait on them to call me. As I patiently waited for the call on the job opportunity, on December 11th I received a call from Jade. She said that she felt I was wrong to not allow Chad to bring Bree around her. Jade threatened me several times stating she would hire an attorney and take my daughter from me. She also said she was going to call the cops and have them take Bree away from me. At first I just thought this woman was as bipolar as Chad. He would call and apologize for Jade calling me names, then he would call and cuss me out with her in the background. It was complete madness. Jade was out of control and I had too much to worry about to be concerned with her empty threats and childish name calling.

It wasn't until that phone call that I realized where some of the hate Jade had toward me had come from. Chad had told Jade some really twisted stories about our marriage and about me. It was the only thing that made sense. She was calling me names like drug addict, stupid bitch and dumb cunt. This woman didn't know anything about me except what she was told. Jade felt she had a right to judge me from every story she had heard about me and half of them weren't even true. I just brushed it off because I was fully dedicated to doing the best I could for Bree. I had a lot to overcome and pull together on my own and Jade was the least of my concerns. I may not be a perfect mother, but I gave and give Bree all my love. Who was Jade to judge me anyway? Who was she to threaten me? I was doing what I thought was best for my child. I felt that being around someone who talked bad about me in front of her was extremely unhealthy for Bree, not to mention the fighting that she was being exposed to.

In mid-December I still wasn't working. Bree and I enjoyed preparing for the Christmas holiday. It was always one of our favorites because we baked cookies, decorated and always spent time together building our own traditions. One day out of the blue I received a call from Ina. She said Derek was in jail and she needed help with Jeremy and Luke. Ina asked if she could bring them down to me and if I could keep them for about a week. I didn't have a job so I thought it would be a perfect time to get to know my nephews and Bree get to know her cousins. I explained to her it could only be for a week because I was waiting to get a call on a job I was trying to get.

Ina agreed and brought the boys down to me. I must admit it was so good to be able to spend time with both of my nephews and the kids played so good together. Bree was in heaven having her cousins at the house to hang out and play with. About two days before Ina made it down to pick up the boys, I received a call for the position at the factory I had been waiting on. I was so excited and everything worked out really well with the boys and timing for all of it. I think it's safe to say Bree and I were both sad to see the boys go.

Soon after Ina came and picked up the boys I started my new job. I was happy to be working, but I was in another temp position and bills were already behind. I knew there was no way I was going to make it till taxes and I was stressed about what I was going to do. I kept praying for God to lead me and show me what he wanted me to do, yet it just didn't feel like he was listening to me.

During the holidays Chad came to our house to pick Bree up and take her to see his family, which I thought was awesome. We both sat down and agreed to a visitation schedule and talked about how we would always remain good to one another for Bree's sake. Chad and I had no problems talking to one another when we didn't have to deal with Jade's anger issues and her yelling cuss words in the background. Jade was a very hostile woman toward me and she wasn't shy to express her dislike of me, apparently in front of anyone. I expressed my concern to Chad again about Jade being alone with Bree, but he assured me that he wouldn't let anything happen. Chad seemed so understanding of how I felt and why I was uncomfortable with Bree going out of state. I expressed it even more now that Jade had threatened to hire an attorney to take my daughter. What was crazy is Chad and I were communicating fine, so I truly believed that I didn't have to worry about Jade or her outbursts. My only concern was what was best for Bree and how Chad and I could work together to provide that for her as her parents.

After Chad's visit and Bree was home safe, Paul came to visit us. We ended up loading his car and taking a small trip to Michigan to see Paul's oldest, Samantha, and her boyfriend (now husband). We got to stop in and visit with Dean, too. It was always such a blessing to see the kids. They just kept getting bigger every time I saw each of them as if they wouldn't stop growing. Darn kids. Bree would light up every time she would see any of Paul's kids. She loves every single one of them very much. I felt blessed to be with family and, even though the stress of bills and making sure I took care of everything was on my shoulders, I was making it work. Bree was okay, I was okay and life was good. Bree and I had a wonderful Christmas together and a good New Year, too.

Chapter FIFTEEN

2004: I went into the New Year focused. I loved being independent and providing for Bree. I was so determined to take care of our bills and daily life that I didn't see what was coming. I have to take a moment here to say that, without our haters, who encourage us to be better? Jade truly helped me become a better woman and a far better mother than I could have been on my own. She pushed me to give my all and to always think about what's most important. For me, Bree is and always will be one of the top on my most important list.

We can only forgive those who try to hurt us or come against us. Trying to defeat your enemies alone can truly take you to their low. The following chapters you are about to read are where I learned some of my toughest lessons about the power of forgiveness. We need to understand there is power in forgiving ourselves and others. I thought it made me a pussy or something but, the truth is, it didn't make me weak. The events that took place over the next years not only taught me the power of forgiveness, but also made me stronger.

In February, I filed for a divorce on my own. Chad was coming up to visit Bree as often as he could. He stayed in Indiana when he would come get her. I truly believed that Jade was crazy and it was unhealthy for Bree to be around her. Chad and I were actually on good terms and didn't have any problems. On many occasions he continued to apologize for Jade's behavior. He tried so hard to work things out with me. Chad loved me and wanted to get back together more than anything, but I was enjoying learning who I was as a woman and mother. I hadn't ever been single for very long and I was liking it. I kept telling him we didn't get along this well when we were a couple. I was comfortable with the way things were between us and we got along and communicated better than we ever had.

I actually enjoyed my time with Chad when he would visit, but it wasn't long before I found myself in a rut. I knew there was no way to keep everything caught up at my house by myself. The time, I knew, was approaching and I was about to lose my home. I had been going through layoff after layoff and had no idea what I was going to do. I wasn't stressed though, I was at peace and kept faith that the Lord would work everything out.

Chad was a sense of comfort and familiarity to me. I really embraced the time we shared when he would come around. We would touch, hug and talk as if we were an older couple that had been together 50 years. One time when Chad came up we took Bree to the bowling alley. As Bree was off playing games, Chad looked at me and said, "Let's just run away together. We can go west like you've always wanted. I'll take one last ride on the bike and we'll go." See, Jade owned a custom-built Harley Davidson. Personally, it wasn't the words I had dreamed that would sweep me off my feet and I just smiled at Chad after he said it.

I just couldn't bring myself to go back to Chad. We had tried on and off for so long that I knew my heart didn't belong to him. Still, the only man I dreamed about and looked for was that skateboarding, Army man. I knew I couldn't love a man correctly until I got myself together. I just continued to remind Chad of how much better we were as friends, but I felt so bad for him. It was obvious that Chad wasn't happy with Jade, there was no hiding that, but Chad didn't want to be alone.

It quickly got to a point that it was impossible to communicate with Chad at any time Jade was around him. I have truly only met this woman the one time at my home, but she was so volatile toward me. I didn't really care what Jade thought of me or about her judgments, what I was mad at was how she had no problem talking so bad about me in front of Bree every time she got the chance. I truly believed she had some kind of mental disorder. Every single time Chad and I would work something out for a visit or time, Jade would get mad and disagree with the terms. I have never dealt with an adult who behaved so ridiculously. If I had been in middle school I would have beat that woman's ass; however, I was a grown adult and an example to my daughter. At this point I just allowed Chad to handle Jade.

One night Chad ended up spending the night of his visit at my house. After Bree's bedtime story and prayers she went right to sleep, as she always did. Chad and I had a few beers and the next thing I knew we were all over one another. I am not sure if it was the intensity of the circumstances or what. That night we shared some wild and passionate sex. It was so intense for both of us that we lost ourselves for a moment. I do admit there was one point that night the bitch in me did think to myself that having sex with Chad was just a payback to Jade. I was growing very weary of her name calling and the fact that I didn't feel Bree was safe with her around.

Chad and I continued to remain close and continued to work things out with Bree despite Jade's ruthless behavior. In March I was finally placed on probation for the D.U.I. (Driving Under the Influence) I received in 2002. Work was finally staying steady for me, and I made a few new friends. This really sweet guy named Brad actually wrote me a letter and placed it on my car asking me on a date. I agreed to go out with him, but we kept it simple. After that night Brad and I became good friends. Brad owned his own home and he knew the bind I was in financially. He ended up offering to help Bree and me with a place to stay, no strings attached. I knew I was losing my home and there was no way around it, but I told him I would think about it. Brad and his family ended up being a true blessing for Bree and me.

I believe Chad was holding onto the idea of us working things out because, in March, I had to file a Contempt Citation on him. Chad and I had court in April for the divorce and he wasn't completing the 'Helping Children Cope with Divorce' class that was required. Due to Jade's erratic behavior, I also filed a Petition for an Ex Parte Order. I just requested that the court grant me temporary custody of Bree until we went to court for our divorce in order to have something officially 'Ordered'. I knew if I had an order I wouldn't be as uncomfortable with Bree going out of state with Chad.

I was afraid that Jade may try to open a case there in Tennessee and Chad wouldn't bring Bree home. Chad was his normal self where he would bounce one day and then be angry at me the next. I wasn't concerned with him, but I had no idea what Jade was capable of. The reason I made the decision was solely based off of the way Jade was behaving and threats she had made to me. I really thought the woman was sick so I didn't want to risk counting on Chad to protect our daughter. I knew Chad well enough to know that he was not a leader and I wasn't taking any chances with our daughter's wellbeing. When we were together, Chad usually always did as I told him and the woman leading him now was not healthy.

When Chad and I would talk on the phone, Jade would say things about me being a bad mother because I had a criminal record. She even mentioned that I left Chad with some debt to a drug dealer (assuming she was talking about Chad's good friend that gave us the front). Jade was touching on things that only Chad could have shared with her; however, what Chad led her to believe was insane and not all accurate. I was mad at him for talking so badly about me and explained to him that it made things harder to be friends with someone who thought so ill of me. He swore that he didn't talk bad about me and they fought all the time because he wasn't allowing her to either. I was confused as to why Jade even felt she had a right to judge me when she didn't even know me.

Jade didn't know my battles, where and what I had already survived. She didn't know how many times I dropped to the floor and prayed. That woman seemed like she was pure evil from the very first day I had met her. I continued to be mad at Chad for sharing some of our personal stories with a woman that thought she had the right to throw my mistakes in my face. Was she perfect or better than me? As time went on Jade's true colors came out even more.

When I learned who Jade really was, I began to worry about the situation I was finding myself in. She wasn't just some woman who happened to dislike me with her every pore on her body; No, Jade was a multimillionaire with nothing but time and money on her hands.

From the research I have done, it is my understanding Jade and her sister were in a truck and it flipped. They both got hurt really bad. Jade's family sued the vehicle company and won due to that year of the truck being built too top heavy. There was an appeal but, in the end, all family members, including Jade's mom, Jade and her sister, walked away with $13.8 million each. My attitude changed real quick when I realized this woman acting like a psycho towards me had the means and money to do anything she wanted to me. I instantly had an ill feeling in my stomach and wasn't sure what was to come.

Jade and her family came from nothing and now had everything. All of her behavior was making sense, especially why she felt so inferior over Chad and our daughter. It finally registered why she wasn't shy to cuss and act like I should somehow give in to all she wanted. I wasn't afraid or intimidated by Jade, her money or her opinions of me. I only had one concern: What Jade was saying around my child. I became very aware of the fact that I didn't know this woman. I had no idea how intelligent she was or was not, nor did I know what Jade was capable of. She had already threatened to take my daughter so I wasn't putting anything past Jade.

After struggling to figure out what I needed to do, I finally made the decision to take Brad up on his offer to help Bree and me. There was just no way I could keep the house even though I tried my best to. I just wasn't making enough to support a home as a single mother.

Chad ended up finally complying with the required class and, in April, we went to court for our divorce. Our divorce wasn't bad in any way. We both ended up crying by the end of the whole thing. In fact, the judge even complimented the way Chad and I were working together and mentioned he wished other parents would behave in such a manner. Chad and I had agreed how to do visitation. We agreed to $50 a week in child support and, as soon as Chad got employment, he agreed he would also get Bree on his insurance. I just happened to be in the middle of moving from my home to Brad's house on the day of our divorce. Chad had met Brad and knew that we were just friends. He even thanked Brad for helping Bree and I out.

After Chad and I got out of court and were officially divorced, we ended up going to a local bar together. We sat there and drank shots as we talked about all we had been through. He returned my father's wedding ring, which I had been requesting for a while. He told me he just wanted to hold onto it as long as he could. As we continued to talk and drink Chad asked me if I wanted to get an eight ball. I looked at him like he was crazy and said we don't have money for that. I wasn't interested and thought the mention of money would throw Chad off, but that didn't work as planned. Arrogantly, Chad stood up and went to the ATM and pulled out $200 with Jade's card. When he came back and sat down he said he could get more money in a little bit. I told him I didn't mess with that shit anymore and I wouldn't even know where to get it if I did. I was quickly able to change the conversation when I began talking about our daughter. I explained to him I was really trying to do right by Bree. For hours we continued to drink and talk to one another as best friends. I knew we couldn't find happiness as a couple, but I had good faith in how we were going to raise our daughter.

After getting pretty intoxicated we ended up going to my old house that I was in the process of moving out of. I realized once we got to the house, I had left my keys at Brad's house so Chad and I decided to break into my house through the window. As he helped push me through the window and his hand started moving up my thigh, it was over. He kept touching me as I worked my way through the window and it turned me on so much. When I finally got in the house I opened the door with anticipation. Chad came rushing through and grabbed me into his arms. I believe we had the best sex we ever had in our entire relationship that night. Chad made it very clear that he wanted me to come back to him. He kept talking about just running away and never looking back. I knew I didn't want to be with Chad but, again, I knew

I would always love him as Bree's father. We spent the night holding one another and talking.

Within the next few days that followed, Bree and I left our old house behind and had everything moved into Brad's. Once we got settled into Brad's house, a position opened up at the factory I was working at and it was full time. It was a CNC Burn Operator position. I knew that not one woman had ever run the machine nor was successful at trying; however, I also knew the position could change everything for Bree and me. Plus, I wasn't the average woman. I qualified to apply for the position, but felt a little discouraged because I knew all of the current full-time employees would be considered before me.

I diligently prayed and made a pact with God. I agreed that if it was his will for me to get the job, I promised to give it my all and fulfill my part. Once they went through all the full-time employees that signed up to try for the position, to my surprise the day came when I was called back for training. It was my turn to show the guys what I could do and I was ecstatic. I was only three days into training and everything was going really good when I got called to the office. Some of the other full-time women felt it was unfair they didn't get to try for the position and claimed that it wasn't posted properly. I was so upset. It was a bunch of bull, but I was told they would call me back if the position didn't get filled.

Chad and I were staying in touch when he could. On May 21st he did end up coming to the house and spent time with Bree and me. He was really in a bad spot emotionally. Chad shared with me about how the fights between him and Jade were worse. He kept telling me that he didn't know what he was going to do. I really felt bad for Chad and could see how hurt he was. I tried to stay out of their business when I could but, when it affected Bree, I was all over the situation. It was at these moments when Chad would confide in me that I knew the decisions I was making in regard to our daughter's wellbeing were the right ones.

Although I did feel bad for Chad, I was anxiously waiting for the factory to call me back and tell me that no one else wanted the position. I knew most of the women couldn't handle the work because it was a very physical job. The burn table was operated manually and the sheets of steel were 240" by 72." Those are really big sheets of steel. You have to wear a hard hat and use a crane to lift the steel, then you place the sheet on the burn table and make sure you have everything lined up, download the program and manually adjust the height of the laser as it runs through the entire program. Once the program is complete you have to clear the table. You blow torch what is scrap and needs broke down and you lift steel throughout the entire day. Once done, the steel lasered out went to the press where it was formed. The CNC Burn Machine was only one of seven in the United States. I wanted to prove to everyone that a woman could operate it just as good as a man. Brad also worked in the same factory and was full time already. He really provided a good reference for me when I was going for the job.

Brad has one of the best family units I have ever truly been a part of. His mother and step-father are the friendliest, God loving and beautiful people. They are both dedicated to their church, God and their family. His mother accepted Bree and I as one of her own the first time we met. After a month of living with one another Brad and I did end up sleeping together and decided to try to make something work between us and our relationship began to grow.

It wasn't long before we started going to church with Brad's parents. I fell in love with the church the moment I walked through the door. What was wild was the church was held in a local school's auditorium because the actual church was under construction. It didn't matter we were in a school auditorium because it was the people that made me feel so welcome. It was tough for me to find a place that I could be accepted and embraced. I felt like I was covered in shame from all the things I had been through and all the mistakes I had made. Bree and I both embraced the church and they embraced us. The feeling I couldn't fit in anywhere changed the day I attended the first sermon there. After that day, Bree and I never missed another Sunday unless she was with her dad, which I would still go and later talk to her about it. I couldn't get enough of the worship, the music and the love.

It took about ten days until the phone call came in. The factory finally called me back and they wanted to offer me the position. I told them I accepted, very calmly. Once I hung up the phone I began jumping around and screaming like an excited little girl. I knew this changed everything. This meant full-time employment, overtime and benefits. I would be able to afford to take care of Bree no matter what happened and I knew I didn't have to rely on anyone except myself.

Not long after I started my new job, Chad was supposed to come and get Bree for a weekend visit but no one could get a hold of him. I even called his mom and she wasn't sure where he was either. Tracy even told me that Jade was looking for him, too, so we knew he was in Indiana somewhere. Bree was so upset and crying because she was all packed, ready to go and Chad wasn't coming. It really just broke my heart seeing Bree hurt for Chad like that. So I asked to borrow Brad's truck and I headed out to find Chad. My objective was to find his butt and get him down to Bree because I had promised her I would go find her dad and bring him back to her.

Tracy ended up finding out where Chad was and let me know. I went to where he was hiding out. Chad looked so rough, hung over and just not doing too good at all. He admitted that Jade and he were fighting again and he was just trying to stay hid to think about what to do. Chad was just lost and I could relate with the feeling all too well. I tried to explain to him that he needed to pull it together because we had a little girl that was counting on us. I explained how upset Bree was and I was able to talk him into coming over and staying the night. He could just spend some time with Bree and she always made him feel better. I followed Chad down as he drove because he had been drinking for a few days. When we got halfway there Chad pulled over and we ended up talking a little more. It really did break my heart to see Chad going through what he was.

I knew I couldn't help him or ease his pain. There was nothing I could do but tell him I was sorry and I would always be there for him. I gave him a hug and told him everything was going to work out. As the father of my child, I truly thought I would always have a love for Chad. I had stopped fooling around with Chad once Brad and I committed to one another. I was trying to stay faithful to Brad. Chad came and stayed most of the night and got time with Bree. Once she was down for the night, Chad ended up on the computer emailing back and forth with Jade. When I woke up in the morning he was gone.

For the summer visit, Chad and I had come to the agreement that Bree would stay with him June and July with her coming home every other weekend. She was with him from May 24th to July 8th with the visits home on every other weekend, of course. However, when I would try to call just to say hi to Bree, Jade made it impossible and wouldn't allow me to talk to Bree. She would just straight hang up on me. I just began to communicate with Chad through email because it was impossible to talk any other way.

Even though his spelling, capitalization and punctuation have never been good, I was still able to understand what Chad was emailing to me. He reassured me that Bree was doing good and always ended his emails with him saying he loved me. I had a hard time with what could be occurring at the house because of the way things had continued to get worse with Jade. Jade also had a daughter who was ten years old and a son who was nine years old. I couldn't help but think that God only knew what those kids heard about me from their mother and might repeat to my daughter.

It was sometime during June that Chad got drunk and wrecked his car. I offered him my car to help, but he declined and worried Jade would be mad about that. Since Chad had moved to Tennessee, we were meeting in Kentucky for our transfers. It was a four hour drive round trip every other Friday and then again on Sunday. That drive really took its toll on Bree and me. Before I knew it, July was upon us and it was time to celebrate Bree's fifth birthday. I invited my mother and Dakota, all of Chad's family and Brad's family. It was a great turnout and I took lots of pictures as I always did. The party was Dora the Explorer themed and Bree was so happy to have everyone there. Bree and I were doing good and we were both happy. My job had enabled me to get off of all state assistance for the first time in years. I was able to provide for my daughter and I with our own insurance and my relationship with Brad was good.

I was joking around with Tracy and mentioned that I should move in with my mother in Tennessee, which is where my mother, Oscar and Dakota were living at this time. I made the comment that it would make transfers so much easier on everybody, but I said it with a smile. I knew with my job I wasn't going anywhere and living with my mother again was never happening. Tracy and I got a chance to talk about a few things and I was even honest with her about my concern of Bree being alone around Jade. Tracy told me not to worry about it and shared with me that she hadn't seen Bree in close to a month. I knew I had to change that because I wanted Bree to stay close to her Grandma and Aunt Stacy. The party went good and ended well. My mom and Dakota stayed because they were planning to head back home the next morning.

Chad and I were trying to work out getting Bree down to him by meeting my mother half way. She was leaving the next morning and headed in the right direction and I thought it would be easier if Chad just picked Bree up from my mother. As we were on the phone that evening I MapQuested the distance and trying to come to an agreement with Chad on where he could meet my mom. Chad and I were talking about where would be a fair place and, as always, Jade was in the background running her mouth about how stupid I was. I could hear her yelling that I was stupid because I didn't know the distance correctly. Then I heard her comment about me being a "fucking idiot," and how I couldn't read a map. I don't know if it was the fact that Bree had already expressed that she didn't want to go back or if I had just had enough, but something inside of me snapped in that instant. I was done with this woman. In my opinion, she was poison and I wasn't going to be bullied by her anymore. I told Chad that he and his fucking idiot were done. When I had picked Bree up just a few days earlier she told me about Chad and Jade fighting. It was always the same stories of yelling and fighting that came from Bree when she would come back from their house. Yes, Chad was supposedly standing up to a woman that was talking bad about me in front of our child, but Bree was still being exposed and suffering from it. I was so angry at the continual harassment I made the mistake of taking matters into my own hands.

I emailed a letter to Chad as soon as I hung up with him and I reacted out of complete anger and frustration. Many times I regretted sending this letter, but it went exactly like this:

Subject: *Definition of a true Idiot*
"A woman who pays for a man's fines, car payment, bills, cost of living, and Child Support; while he has sex with the ex-wife twice after he hands the money of the true idiot over to her!!!!! How about a woman whose boyfriend pulls $200 out of her account to spend on his ex-wife, after already handing her child support the true idiot gave him to pay the ex-wife. That $200 was pulled out of a ATM in &^%$#(, at the *&^%* Pub on $#@!* Street…. And the man is still able to get the true idiot to pay for him and his bills…. THE DEFINITION OF A IDIOT!"
~ Zara Banks

I not only emailed this to Chad, but I made a couple copies and mailed one through USPS postmarked directly to Jade. I didn't care how much money she had nor how important she thought her opinion was, she had no power over me and I wasn't going to sit back while she continued to disrespect me, especially in front of my own daughter. I was taking a stand against all of it, against her. Chad had always been a man who followed and not one that led. I knew that we couldn't be parents to our daughter because Jade wouldn't allow it.

That phone call with Chad took place on July 11th. On July 13th I filed a Verified Petition for Modification of Visitation. Our Degree stated that we could do our visits as long as we agreed and, if we disagreed, we needed to follow the 'Indiana Parenting Time Guidelines'. I was trying to make the Court aware of the verbal abuse that Jade was continuing to exhibit toward me and in front of our daughter. In the Petition I begged for the Court to support me in only allowing visits with Chad and Bree to be held in Indiana. In the Petition I explained in detail the events that not only Bree had described to me but Chad had admitted to me in regard to their fights. I told the Courts the truth and asked for a decision be made in the best interest of Bree. I also requested that Jade be ordered to stay away from our daughter during Bree's visitation with her father. I truly felt like the fights Bree was being exposed to and talking about were causing her spiritual and emotional damage.

I was angry and believed that this woman was causing bruises on my daughter's spirit and there was no one to defend Bree. The words Bree was exposed to could not be taken back even if she did see her father fighting for her mother. I knew I had to protect my daughter and felt like I had to do something. I didn't understand the specifics of the law at this time and I just wanted what was best for Bree. I continually stood on the truth and I kept faith the truth would set me free.

A few days passed since I filed the Petitions and sent the email to Jade. Chad ended up calling me crying and asked me why I sent that letter and told me it wasn't right. I could hear Jade in the background doing her normal vocals, and I told Chad right off, "You made your bed now lie in it. That woman won't stop and she is hurting our daughter and I am not taking her shit anymore." I listened to him cry for a bit, but the entire time Jade was in the background yelling at him and cursing me. He was just quiet and kept crying the entire time Jade was yelling. I did feel bad at that moment and questioned why I allowed my anger to lead me. I wasn't trying to hurt Chad and I really didn't mean to. Chad and I weren't even having sex at that time. I was just so tired of being treated like I was parenting with Jade and not Chad.

I was hoping the letter would get Jade to stop interfering with every-thing. I am not sure why I thought that was going to be the answer. For the first time I was finally getting my life together, I wasn't about to allow some woman that knew nothing about my past come in and hurt our baby girl or me. I really thought Chad had grown some balls with all the fighting he had been doing with Jade, but I was beyond wrong. I hung up on Chad because he wasn't talking to me, he just kept crying and all I could hear was him being scolded like a child. Bree was suffering from all the fighting, not only between Chad and Jade but the continual up and down between Chad and me. God only knows how much abuse she really did go through when she was in the care of Jade, but it hasn't made her a victim. In the end, my daughter faced a war at a young age and, because of her faith and trust, she came out of it stronger. She's more like her mother then I admit most of the time.

Now I have made many mistakes and still do, but I always strive to be a positive example for my daughter. Bree is also a warrior of God and she is growing into an amazing young woman. She is a great example of how God can pull you out of a mess and dust you off. Haters shouldn't phase you and impressing others is not your purpose. Be yourself, don't be afraid to hurt, make mistakes and grow. We need to love one another before hate consumes all of us. As time went on things were easier on Bree because I was not allowing her to stay with Chad. I wanted to know what the Courts were going to do about Jade's behavior first.

My job and relationship were going good. Brad, Bree and I were still going to Church every week, and I was also getting in the best shape of my life. I was lifting steel daily and it was the best workout. I dealt with steel dust and all the manly environment a woman could bear. It was a great job and I felt so blessed to have it. I also used it as an example to Bree that when you work hard for something you can achieve it and it didn't matter what gender you were.

For the first time in my life I really felt like I was on track. I was proud of myself and what I was achieving. I also purchased a nice new car, even if it was through a high financing company. As much as I felt like I was doing everything right, I still had a heavy heart for my daughter. I had no idea what was going to happen or if the judge would approve my Petitions. It was in early August I heard through a few friends that Chad and Jade were in Indiana. I emailed him to see if he wanted to get some time with Bree, but his response was short and cold. I never worried about Chad getting time with Bree, he wasn't the problem. I also offered to give him a ride or pay for him to have Stacy bring him, but he again refused.

I wasn't trying to be a bitch, but I was standing firm on waiting for the Court's answer. I was 100% willing to allow Chad to see Bree but not Jade. After two weeks, and knowing Chad and Jade were back in Tennessee, I emailed Chad again and told him I was sorry he didn't make it to see Bree. I tried really hard to be polite, but I wasn't sure what was going on. I knew Chad was mad at me for the letter, but not coming to see Bree surprised me. It was the response to that apology email that made me realize I wasn't speaking to Chad anymore. The only response that came back to me was if Chad couldn't see Bree with Jade he wasn't coming to see her.

On August 20th I was continuing to check with the Courts to see if there was any response to my Petition for the Modification. On my first break at work I decided to call and check to see if we had a court date set yet. To my absolute shock, the woman from the Clerk of Courts office told me there were now six other Petitions filed, including one for a change in custody. My heart dropped. What did Chad do? I instantly went to my boss and told him I had to leave.

The tears started coming down and I knew this was going to be a war. I couldn't wrap my head around why Chad would allow this woman to convince him to try and take our daughter from me like this. I ended up going to the sheriff's office to pick everything up. Once I received the Petitions that were processed, I started reading them right away. I couldn't believe the things that Chad was saying about me.

I went straight to my daughter's school and took her out of class. Then we went straight to a friend's house and I took the time to read every word in each Petition. The Petitions filed were as follows;

Appearance by Attorney and the Attorney's Certificate. Chad and Jade had spent their time in Indiana hiring an attorney, obviously. Chad still didn't have a job and support was $50 a week, which he was behind on. Keep in mind, Jade is a multimillionaire and her money supported all of this.

Verified Petition for Contempt Citation and Order to Appear.
This stated I was forcing Chad to visit in Indiana only, which was true at
the time. It stated that Chad didn't have a license so Jade had to provide
all transportation for him and it was causing a hardship for him. I found
that funny since Chad drove by himself all the time. It further stated that
Chad feared I would disappear and move to Tennessee with my mother.
The evidence to that was his mom had overheard me mention moving
at Bree's birthday party. Chad even claimed that I had previously disappeared with Bree to Florida without warning. He claimed he feared
I would leave and he would never see his child again. In closing, Chad
requested that I be incarcerated for not allowing him to take Bree out of
state and I pay his attorney fees and child support.

The next Petition was an **Emergency Verified Petition for Modification of Decree of Dissolution as to Change of Custody**. This one was
a great read. It stated that I am a drug addict and unable to adequately
provide for Bree. It states that Chad believed that the environment of a
drug addict is inherently dangerous and he feared for Bree's physical,
emotional and developmental wellbeing. Chad claimed that Bree was
endangered when in my care. I was in tears and found myself yet again
dropping to my knees. I couldn't believe that Chad would do this. I
was convinced that it all had to be Jade. All I could come up with was
Chad was given some kind of an ultimatum. He choose to stay with
Jade, not communicate with me and to fight to take our daughter away.
I never had a normal friendly conversation with Chad ever again, even
to this very day.

There was a **Verified Application for Preliminary Injunction.**
This was a request to grant physical custody of Bree to Chad because I
requested his girlfriend not be present during visitation and that was causing hardship since Chad had no license. It also stated that Chad believed
my "drug addiction to cocaine and marijuana engenders erratic behavior"
in me. Some of the exact words went as follows, "Father fears for his
daughter's emotional and physical health if she continues to live with the
irresponsible, unpredictable, and unreliable behavior of a drug addict."

The last of the papers was **Verified Petition for Appointment of Guardian Ad Litem:** This I thought was a blessing because an Ad Litem is designed to represent the child and not the adults.

If I ever felt like my world was falling apart, it was in that moment I received the Petitions. I had been through so much and I knew the one thing I was doing right in my life was how I was raising and loving my daughter. I just couldn't bring myself to believe Chad would do this. There were several times I thought about just telling him, "Fuck it let's go west."

I just wanted to stop all the crazy fighting that had no purpose. In the end of all of this Bree was the only one being hurt. Jade didn't want Bree, she just wanted to hurt me. I can't express how bad nor how hard it was for me to pull it together. I realize it was time to armor up for my daughter's sake. Her dad was doing as he was being told and our daughter was no longer his priority. This was never about what was in the best interest of Bree, for either Chad or Jade, this was about Jade getting revenge for me fooling around with Chad. She was out to hurt me in the worst way she could.

Once I finished reading all of the papers, my first call was to Chad's mom. I thought she would know exactly what was going on. Once she was on the phone she acted as if she had no clue. After I told her everything that happened she just asked me why I would send Jade that letter. I responded with, "It was the truth." I tried to explain that Jade really was hurting Bree by always talking bad about me in front of her. I even told her about the fights Bree had listened to that made her cry just when she would share them with me, let alone what Jade's two children were hearing and possibly repeating to Bree. I just couldn't believe that this was actually happening to me after everything I had overcome and was working through. I pulled it together and, after I got off the phone with Tracy, my next call was to legal aid. They talked to me for a little bit, but I didn't qualify for any assistance. I really didn't know what I was going to do. It seemed like as soon as I was getting things right everything was falling apart again. I just couldn't win in life, so I thought.

Along with the Petitions I picked up several things the Judge had already ordered. Such as the Guardian Ad Litem, Mrs. Jill Mayor, who was appointed to Bree. Our Court date for all Petitions was set for August 25th at 11:30 am. I contacted the Ad Litem, Mrs. Mayor, for my third phone call. I invited her to the house, but she declined and said it wasn't necessary.

I began to explain my job to Mrs. Mayor, which you can't do while high or on drugs. I then loaded Bree into the car and we headed to the local library. After several conversations with professionals, I took it upon myself to type up Verified Request for a Postponement. In the Petition I asked the court to give me time to retain counsel. Some of what I wrote in the Petition was:

"Bree is enrolled in kindergarten and also attends a licensed daycare. Her safety and well-being are in no danger and I am willing to provide the Court with any and all information and/or evidence of such. Bree is currently in my care and covered in all medical, dental, and vision insurance thru my work."

Since I was unaware of what the Court's response would be to my Petition, I began preparing and putting together my case. I couldn't sleep and I kept praying as deeply as I ever had. Brad and I fell apart at this time because I was consumed with not losing my only child.

As I began preparing to represent my case, I gathered letters from my mother, who, as crazy as she is, was there the night of the phone call with Chad on Bree's birthday. She heard Jade cussing and yelling at me. I also got a letter from my probation officer. I was still on probation from the 2002 D.U.I. (Driving Under the Influence). I brought prior drug test results. I was attending all alcohol classes, and I was compliant with everything I was required to do. I wasn't even smoking marijuana at this time in my life. I was truly trying to make the right choices for myself, then here came this woman whose sole purpose seemed to be to tear me apart.

I gathered all of my pictures and physical evidence, including the phone records from when Bree and I were in Florida. Chad had even come down for Christmas with us and I had the pictures to prove it. To this day, I still have all copies and physical evidence in this case. I found it humorous how Chad claimed I took Bree and, "Disappeared to Florida." The anger levels in me were beyond anything I had ever felt.

I couldn't believe I was battling Jade and Chad for my daughter. It was just months earlier I was looking for Chad in his hometown and begged his hungover self to come see Bree. I couldn't believe the same man that agreed to always pull together for our daughter was now trying to take her somewhere with a woman who was emotionally abusing her. I can't explain the hate that was building inside of me. Revenge by using a child is pathetic and sad. No one should allow their children to be abused, emotionally or physically.

On the day of Court I dressed in my best pinstriped two-piece suit and walked in the Courthouse with my briefcase in hand. I was ready to defend myself and fight for my daughter's wellbeing. I had references from my daughter's school, daycare, my work and proof of my daughter's insurance coverage. I was as prepared as I could be. I had all of Bree's medical records, school records and shot records. I walked in prepared to prove that I was a good mom and doing the best I could to take care of my daughter. Chad's attorney's jaw dropped to the floor the moment he saw me. He was expecting some strung out, struggling drug addict and I was anything but. I was dressed and ready to not only represent myself, but represent Bree.

As odd as it may sound, I really enjoyed the first hearing. It was interesting to me because we meet in the Judge's chambers and not in the courtroom. Mrs. Jill Mayor, the Ad Litem, was also present. In the chambers sat the Judge, Mrs. Mayor, me and Chad's attorney. I'll never forget the feeling of sitting there with all of them. I knew that I was there to fight for the best interest of my daughter and I wasn't intimidated by any of them. My biggest problem was that everyone involved seemed to think that I just didn't like Jade and that was why I didn't want Bree around her. That was never my problem and no one would listen to me about it. I knew this was never about me, it was always about Bree, but convincing others was not going well for me.

The Judge asked me a few questions, then Jill would speak. When the Judge would talk to Chad's attorney it was funny watching him scramble and unsure of how to answer the Judge. Every time Chad's attorney would try to claim one of the lies Chad was using, I would pull out proof of the complete opposite. I requested that I be drug tested and that Chad and Jade be ordered to do the same. I had all the evidence to prove that I was taking good care of Bree and providing for her. What I couldn't understand is why no one cared or paid attention to what led all of us to where we were at that moment. It was simply a wealthy, scorned woman out for revenge and my daughter was placed right in the center. Unfortunately, Bree became an even bigger target for Jade.

The Judge was not happy about Chad's attorney wasting the Court's time, but I could tell they dealt with this all the time. I really feel like that is why no one really paid attention to this case. It was treated as if this was all the adults just arguing, which was normal and sad. No one would acknowledge what I was saying Bree was being put through. It really angered me that this case was treated as such, especially for as long as it took for the truth to really come out. It is not easy to prove emotional abuse. I admit I did find it great that Chad's attorney never saw me coming and was so unprepared for an intelligent woman.

When I walked out of the Judge's chambers I wasn't happy. I was ordered to allow Bree to go back to Chad for visitation and nothing was done about Jade. She didn't seem to be a concern to anyone. The Judge also declared that this was not an emergency case and a later date would be set for trial to answer all Petitions filed. I was ordered to go with Mrs. Mayor to take a drug screening, as well as Chad. Jade could only be requested, but she agreed to the drug test. Privately, Mrs. Mayor made the comment to me that Jade was trying to show some kind of power over Chad the way she made sure to hold onto his hand the entire time. I thought that Mrs. Mayor was going to be perfect for this case because she could already see how controlling Jade was.

In each interview with Mrs. Mayor I would claim Chad wasn't behind all of this, but it made me sound crazy because Chad would claim everything being said and done was him. I guess I just couldn't believe Chad would ever do this. I began seeing Jade more as a puppet master and Chad was the puppet. Truth is, it took a long time for me to realize that Chad made his choices on his own and stuck to them. After the three of us took our drug screening the end results were all three of us passed with no problems. I was even more worried about Bree having to go to Chad and Jade's house. The entire situation made my stomach ill. I was allowing Bree to go stay with Stacy and Tracy on some of my weekends. They didn't get time with one another when Bree was with Chad due to his out-of-state residency. On August 27th I agreed to take Tracy with Bree to Kentucky so that she, too, could visit with Chad and Bree.

At one point I did reach out to my mother and her parents for help with an attorney. I was told that my grandparents had loaned Derek money and he never paid it back, so they refused to help me. My mother was never able to help me financially so there was no luck there either. I ended up calling the one person I knew would be there for me -- I called Paul. I explained everything that had been happening and my concern for Bree when she was around Jade. I told Paul about how Chad wouldn't even talk to me and he was a completely different man. Paul ended up helping me retain an attorney who, in the end, was pretty useless. Okay, to put it politely, he wasn't very good and I did most of the footwork for my case myself.

Once again, I began meeting Chad in Kentucky for transfers every other weekend. I felt it was wrong I had to spend the gas money and eight hours every other weekend driving since he was the one who decided to move so far away. But, it was ordered through the court so I had no choice. My biggest issue with the drive was, when we would finally get there, Chad was continually late. I'm not talking ten or 15 minutes late, I'm talking about a half hour to an hour and a half late. It was seriously taking its toll on Bree and me. The trips were long and tiring. For two hours Bree would tell me about how she didn't want to go and she just wanted to stay home.

At one point, I looked into child hesitation, which is where a child acts like they don't want to go with the other parent, but they really don't have any problem with going. I also studied separation anxiety thinking perhaps that could be part of the issue. In a strange way, I was really hoping that I was overreacting about everything. It didn't take long, however, until I knew I was fighting the right battle. Soon Jade became involved with our transfers also. It was heartbreaking to not be able to help my daughter and tell her she had to go. It was hard on Bree each time Jade would call me names during our transfers, but, in the end, it helped me to become a better example for Bree.

During transfers Jade began to come and just stand back with her evil eye. Most times she would verbally attack me and I would just put my head down. I didn't want Bree to see me kill someone and, at that point, Jade's mouth brought out real evil thoughts for me. I just wanted to bash her teeth down her throat and it was very hard not to do so. It helped, though, when I would remind myself that my daughter was watching and I needed to be the example for her.

Jade would cuss me in front of my child and talk about how much better of a mother she was. Chad would stand there like a puppet and say nothing. I had lost all respect and love for that man. The feelings of being blessed to raise our daughter and working together were long gone. Jade told Bree she was a better mom than me because she had been a mom longer. I still swear Jade has severe mental issues. Who would tell a child something like that?

Once Bree was turned over, I would cry the entire two hour drive home. I felt so helpless as a mother. I felt bad that Bree had to go through what she did. On transfers, when Jade would act like a fool and Bree was coming home, it was those moments I would try to use as good lessons for Bree. What else was I supposed to do? I would tell Bree to notice how I didn't respond to Jade and how I would walk away when she called me bad names. I told Bree that sometimes you just have to be the bigger woman and walk away.

Work was still going really good for me, except I was suffering from severe pain in my lower stomach and couldn't figure out what was going on. It got so bad that I would be lifting steel overhead and would almost drop to my knees from the pain. I was in great physical health looking at me, but something was really off inside of me. I ended up making an appointment with a gynecologist.

After all the tests and the reassurance of another clear AIDS and STD test, the doctor discovered that I had multiple cysts on my ovaries. He was shocked that I had my tubes tied and the other doctor allowed me to do it at such a young age having only one child. After that visit to the doctor, I was scheduled for surgery in November. The doctor wanted to laser the cysts off in hopes they would not return. The problem that was causing the pain was the cysts on my ovaries had an ooze coming out causing my ovaries to stick to my insides. It was extremely painful.

It was around this time that Chad announced he and Jade were engaged and going to get married in Hawaii. Chad needed me to give him Bree's social security card and birth certificate so he could get her I.D. for the plane ticket. Truth is, I didn't want to give either of them to him. He could go get his own copies himself, yet he wanted mine. I knew this marriage was just going to make things worse for Bree and me both. Transfers were not getting easier and Bree was really starting to act out worse when she would return from their home.   For a short time she even started to wet her bed at night making me grow an even greater concern for her emotional wellbeing. After repeatedly complaining about the continued verbal attacks by Jade, the Ad Litem told me I needed to start recording all of our interactions; including, but not limited to transfers and phone calls. That was great for Jade's verbal attacks on me, but I still had no idea how to prove Jade was still saying horrific things to Bree.

In November, my very useless attorney wrote Chad's attorney a letter to ask him to tell Chad that he needed to please stop being late during transfers. It felt insane to have to communicate to the father of my child through attorneys.

I have no doubt from the moment all the Petitions were filed I was forced to communicate with and fought for parenting time from Jade, not Chad. When emails did begin between Chad and I, each one was so proper; perfect spelling, capitalization and punctuation. I knew then it wasn't Chad behind the keyboard. It was so frustrating to be in that situation with Jade. I also believe with all of my heart that each email to the Ad Litem was also written by Jade, even if Chad took the claim for it. He was doing nothing because he was in the dog house. Even with the stress of Chad and Jade's continual attacks, I still had to face surgery for the cysts that were hurting me. Thankfully, on the day of my surgery everything went well and I was able to get back to work within a week.

As expected, the fight for custody began taking a toll on my relationship with Brad. I was still going to church, but on weekends Bree wasn't home I felt lost. I hated thinking about what Bree might be going through or hearing out of Jade's mouth. During the week I stayed on track and had a very consistent schedule for Bree, but when she was gone I didn't know what to do. Brad and I stopped communicating and I tried to absorb everything I could about a mother's parental rights. I spent many hours at the library trying to understand what I could do legally for Bree and how to do it.

Then fights started with little things such as Bree's clothes. She would wear an outfit there and then wear a different one home. It seemed normal to me, however, it became a problem to Jade because she felt that I didn't dress Bree in good clothes. Jade felt that what she had for Bree was better. It really made no sense to me because my daughter had good clothes and was always dressed very well. This was just another way for Jade to nitpick and try to start a fight. Bree began wearing her clothes there and then the same outfit home, which was fine with me. I felt the problem was easily solved.

As the year came to a close, Brad and I continued to grow apart. I didn't sleep well at night. My mind was consumed, and I just couldn't slow it down. I had read many books and knew that I couldn't and shouldn't ask or quiz Bree about her visits when she would come home from Chad and Jade's house. I learned quickly that I didn't have to ask her. The moment she would get in the car she would unload all of the events of her weekend. Most of the time it was almost as if she was releasing a lot of weight she had carried around the entire weekend. I would just listen to her and would later take notes for my records. I also knew that I could never speak badly about Chad or Jade in front of Bree, despite what they were doing. I had read it would hurt Bree more in the end, so I did my best to encourage positive feelings and words about Chad. After spending so much time in self-help books and studying all the parenting books I could get my hands on, I did feel a little more confident about myself and about being a mother.

When Christmas finally came around, Brad's mom held what she called a "tea party." It was all of the women in the family doing baked goods and arts and crafts. Bree and I loved going there. Brad's mom even held a princess tea party for all the younger girls in the family. Bree had a blast with getting her nails and hair done, trying on dresses and posing for pictures. It was awesome how Brad's mom was so involved and loved Bree and I wholeheartedly. She is one of the nicest people and I still love her dearly. Brad's mom was also really big into scrapbooking and gave me all of my starter items. I eventually ended up growing a huge love for scrapbooking.

On New Year's Eve, Brad and I were talking and I asked him if there was anything I should know as far as his criminal record went. I explained to him that I was trying to make sure that Chad and Jade couldn't use anything against me in Court to help them take my daughter away. Brad reluctantly confessed that when he was 19 years old he dated a 16 year old. The parents didn't agree with the relationship and prosecuted him, so he was a registered sex offender.

After talking to his mom and confirming the story was true, my heart ached. I knew there was no way I could stay with Brad. As soon as Jade got her hands on that it would be an issue. No matter what the story was, consensual or not, he was a registered sex offender. I had to make a plan and it was so frustrating how much my life was affected by the entire

225

case. I am still thankful to this day for Brad and his family. They were very supportive and encouraging. The holidays passed and I had no clue what to expect in the New Year. My mom also called and got me up to date on what was going on with Ina and Derek. I was told that Derek moved away to Florida and he and Ina had broken up. It looked like we all had some changes to face in 2005.

Chapter SIXTEEN

2005: Bree and I appreciated Brad and his family greatly. Spending the holidays with them reminded me of the holidays from when I was a kid, all the decorations and everyone gathered together. My job was also going really well. For a short time I was content. I loved our church and Bree did, too. We were both involved in all the weekly activities as well as Sundays. If I could have moved Bree and me into that church I would have. It wasn't long until construction was complete and we were all able to attend services in the actual church building. It was very big and had so many activities for everyone.

I started looking more into the local schools and wasn't really happy with the results. I felt that a better place for Bree would be in the beautiful small town that Brad's parents lived in. They had a better school rating, it was only 15 minutes away and the schools were much smaller. Brad's mother and stepfather were willing to let me use their address, so I began praying on what I should do. I did a lot of praying and still do. Sometimes I felt like the Lord heard and answered me, other times I felt like he wasn't near me at all. I made the decision to believe he was near me, even when I didn't feel him. I believe that is where our faith is tested. In the dark, lost and convinced that moving forward is impossible, is when we need to have faith the most.

I was uncomfortable with the school Bree was in because of the overabundance of kids, which meant the teacher wasn't able to get one-on-one time with students. Bree was very smart and I spent every chance I could, from the day she was born, helping her learn as much as she could. We lived on a schedule and consistency. Every night I would do homework with Bree after I cooked dinner and then we usually did crafts together. I don't care too much for T.V. and always tried to stay active with Bree. I was doing everything that I thought I was supposed to, including our normal bedtime bible story and nighttime prayer. I knew that it was important as a parent to keep a schedule and as much consistency for Bree as possible. I also knew that Bree didn't have structure at Chad's, so I tried to make sure she always knew the schedule when she was with me.

I continued to do as much research as I could on how to be a better parent and even became very involved with a women's bible study at my church. I needed all the support and prayers I could get. I finally did come to the decision to enroll Bree in the school where Brad's parents lived. I was really happy with the school and soon discovered they had an excellent program that allowed her to be there early when I had to go to work and stay until I was off work, which was only a half hour after school was out. It was a great daycare program that was in the school. Usually, two or three of the most wonderful young women would be watching the children, so I also decided to change Bree's daycare. She was very excited and it actually turned out to be a huge blessing for both of us.

In March I had completed my probation and complied with all of the requirements. I was a free woman and standing strong. I even started learning about how credit worked and began making small payments toward debts in order to help build my credit score. It was also at this time the Ad Litem, Mrs. Mayor, asked for a letter from Chad and I describing how we felt things were going. As I sit here and re-read all of these documents and letters for this book, it really amazes me that no one paid attention to what was really happening. Emotional abuse causes inner bruises no one can see and it is extremely hard to prove. In part of my response letter to the Ad Litem, mailed on March 4, 2005, I specifically wrote:

"Bree no longer wets the bed upon returning from Chad's. She has however become more aggressive and rebellious after her

return, so much so that her teacher has commented on now being able to tell when Bree has had a weekend with her father. I believe though; that through all of this she will need some kind of counseling in a few years due to the fact that it seems the only concern for her, from everyone involved, at this current time is her physical well-being, rather than her emotional well-being. I am not worried about her physical safety nor have I had that concern, but I do realize with the petitions Chad filed that is a factor in "his" statements."

I also wrote about the fact that Chad moved to Tennessee and that I was being required to drive 50 more miles than Chad. It may seem silly, but it was about 45 minutes extra on the road for me, not to mention the gas money it was taking. I discussed how Chad only called Bree on rare occasions, yet he was claiming that I didn't allow him to talk to her. It seemed apparent to me, while Chad was out riding his custom built chopper, driving the Cadillac and taking wonderful vacations, he completely forgot that being a father to our daughter was important. The recommendation letter that the Ad Litem wrote to the Judge confused me so much. I really thought after Mrs. Mayor spoke with Bree and heard about all the things Jade had done and said the truth would set us free, but it didn't at this time. Once Mrs. Mayor received the letters from both Chad and me, she responded to the Court and wrote:

"Zara does report that the visits are going o.k. in a letter to me on 4/4/05. She reports that her daughter's teacher has commented on being able to tell what weekends Bree goes to her fathers because of her behavior. Zara has felt all along that the distance between her and Chad and transporting her daughter every other weekend is too hard on such a young child."

I thought, wait a minute, did she just twist my words? Bree's behavior issues had nothing to do with the traveling. In summary, Mrs. Mayor suggested that the distance between Chad and I was going to hurt Bree in every aspect including Girl Scouts, sports and even school.

The letter also stated:

"The determining factor in this type of custody is doing what is best for the child, I feel Chad and Zara can put their animosities aside and accomplish this."

What was wrong with this Ad Litem? Chad and I weren't even allowed to communicate without Jade. All email communication was Jade and not Chad. I was so angry that no one could see the truth. How was I supposed to co-parent with Jade? Jade couldn't even stop calling me names. I prayed for the Lord to take away the anger and to just allow the truth to be exposed. I began suffering from violent nightmares of hurting Jade. It got so bad the nightmares became daydreams. I had no idea how to overcome what was happening. I continued to volunteer at church every chance I got. I just tried to keep my mind as busy as possible. I tried to convince myself Jade would get over this someday and everything would be okay.

I was extremely happy with Bree's new school and the way things were going for her. She was making many friends and growing fast. I would hear from friends here and there that Chad was working. By the time I would request he provide insurance, he wouldn't be working anymore. I'm not sure he held a job for over four months in the last 11 years. I never held that against him, though. If I married a millionaire, I am pretty sure I wouldn't want to work either. Plus, I had Bree covered on my insurance so it wasn't a big deal.

One day my mom called me all upset and told me she needed my help. She proceeded to tell me that Dakota had come to her and confessed that he was addicted to crack cocaine and he needed help. My mother said she had no idea what to do to help him and told him she would call me. I couldn't believe what she was telling me. I asked her to let me talk to Dakota and he got on the phone. I could feel his pain and hear his tears through the phone. I told him everything would be okay and I was going to have mom bring him to me that day. When he gave the phone back to my mother, I said, "Have him pack his shit right now, mom, and get him up here. He cannot stay there for one more night."

230

Mom and Oscar both agreed with me. My mom and Dakota arrived at my house that night.

My mother and Oscar were still living in Tennessee and Dakota had been in a lot of trouble from when they were living in Florida. Unfortunately, things didn't get much better for my little brother. About a year prior to this, before we moved in with Brad, Bree and I went down to Tennessee for a weekend. It was always interesting when I would go visit my mother. She isn't a dull woman at all and never has been. Mom and Oscar lived at the end of Land of the Lakes, which is a gorgeous stretch of land with buffalo included. When Bree and I arrived, my mother took me on a tour of her house. It was absolutely beautiful and my mother said it used to be the governor's home. I don't know if that was true. As she took me through the house she explained all of her plans on the remodel she dreamed of. My mother said that they purchased the home to turn it into a swinger's club. For some reason I wasn't even caught off guard by that. Mom told me all the details of each room. She even talked to me about the money side of the business. She promoted how it could benefit me if I was to come down and help running it. Truth is, I accepted that my mother was just who she was. I had to accept that; however, Dakota was still living with her and had to deal with all her craziness daily and that is what kept me going back. I didn't ever want Dakota to feel like I abandoned him in any way. I love my little brother.

After mom left and Dakota was with me to stay for a while, I locked him down. Dakota was 18 years old at this time. It was really hard for him at first, but Bree helped him through that moment in his life more than she even realizes. I made sure that Bree and Dakota stayed inseparable because she was like a little sister to Dakota. It meant a lot to him that she looked up to him and loved him so much. When Dakota would ask me if he could go for a walk, I would sit Bree next to him. I would tell him I had to go take care of something and would leave the house. Dakota would get so upset at me, but I didn't want him out wondering around the streets looking for crack. Most of the time I would just go around the block. Once Dakota got through the withdrawals he has never touched crack again. Now he actually hates it with a passion.

I was praying so much for Dakota's recovery. At the same time, I was still battling my own issues but there is so much power in prayer. Even if you are surrounded by darkness your prayers for another have a lot of power. The custody case completely consumed my mind. I was always thinking about who could be hired to pretend to be my friend or would Jade go as far as to have my daughter kidnapped? Was she crazy enough to have me killed? It ate me up daily trying to figure out what the next move was going to be. After about five weeks, mom and Oscar decided to move to Michigan. Dakota was doing really good. He overcame the withdrawals and felt much stronger. Moving away from where he was in Tennessee was going to help a lot, too. On their way to Michigan, Oscar and mom picked Dakota up.

Brad and I had our differences, but for the most part got along well. Due to his record and the custody case, we both knew I would have to move out and get my own place. We discussed it and I began house hunting. It didn't take me long to find a small house that was affordable for Bree and I. When it was time for Bree and me to move out, we were able to get everything moved in one trip. Brad and I weren't in love so the move wasn't hard on Bree or me. We remained friends and to this day I would help Brad or anyone in his family anytime if they needed me.

I have to say, the first night in our new house was awesome. It was a blessing to have our own home and I knew it was a good fresh start for us. Nothing changed for Bree and I except the house we went home to at the end of the day. I worked, Bree went to school and at night we did everything together. We kept a schedule and stuck to it. Paul even came to visit Bree and me soon after we moved into the new house. He surprised Bree and me with an air conditioner for the house, which was a wonderful gift.

Before the beginning of the new school year I made a dreaded phone call to Chad to see if he could help me with Bree's school supplies and school clothes. As we talked, I explained that I was trying to pay for a house by myself and that I could really use his help. Child support has never been real reliable so it was a long shot even asking for his help with anything. As Chad started to say he would see what he could do, it began again. Jade began yelling in the background, "If she can't afford to take care of that little girl then she needs to let her come live here." I just responded with, "Never mind and fuck you and your woman." Truth is, Chad's mom was a true blessing. She helped for several years on and off with Bree's school supplies and clothes, plus my mom would help when she could. I am and was very thankful for their help.

Bree would always be so happy to come home from her visits with her dad. A part of me really enjoyed that, but the other part of me knew it was because of the way Jade treated her. It didn't matter what occurred that weekend, Bree was always ready to talk to me and share. Sometimes it was good and they took the kids somewhere exciting and she loved her time with her dad. Other times were filled with tears and stories that broke my heart. I tried my best to just listen and be there for Bree during her rough visits. I knew I couldn't do anything, but I would tell anyone who would listen what was happening. During one visit, Bree had been at Jade's mother's one day during her visit because Chad and Jade had gone out somewhere. When they all got home, Jade asked Bree if she had anything to eat yet. As Bree told me the story she started crying and said, "Mom I just forgot." I just felt anger rising inside of me because you could see the pain in Bree's tears. I just smiled at Bree and told her, "It's okay, I forget things all the time baby girl." I didn't even understand what she had forgotten, but I just let her talk whenever she was ready.

When Jade asked Bree if she had anything to eat while being babysat, Bree told Jade no. It is my understanding that Jade then called her mom and asked if Bree had ate. Bree said she had forgot that she had a peanut butter sandwich and, because Bree said she hadn't ate, Jade took it to the extreme. Jade made Bree write on a piece of paper, "I am a liar." Jade then pinned the paper to Bree's shirt and made her sit in the middle of their living room for hours as everyone walked around her. My daughter was five years old when this happened, she turned six in July. I can't even begin to explain how badly I wanted to just hurt and beat the hell out of Jade with everything inside of me. I was growing a very evil way of thinking and I kept praying for the thoughts to be lifted from my mind.

I knew Jade was being mean to Bree because she hated me. It wasn't fair to Bree in any way. I hated Chad for allowing this woman to do the things she was doing to our daughter. What kind of father stands back and allows someone else to hurt their baby?

I still couldn't sleep at night because I suffered from horrible, gory visuals of the things I wanted to do to Jade and it was always in front of her children. I wanted her to feel exactly what she was doing to me in front of my child -- tearing me down, trying to humiliate me, talking bad about me and telling stories she had no clue about all in front of my own child. I was being forced to co-parent with a woman who was throwing spiritual punches at my daughter. I realized quickly she wasn't the most intelligent woman in the world and came to the conclusion that she was just crazy. She didn't know me. She had no clue. Jade was just pissed and out for revenge no matter the cost.

I began shutting people out and being extremely cautious of who I talked to about anything. I had already stopped smoking pot completely and if I did drink it was on the weekends Bree was gone. I was never prepared or imagined I would be at war with anyone for my child's safety, especially Chad. After Bree's sixth birthday my mother came to visit. I didn't want to do anything but drink when she came around. I would get shit-face drunk and then yell at her about things from the past. Honestly, I would drink so heavy that I would black out and wouldn't even know what I had said to her.

As Jade continued to emotionally hurt Bree, I was afraid it would turn into physical abuse. Some days I felt like I was losing myself spiritually because I felt like I was under complete attack. The truth is, I <u>was</u> under attack. Looking back now, Jade was my Goliath. The women's bible study group that I joined began a new study and we were all given a book called, *"The Ultimate Makeover"*, written by Sharon Jaynes.

I started believing that there was a chance God could help me with the nightmares and all the hateful things I was struggling with. The worst thing in the world is to watch any child being hurt, especially your own. Not being able to do anything about it is a nightmare within itself. Worse than that is anyone that could help was beyond convinced that I was just jealous of some rich, crazy and spiritually lost woman. I couldn't understand what was so hard about seeing Jade was emotionally torturing my child.

When I started reading, *"The Ultimate Makeover"*, by Sharon Jaynes, I started thinking about things deeper. In the book Sharon Jaynes writes, ***"No longer are we simply a product of our past failures, hurts, and disappointments, but a result of Jesus Christ's finished work on the cross. We are saints (by calling) who sometimes sin. A saint is not a person who is perfect, but one who is set apart."*** (*Pages 52 & 53*). It made me realize that no one is perfect and, the more I tried to be, the more I was hurting myself.

It was getting close to the time of Chad and Jade's wedding and I had a lot going on. I had honestly forgot about trying to get Chad a copy of Bree's birth certificate and social security card. I was working a lot of overtime and keeping the house up. Our home wasn't very big at all, but it was perfect for Bree and me. On one of our transfers when it was time for me to pick Bree up, Chad and Jade were already in Indiana and we made arrangements to meet at a park near a beach Bree and I loved. I had planned to surprise Bree and take her to the beach as soon as I picked her up. I made sure I had everything packed and ready, including her swimsuit. I even loaded our cooler up for a cookout while we were at the beach. I completely forgot the wire I had started wearing for our transfers (it was a wired tape recorder). I was doing really well financially and it felt so good to be able to do extra fun things with Bree. When I arrived at the park, there stood Chad with Bree and Jade was just a few feet back. Unexpectedly, Chad asked me if I had the birth certificate and social security card with me. I told him I hadn't had a chance to get them together yet. I let him know that he had access to all of that as Bree's father and that he could get his own copies if he wanted. I wasn't real comfortable giving him my copies, in all honesty, but me saying that was all it took. Jade started running her mouth and Chad followed suit. They were really starting to make a great team together.

As Jade continued calling me names, I told Chad his wants were not at the top of my priority list and I began to put Bree in my car. The entire time Jade was yelling at me, calling me a stupid bitch and more. All in front of not only my daughter, but the entire park. I just kept smiling and got into my car. It was hilarious to me because, as I drove off, Jade was actually running after my car cursing and yelling very foul things at me. We were in the middle of a park. Families that were there enjoying their day were looking at her like she was the craziest person on earth.

I can't explain how many times I wished that I should have just let her attack me. I tried to prepare myself for the next time she came at me. I decided that if she tried to come at me again, I would just let her hit me as much as she wanted. I thought that maybe it would be proof enough for the Court to see how violent and crazy Jade really was and what she was capable of doing. Jade was so blinded with anger, jealousy and hate. Bree and I left the park happy and we headed to the beach. I wasn't allowing Jade to ruin our day, I was getting used to her outbursts.

I was very proud being single and not going all wild and crazy. The attacks from Chad and Jade truly helped me stay focused on my daughter. When Bree and I arrived at the beach, we got suited up and set up at our favorite spot. We spent a lot of time at the Whitewater National Park that year. It is a beautiful and peaceful place. At that time in my life I wasn't looking for or even thinking much about getting into a relationship as I was too wrapped up fighting for my daughter and trying to do right by her. Plus, I was truly happy single.

As our afternoon continued, Bree and I played and swam in the lake. She always made friends quickly and soon found a little girl to play with. I'm pretty sure you have gathered by now that I am not what most would consider an ugly woman and, at that time in my life, I was very comfortable in my skin. I was still lifting steel and, as you know, my workouts were very extreme. As I was walking up to our towels, this really good looking man was walking past me. I tried not to take notice that he was staring at me. When we got to our towels I layed down and noticed that he had walked up to the same people that I had just talked with. Their little girl was who Bree was playing with.

I was being extra cautious because I was unaware of exactly how crazy Jade could be. I never underestimated her resources either. Meeting new people was not something I was enjoying like I had always done. I was doing good staying focused on Bree and not worrying about anything or anyone else, so when this good looking man started to approach me my defenses went right up.

The man asked if he could sit with me and I told him that I was actually waiting for someone that I had a date with. It wasn't true, but I figured it would chase him off. His next question caught me completely off guard. Most men usually walked away from me after I would say that. I used a fake boyfriend or date often when men would approach me. This guy, however, looked me right in the eyes and said, "Can I sit with you till your date arrives?" I have to admit that I was a little dumbfounded, and the fact he was so good looking didn't help. I thought about it and ended up saying yes.

His name was Ian and he had his son with him who was only a few years older than Bree. Ian said he was there with his family and pointed to the top of the hill and everyone sitting there began waving at him. He said he was a mason and laid stone for a living. Ian was well built and, as the day turned into early evening, I took notice of how he was so great with his son. His son and Bree became friends quickly and played well together. I ended up inviting Ian and his son, Bud, to cook out with Bree and me for dinner. The offer also came with a ride home since Ian and his son rode there with their family. Both of the boys accepted the invitation and I grilled hamburgers for all of us. The entire time with Ian and his son was a lot of fun.

Ian was charismatic, charming, younger, intelligent and very handsome. The evening we spent together seemed magical and he swept me off my feet. I had never met anyone like Ian. I still compared him to Ezra, but Ian was one man that hit so many marks that I couldn't get enough of him.

Everything happened very quickly. That night, after Bree and I took the boys home, both of the kids fell asleep on the couch watching T.V. Ian and I ended up having a couple of drinks and, out of the blue, Ian offered for Bree and me to stay the night. I looked at Bree sleeping, considered that I was going on my third drink, and thought it best to accept the offer. Ian and I continued to get to know one another and talked for hours. Ian said he had just recently got out of a relationship because his girlfriend was addicted to drugs. I really felt bad for his circumstances.

I can't explain what it was; maybe because it had been so long since I had been touched or the smooth swagger that seeped from Ian or perhaps it was just the alcohol. Either way, we ended up having sex. It was a great night and Ian was a very good lover. He was rough enough, passionate enough, knew what and where to touch and kiss. The man took my breath away that night.

In the morning, I was up before everyone and had a plan to sneak out. I didn't want to get caught up in anything, even though the night had been wonderful. I woke Bree up and got her loaded in the car when all of a sudden Ian walked out and asked if I was trying to run away. He called me out for trying to sneak off and started teasing me about how he didn't want to be used for a one-night stand. He walked right up to me and embraced me tightly. It was a crazy whirlwind of emotions with Ian. It just felt so good to be held the way he held me. Ian explained to me there was a rule not to call for three days after meeting someone or you would seem desperate. He said he would call me in three days, and I smiled and said okay. Bree and I left and talked about what we should do for the day. We both voted on going to the park and spending time together there.

Later that afternoon, while Bree and I were at the park, my phone rang and it was Ian. I told him he was breaking his own three-day rule. He said he couldn't help it, he didn't want to stay away from me. Ian ended up bringing a full picnic basket to the park where Bree and I were at. It felt so good having such a confident man around me. After that day it was on. We both worked a lot and in different towns, but we talked every day.

We would be together every free chance our schedules allowed us to be. When Bree was with Chad for weekend visits, Ian and I would have the most incredible dates. I really fell for him hard and fast.

Eventually, we were able to get both of our children's weekends in sync because Bud's mom was a really nice woman. I was almost envious of the way Ian and her could talk and come to agreements. I longed so bad for that with Chad. The weekends we had both the kids were the best times. It felt like we had the best family unit I could have ever asked for.

Ian was also an assistant baseball coach for Bud's team and appeared to really have his shit together. I did find out that the house he said was his was actually his mother and stepfather's home. I almost walked away from Ian when I found out he lied to me, but he was able to talk me into forgiving his ignorance for lying. He convinced me that no man would admit to a beautiful woman that he lived with his mom. I began to notice that Ian also took pain pills frequently, because of an ACL injury (Anterior Cruciate Ligament). I, myself, rarely even took Tylenol and wasn't a big pain pill fan.

To help Ian, I started researching how to ease the injury without pills. I found that there were some braces, certain massages and even oils that could help with the pain. I tried to show Ian the alternatives, but he would say that the pain was too much when he was working. I had never really been around anyone that consistently took pain pills, so I thought since the Doctor prescribed them it couldn't be that bad. It wasn't long before Ian was staying at my house all the time. We wanted to make things work between us and Ian agreed to find a job closer to the house so we could do just that.

Soon Ian got a job with a Kirby Distributorship. It was a perfect position for a man like Ian. Sales was truly a calling for Ian. When he started with the company I couldn't believe the hours. He was gone from 9 am till 10 pm or 11 pm at night. I questioned the job and thought something wasn't right with that. It wasn't until I started hanging out at the office and talking with more of the women that husbands worked there I learned the hours were always like that.

By September, my health wasn't at its best. I had always had a small hemorrhoid since the birth of my daughter and at this time it wasn't so small. I ended up having surgery scheduled. I let Chad know right away in an email that I wasn't going to be able to drive the distance for transfers for a short time. I was ordered to take time off work and relax after the surgery. After I had the surgery I ended up with an infection that caused me to be out of work for a month longer than I anticipated.

That experience caused me some of the worst pain I ever had. If you have ever had an inflamed hemorrhoid, which many of us do at least once, you know what I am talking about. From September 16th to October 16th, I was ordered by the doctor to do nothing but sit with my butt on a donut or in the air. I also had to soak in warm baths a minimum of three times a day. Ian really won my heart over during this time because he was doing everything he could to help me. He would get up in the middle of the night to help me adjust or just to check on me.

Since I was unable to drive the distance to exchange Bree, Chad and I agreed that his mother, Tracy, would come get Bree for his visit instead. This was in September. Due to the infection, I was still unable to make the trips to Kentucky when Chad's next visit came up and he put no effort into coming to get Bree. I notified Chad and his attorney about everything that was going on during this time. Soon after I began healing up, Chad and Jade's wedding neared. Bree was able to go to Hawaii with them for their wedding and, I admit, I was jealous of her. I kept teasing her that she got to go somewhere I had never been. She was excited about that.

After the wedding, Jade and Chad had their honeymoon. Bree was gone for two weeks and no one would let me talk to her. I even called Jade's parents' house because a week had passed and I hadn't heard anything from Bree. I was sincerely afraid they would arrange a kidnapping or something worse. I refused to put anything past either of them. I was extremely concerned for my daughter. I was pretty upset, yet relieved to learn that the entire time Bree was only an hour away from me at Chad's mother's house. Bree had only been with Chad for the wedding, then she was flown back with Tracy for the remainder of Chad's visitation.

I admit I was relieved to find out Bree was at Tracy's. I knew she was safer there than with Jade. Ian was doing really good in Kirby and he loved the job. The office he was working for was preparing for a move to an office that was an hour away from where we were living. Ian asked Bree and me to move with him. He told me that I could go pick any house out that I wanted for our family and he would cover rent and all expenses. He told me that we would be a family and reassured me that he would take care of us no matter what happened.

There was a town right in the middle that was only half an hour away from my work and Bree's school. It also put Ian's new office only half an hour away as well. I thought about how easy it would be to still get Bree and me back and forth to work and school. I really wanted Ian to be the perfect man for me and convinced myself of that. Things between us were going great and Bree really grew to love Ian and Bud by this time. After I talked with Bree about the move, I decided we would give it a try. I believed with all my heart that I was making the right decision for both Bree and myself.

I ended up setting a day aside to go house shopping. I had Bud and a couple of my friends' kids with me. We spent the day in and out of houses, but I didn't see anything I liked. It was a much smaller town than I expected, but, to be honest, I was ready to get out of my tiny house and the city we were currently living in.

There was one house left on our list that the landlord couldn't show us until 5pm. When we finished looking at all the other houses it was about 3:30 pm. I decided we would drive past the house just to see if it was worth waiting an hour and a half for. When we pulled up I thought we had the wrong place. It was a two-story, corner house in a great looking neighborhood. It was huge, had a good sized yard, full roofed front porch, a large back deck, not to mention affordable. I remember thinking, with my job I could take care of this place on my own if I had to. So there we were, anxiously waiting for 5 pm. Bud was so excited about all of us moving in together and becoming a family. He always loved coming over and playing with Bree. He was such a good kid. I felt blessed to be a part of Bud's life. I was starting to feel like life could possibly be worth all the struggles I had overcome.

When the landlord showed up and let us in the house, I knew the moment I walked in that it was going to be mine. The ceilings were really high and all the trimming was a deep cherry wood. It was so beautiful. When you walked into the house you walked into the foyer first. Then to the left was this large living room. Walking through there you ended up in the full dining room. Downstairs also had a small bathroom, utility room, a half basement, plus a good sized kitchen.

When we went upstairs it just got better. There were two bedrooms and the master bedroom. Bud was already claiming which bedroom he wanted and which one Bree could have. The master bedroom had a closet around ten feet deep. Yes, it was a walk-in closet. The upstairs bathroom was very large. I wanted it even more when the landlord said I could paint and decorate. I was in heaven and knew I just had to have this house. I spoke with the landlord and sold him on the fact that this house was meant for me. Ian stood by his word and, before he ever saw the house, we met with the landlord, signed our lease and Ian kept his word and paid for everything up front.

I was so excited about this move. I had a good looking man, beautiful home, wonderful daughter, the coolest stepson and a good job. I will never forget how excited I was to show Bree and Ian our new home. Bree had been at her dad's when I went house shopping so she hadn't seen the house yet either. After we signed the lease and had the keys in hand, I drove Bree and Ian over to our new house. Their excitement and disbelief in the house was amazing and all I had hoped it would be.

Ian just kept walking through the house saying, "I can't believe this is our house." I couldn't believe that things were coming together so well for us. I didn't think I would ever find happiness like that and yet there

I was. The move and making sure we had everything organized with the U-Haul was taken care of and the move went pretty smooth. This was the beginning of November.

All of a sudden, out of nowhere, Chad started claiming he didn't get his visits in September and October. That was during the time I had surgery and suffered from an infection. At the time of my surgery I had taken the doctor's notes to his attorney's office and let Chad know what was going on. Bree even went to Chad's mother's house, which we agreed to. I still have the phone records from when she was there. Chad was claiming he wanted makeup time for the visits he missed.

Now Chad was asking for Bree every weekend and the entire Christmas break until the end of the year. His attorney said if I didn't comply and agree he would file for contempt on me. My answer was simple, bring it on. Bree hated going there so I did my best to only make her go when she had to. Anytime Chad tried for extra time with Bree, I fought it. No one believed that Jade was hurting Bree, but I knew the truth and Bree was being made to live through it. I didn't care what Chad and Jade tried this time. In my opinion, our lives were so good that there was no one that could bring us down. Sadly, I was growing accustomed to Chad and Jade's lies and immature behavior.

Although Ian's hours were really tough to adjust to, we made it work. When Bud would come every other weekend, I would be the one taking care of the kids and we always had a blast. We would do movie night with pizza and popcorn. The kids and I had some of the best popcorn fights. Bree and Bud rarely ever argued about anything, which I thought was awesome. I did start noticing that Ian was taking pain pills more often. At first I thought it was okay with the doctor giving them to him, but I began to notice that he had another doctor who was writing his prescription.

He carried the pain pills with him at all times. It was only when he would call into work that I started questioning his use. When Ian stayed home from work he just laid on the couch and was in so much pain. I learned that he called in when he was out of his pain medicine and the pain he was feeling was his body withdrawing from the narcotic. Before I realized what was going on, I wanted to cry for Ian because of how bad he seemed to hurt. There was nothing I could do to help him. I tried talking to him about looking into help to get off the pain pills, but every time he would cleverly convince me he was okay. He somehow sold me on the idea that he had control. Ian swore to me that he wasn't abusing his medicine.

After Bree, Ian and I got moved in and unpacked, the house seemed so surreal. It was by far the biggest and nicest house we had ever lived in. It took some adjusting to getting up a little earlier for the extra half hour drive, but it was beyond worth it. Soon after our move, I started suffering from the same lower abdominal pains as when my cysts were active on my ovaries. I did my best to push through the pain and continue working. I decided to leave Bree in her school until after the Christmas break, at which time I planned to enroll her in the school in our new town.

I was unwilling to allow Chad or Jade to manipulate extra visits and Chad's attorney wasn't joking. On December 8th there was a Petition for a Contempt Citation and Order to Appear filed against me. I was so upset that this battle just didn't seem to have an end. I even stopped talking to Tracy and Stacy all together because I didn't trust any of them. I knew that I had to follow the Parenting Guidelines and that is exactly what I did. Chad wasn't getting any more time to allow his wife to abuse our daughter. No one else may have been willing to fight for her, but I refused to ever give up.

The Contempt Petition claimed that I, of course, refused his visits in September and October. It stated that I only allowed his visit for Thanksgiving because I was threatened with a contempt citation and most of what Jade and Chad claimed was a complete lie. The Petition also included that Chad hadn't had a Christmas break with Bree since 2001, which I really found funny. In 2001, we spent Christmas as a family in Florida where he claimed I disappeared with Bree.

I still have pictures of Chad, Bree and all the family from Christmas of 1999 to 2002. In 2003, he took her to see his family. He lived with Jade at that time, but he was coming up and hanging out with Bree and me at our house. I found it insane how he would blatantly lie to the Courts and not be held accountable when it was time to show proof. Chad nor Jade ever had any physical evidence to prove their claims. Chad also requested that I again be put in jail and be ordered to pay his attorney fees.

During the same day I received the Contempt Citation, I was rear ended and ended up having to file an insurance claim for my car. I swear it seemed like I couldn't catch a break. On December 13th I fired the attorney that Paul had paid for and told Paul I could do a better job than the attorney. Paul actually agreed and told me that he believed in me. Paul told me that I had to take my stand because I was obviously under attack. The Contempt Citation was set for a hearing on January 17, 2006 at 11:30 am.

Christmas came quickly and, just as set out in the Indiana Parenting Time Guidelines, Bree stayed with me. We actually had both of the kids with us. I can't explain how wonderful it was to wake up Christmas morning and enjoy watching the kids tear into all the gifts. Ian and I had worked hard to provide them with a great Christmas. It was a warm feeling to have all of us together. Our money was also beginning to come in steadily and, with all the bills paid, Ian and I were able to do extra things with the kids all the time.

Again, according to the Parenting Guidelines, Chad had Bree in the afternoon Christmas Day until after New Year's Eve. On December 29th I ended up working a ten hour shift and was pretty worn out. It did turn out to be an excellent afternoon because my insurance payment from my car being rear ended came through. I was really happy with the amount that we had settled on. I had a good chunk of cash money on me.

Ian and I were invited to stay the night at a friend of ours who was also in Kirby. After work, we ended up meeting at our friend's house. All of us were playing poker and having a good time. I was on a crazy roll and kept winning almost every hand. We weren't playing with quarters, either. It was really becoming a great night for me money wise.

Now, Ian and I weren't this picture perfect couple by far. We disagreed, had arguments and butted heads sometimes. We did work through things quickly when we did argue. No matter what we argued about, we were both determined not to do it in front of either of our children. I loved that he also felt the same way about that issue as I did. Ian was great with Bree when he was home.

Ian was also good at talking his way out of things when it came to arguments. He came up with the best alibis I had ever heard. It didn't even matter what we were disagreeing about, I would end up believing him or giving into him. The man just had this way about him that made me not want to argue. Plus, after disagreements with Ian, our making up was the best.

After the poker game, Ian and I went upstairs to lay down in the room our friends had prepared for us. Once we laid down, Ian started being rude to me and told me that I had embarrassed him. I sat up offended and I asked him what he was talking about. He was upset at me for winning at poker all night. He said the way I reacted when I would win a hand embarrassed him. I didn't understand and, when I tried to talk to him, he just cussed me and told me to shut up. Ian hadn't cussed me like that before and that was all it took for me because I wasn't taking that from anyone. I got up, went out of the house, jumped in my car and headed for home.

There were two ways to make it home from our friends. I could either pick the highway or take the back way through a small town. I was half an hour away from our home and I just wanted to get there safely. I was tired from working all day and confused by Ian acting like a total ass. It didn't help that it was getting pretty late, either. The drive home wasn't something I had planned or intended to make. While we were playing poker, I did have a few beer but I wasn't in a drinking mood that night. I made it roughly ten minutes away from my house when I began fighting to keep my eyes open.

I did swerve a bit, but recovered quickly. I rolled down the window and turned my music up. As I sat up to better wake myself the lights began to flash behind me. I had only drank a few beers and I knew I was just tired. I wasn't worried at all when the officer approached me. It was only when I looked in the back seat to grab my purse that I was nervous. I realized I had left my purse in the bedroom with Ian at our friend's house. When the officer approached my window, I was 100% honest with him. I explained that I had worked ten hours that day, I had a disagreement with my boyfriend and I forgot to grab my purse when I left. I gave him all of my information and, when he asked if I had drank anything, I admitted I had a few beers hours earlier.

Now I don't care if you believe or say that the luck of the Irish is true or not. I am almost all Irish and I have never had much luck. I was off probation, completed all requirements, didn't smoke pot, out of trouble all together, standing up for myself and finally making good money. I had a beautiful home, killer job, wonderful daughter and life was finally calming down for me. With or without Ian, I knew that Bree and I weren't going to hurt for anything. I hadn't needed help from welfare or state assistance for almost two years and that really did feel good.

The officer asked me to step out of the vehicle and I knew I was in trouble. I didn't have my license or any form of I.D. on me. All I could think about was what was going to happen to Bree. I couldn't help but wonder how disappointed Bree would be in me, too. I promised her that I would always be there for her. I couldn't do that locked in a jail. What would Jade do to Bree? I started explaining to the officer that I was in a really bad custody case as tears rolled down my face. He didn't really care and decided to give me a field sobriety test. I was tired and, although tears were falling, I was at full attention and did my best.

The officer had me do all the normal, arms out, touch nose, other arm, again. Then the officer told me to count from 100 to 1, but by one-one thousand. So I did as he asked and started at one-one thousand one hundred, one-one thousand ninety-nine, one-one thousand ninety-eight, one-one thousand ninety-seven and so on. Even trying to do that sober is not easy. That man had me count down to one-one thousand twelve and I knew I had it. When he stopped me I said, "Sir, please, just let me go home. I am only ten minutes away and I'm currently fighting for custody of my daughter." He then told me I was under arrest for Driving Under the Influence.

The tears just continued to fall as he placed me under arrest and called for a tow on my car. The officer did reassure me that if I could pass the breathalyzer once we got to the jail he would let me go. I was pretty sure that I could do that; so, with my heart pumping, I patiently waited. When we got to the jail the officer took me to the machine and said, "Ok, if you blow a .07 or below I will let you go."

I blew into the machine while tears streamed down my face. I was so scared of what could happen if I didn't pass. I wasn't worried about me, Bree was the only thing I could think about. I was finally doing things right for myself and for my daughter. The results came back .08 and I was booked into the jail. As much as I wanted to dispute the results and ask for another chance, I couldn't. My hands were tied, or cuffed rather. The only phone number I had memorized was Brad's mom. It was late, but I called her and she was able to get a hold of Ian for me. I was so thankful for that woman. Ian had me out within hours and I was home.

Once home, Ian and I talked and he apologized to me for everything. Honestly, he was the least of my concerns. I knew that things were about to get crazy and much harder for me in my custody case, not to mention I worked a half hour from home. I knew I was going to lose my license, again. I was angry at myself for ever getting in the car and leaving that night. As against drinking and driving as I am in any circumstances, I couldn't believe I was facing my third D.U.I. (Driving Under the Influence).

I knew I had to face the consequences of my actions, and I was prepared to do that. I was and am a grown woman. The bible teaches us that at age 12 we are held accountable. Our childhood and the people who hurt us throughout life do not define our decisions. Some of us just tend to use them, or the pain they caused, as our alibi (*an excuse, especially to avoid blame*). I didn't and I don't. I knew I had to put my big girl panties on and face what was to come. With every one of our choices and decisions there come consequences. I knew I could get through what I had to face, but what worried me was how Jade would use this against me.

On New Year's Eve I tried to call Bree. When Jade answered the phone I said, "I am sorry to bother you, but I just wanted to wish Bree a Happy New Year." To no surprise Jade just laughed at me and hung up the phone. Ian and I spent the early evening at his boss' house, but we didn't stay too long. We ended up just spending the rest of the evening at home. Neither of us were big on the bar scene, but we just took advantage of having alone time. We usually always enjoyed that because we didn't get a lot of alone time with our work schedules. I had a lot to face in the coming year, but I felt like it would all work out. Ian reassured me that I was not facing everything alone anymore. He brought me comfort and it felt good to not feel so alone! Our night ended great and we both brought the New Year in together.

Chapter SEVENTEEN

2006: After the New Year and Christmas break was over, it was time to transfer Bree into her new school. She was in first grade and the transfer went very smooth. I knew I had a lot to face legally, but I just wanted to make sure that everything stayed consistent and secure for Bree. I had accepted there wasn't any way to stop the visits to Jade and Chad's, so when Bree was home I tried my best to keep things scheduled at a constant and healthy level for her. I knew that when Jade found out I was arrested, shit would hit the fan and I wasn't wrong about that.

From Bree's very first day of school she always went by my last name. See, when Bree was born, her father and I were not married. My mother convinced me to give Bree both my last name and Chad's; therefore, her last name was hyphenated. When she was getting ready to start her new school, I asked her if it had been easier to use one of her last names in class and she said yes. I gave her the freedom to choose and explained that both her dad's last name and mine were very good names. I told her, since she was in a new school, she could pick which name to go by and whatever made it easier on her was cool with me. I knew it didn't change her legal name or who her parents were, so to me it wasn't a big deal. After Bree thought about it she ended up saying she would like to continue using my last name. She did express concern about not wanting to hurt her dad's feelings, so I told her she could use his if she wanted. Bree decided, however, she wanted to stick with my last name. After that, I never really thought twice about it.

I made it a point to do my best not to talk about adult issues with Bree and no one should have. She was only six years old at this time and had already been exposed to enough. Bree had no idea about my arrest while she was at her dad's and she didn't need to worry about it. That was my job as her parent. It was fully my responsibility to make sure she enjoyed being a kid. I don't lie to my child and, to this day, I encourage her to know that the truth will set you free. I simply reassure her that she has nothing to worry about. I told her many times that all she needed to worry about was being a kid.

I always told Bree, "I got this," and she would always smile at me. I remain consistent at staying Bree's mom and not her friend. I am a firm believer that we are supposed to be examples for our children and, if you want the best for your children, you should give your best to your children.

I believe as a parent it isn't necessary to worry about if our children like us or not. Our consistency and authority isn't always likable. When the time is right, your children will end up your best friends, but it's not when they need security, guidance and rules to follow. I wanted Bree to just enjoy being young, and I did everything I could to provide that for her. Even as I battled the most evil stepmother, my own demons and what felt like the whole world every single day, I still woke up feeling blessed to be Bree's mom. Truth be told, I am blessed to be this young lady's mother.

Jade was dedicated to tearing me down and using every mistake she thought I made in my life against me. I knew Jade and Chad were watching everything I did, and I was trying to make the best decisions I knew to make. Honestly, Jade's obsession with me really made me change and, in the end, it helped me to become a better mother. Jade's father was the president of a biker club in her hometown, which, come to find out, was only half an hour from our beautiful new home. Learning that made me fully aware and cautious of the things going on around me at all times. It was strange because I knew that Chad and Jade partied, smoked pot, drank and did whatever else they wanted to do. However, my doing anything wrong and any decision I made was put on trial and my mistakes were thrown in my face, literally.

Even doing my best never seemed to be good enough to them; however, I wasn't willing to give up even if I did fall on my face a few times. When I did fall the many times throughout my life, I would get back up and brush myself off. The only thing left to do when we fail or fall on our faces is to get up and try again. Giving up means you're giving in. Bruised, broken, under attack, whatever your circumstances are, get your ass back up. Don't give up because others don't believe in you because you have to believe in yourself. For me, I find peace knowing that Jesus Christ also believes in me even when I am at rock bottom.

In January, there was a monster truck show in town. Ian and I decided to take Bud and enjoy the show because he was such a big fan. Bree, unfortunately, was at her dad's for a visit the day of the show. I think she would have enjoyed it. It was my first time at a monster truck show and I thought it was pretty cool. I could see why the boys loved it so much. Both Ian and Bud were so loud and supportive of the Grave Digger monster truck. It was their favorite. I can't express how much I loved being able to do extra things with the kids and not continually struggle with money every week.

Soon after the monster truck show I was suffering from cysts on my ovaries again, and I met with the gynecologist. All that he felt left to do was a partial hysterectomy. I was truly tired of hurting all the time. The doctor really wasn't big on the surgery because I was only 27 years old, but he felt it was the best option to help me get rid of the severe pain I continued to suffer from. I was scheduled for surgery on February 14, 2006. What a way to celebrate Valentine's Day. A partial hysterectomy for you, Zara, plus being put into full-blown menopause for the rest of my life. Needless to say, I was not excite but I was ready for the pain to be gone for good.

Trying to make arrangements with Chad was still nothing less than a complete challenge. I didn't talk bad about Chad or Jade in front of Bree, but they kept claiming to everyone that I was. Even now, if Bree says she hates her dad, I get on her about how strong the word hate is. He is still her father and nothing can change that. I don't, however, stop her from expressing her feelings about what she has been through. I really don't think Chad actually had or even has a clue of the things that Jade was saying to Bree in secret. Jade actually called Bree a liar so many times that Chad believed Bree was a liar. Bree would tell me about Jade and Chad sitting her down and asking her all kinds of questions about our home and what I was doing. I would call out to the Ad Litem how wrong that was to do to a six year old, but she wouldn't listen.

I learned that when I would say something about what Jade was doing it would make Bree's next visit worse. After encouraging Bree to be honest and talk to Chad about things Jade was saying, Bree just ended up more hurt. Chad always backed Jade up no matter what it was. In the end, Bree was afraid to even tell her dad anything because she felt like he didn't believe her anyway. Chad wasn't fighting for what was right for Bree and, by this time, I knew the truth of what was really happening. Jade had full control over Chad and he transformed into all that woman wanted. Submissive he has always been, you could even say a pussy. But allowing his daughter to be emotionally abused and then contributing to it, that was beyond anything I ever imagined Chad would do.

Looking on the outside, Chad and Jade are the picture perfect wealthy family. They are bikers who are a big part of a biker club that Chad eventually became the president of. They are always running charities and raising a lot of money for others. They reach out and help their community often. Yet, in the privacy of their home, Jade was secretly emotionally abusing Bree. Jade continued to talk horrible about me and claim to be such a better mother. Jade made it a point to try and convince everyone around her that I was this awful, crazy, drug addict and an abusive mother.

Some of the things that happened just made me laugh. I remember when Bree came home one time and told me how Jade allowed her daughter's boyfriend to stay the night. The child was only a young teen at the time. I told Bree there was no way that was ever happening and all parents are different. I encouraged her to understand I was her mom and she had to follow my rules. Whatever I didn't want Bree to do or exposed to was <u>always</u> encouraged when she was with Jade and Chad. I thank God daily that my child still respected my rules enough to not give into their negative encouragement. Shockingly, Jade's daughter ended up pregnant by the age of 16.

I raised Bree to take the hard times, give them to God and use them to help make her stronger. I was always real picky about what T.V. shows and movies Bree watched when she was growing up. I didn't even let her have boy posters in her room until she was 12. I believed that, when she was 12, she would be able to make more independent choices. If Bree would say something like I didn't allow her to watch a certain show while she was at her dad's, Jade would encourage her and tell her she could watch it there. What I loved was Bree would come home and tell me about it. Then say, "Mom, I didn't watch it, even though Jade said I could, because I knew better." That kid amazed me and still does every day. If she did watch a show she knew she wasn't supposed to, she told me about that, too, and would apologize to me. It was funny to me how she would tell on herself and she still does to this day.

Clothes seemed to always be a huge issue for Chad and Jade. They were, again, claiming that they were sending Bree home in good clothes and not getting them back. I laughed at these petty things because we had already been through this once. Bree was going every other weekend for visits and, the very few times she wore something home from their house, she would get in trouble if she didn't wear the same thing back. Jade and Chad tried to claim I was keeping all of the clothes they had for Bree, which was just another lie. I also thought it was hilarious that millionaires were complaining about a few pieces of clothing. In the end, Bree was never allowed to bring anything home from their house. I told the Ad Litem and the attorney that Chad and Jade shouldn't send anything else home with her because nothing they had was worth the way they were behaving. It really didn't bother me because Bree's needs were always met, but it did hurt Bree. Obviously, I wasn't as wealthy as they were, but Bree has always had good clothes.

Can you imagine your child being constantly told negative things about you and you not being able to do anything about it? I lost so much sleep over wondering how the things being said to Bree would affect her in the long run. Sleep was foreign to me. I was both preparing for court and making sure I had everything in order or having horrible, visually violent thoughts of things I wanted to do to Jade. As much as I tried to pray and follow God, I was still under constant attack. Sometimes I felt like I could never get it right with God no matter how hard I tried. I thought that maybe I made too many mistakes and bad choices.

February 3rd to February 6th Ian and I were on our way to St. Petersburg, Florida. It was the first V.I.P Gold trip that Ian had won through his company. There were scheduled events and we had a couple seminars we were required to attend, but, for the most part, it was a free vacation in Florida. After a long delay at the airport, we finally checked into the Trade Winds Island Resort. It was such a stunning and beautiful resort.

I was really falling for the life of luxury. Not that we were rich with money by far, but we weren't hurting. Our room was set up nicely and we were both ecstatic just to be there. Ian even surprised me with a beautiful necklace and earring set that was unexpected and so sweet. Saturday was spent with the women going our own way and the guys going theirs. It was so peaceful and beautiful there. The resort was actually right on the ocean and the view was amazing. I loved the fresh air and beauty of the ocean. For a moment, I imagined how life would be without all the madness.

The entire resort was full of other Kirby office salesmen and women that had also qualified for the free trip. It was never a small event when it came to Kirby. Ian was so excited about his success, but what no one realized, not even myself, was Ian was battling his own demon in the form of a serious pill addiction. I had called him out on some of his behavior, but, with all honesty, I didn't have a clue how bad things really were nor did I understand pill addiction at all. I knew about addiction, but, like I said earlier, the doctors gave him the medicine so I truly believed it wasn't that bad.

Ian was a professional salesman and convinced me to believe that he had a handle on things. I was also swept away in the lifestyle we were living. Ian and I talked many times about owning our own business, and I wanted that to come true more than anything. I wanted to believe in and do all that Ian and I were working for.

Ian had no problem fitting in and being a part of any crowd. He was like me in that sense. We continued talking about our own office and our goals for the kids. By this time, I was also starting to get more involved with the Kirby business. I couldn't help it, I was really drawn in by all the big money and flash. Ian ended up joining a volleyball tournament while we were in Florida. I was his number one fan at all times. I believed he was the man that could lead our family and take us far. I always tried to be supportive of him and wanted him to know I believed in him.

I was proud of Ian and all he was accomplishing. He was doing good and was even winning awards on top of our free trip. Ian and I were both captivated by the money and luxury of it all. There is something that happens to you when you start making good money and you start mingling with others that are making even more money. The gowns and tuxedos, the wild fun and adventures that came with it all were mind blowing.

Working for a company that strives to make you feel good about you so you can go make other people feel good is incredible. In sales, it is important to know how, what and when to say the correct thing. The first thing you need to do is sell yourself. The rest is pretty easy and usually sales will follow, which is when the money comes in. This company had no problem providing the energy and motivation to encourage everyone in the business to strive to do better. They used great motivational speakers, speeches, seminars and, of course, the V.I.P trips. I wasn't interested in going door to door because that was what Ian was good at, I was interested in learning how to run the office and conduct training.

Once we got back from Florida, I tried to make sure that everything was in order for Bree and Chad's visit because I was unable to provide transportation for Bree due to my upcoming surgery. We only communicated through email, and I knew the entire time and through all the years I was talking to Jade. I realized it was what it was, and I had accepted that.

In response to my scheduled surgery, I was emailed and told that Chad would pick our daughter up but he wouldn't be willing to bring her back. I was going in for a partial hysterectomy, they seriously couldn't provide the transportation needed? It was always a constant argument with them. I called and left a message for Chad's attorney and, on February 13th, I even dropped a letter off to his office. In the letter I was very direct in telling him that Chad was to pick up and return our daughter until I recovered from my surgery and the doctor released me.

On the day of my scheduled partial hysterectomy, my mother had come down to offer me help while I recovered. Ian was working all the time, and I honestly needed the help. The surgery went well, and I was allowed to leave after several hours. My mother was in the passenger seat, Ian driving and me laying in the backseat in complete misery and confusion. My emotions were out of control and I had no clue why. I was angry, sad, confused, happy and even a little depressed all at once. I can't explain how much I changed emotionally after my surgery. Yay to menopause. I dove straight into instant menopause. There was no slow approach to it for me.

We were half an hour away from home when Ian pulled into a plaza and told my mother and me he would be right back. I was getting so mad and hurt he would even consider stopping anywhere. Here I was, fresh out of the recovery room from surgery and now allowed to go home and that's all I wanted to do --- Go home! As I laid in the backseat crying to my mother, she agreed that Ian was being thoughtless.

It ended up taking Ian about 20 minutes to come back to the car. When he finally came out, he had two boxes with him and presented one to my mother and one to me. He said, "Happy Valentine's ladies." I was so out of it and angry I had forgotten it was Valentine's Day! For some reason that man actually thought on the way home from surgery would be a meaningful moment to give me and my mother a gold dipped rose. It was beautiful, but to this day that rose reminds me of my surgery and Ian making me wait in that backseat hurting.

I didn't notice that Ian was taking even more pain pills then he had before. He was a big boy and handled his own business. Plus, he was working all of the time, so I was usually in bed when he came home and he was in bed when Bree and I got up and left in the morning. I was consumed with my custody case, taking care of my daughter, my health, our new home and work. I didn't really notice or pay attention to how bad Ian was getting.

Due to the pain medication I was given, I was really out of it most of the time after my surgery. I was extremely thankful for my mother being there. She was really helpful with Bree and my recovery. Physically I remember being uncomfortable, but I don't recall much pain. I hated taking any pills, but the medication helped me a great deal. Emotionally it was a horrific experience. I am a firm believer that our spirit can control our mind and body. I feel it is important to allow your spirit to lead you in life. This was a moment in my life I felt like I had no control of anything, including my own thoughts or emotions. One moment I was crying, the next I was laughing and then I would be sleeping. Not only was I on an emotional roller coaster, I was also drugged up with pain medication and hormone replacements. I asked my mother to handle all my medication after my surgery since she was always there with me while Ian was working.

Ian came in one night and woke me up. My mother was so angry because he kept asking where my medication was. He kept trying to talk me out of my pain medication. I was pretty out of it. I remember crying and telling him that I needed my medicine. I told him he couldn't have any. Ian got really upset and ended up leaving for hours that night. My hormones and emotions continued to be all over the place. It took me about three months taking hormone replacements before I realized that the hormone replacements weren't working for me. In fact, they were what was causing me to be really emotionally unstable. I ended up getting off them and began herbal supplements, which have worked for me for nine years now.

I couldn't believe it was now March and Jade and Chad weren't coming at me about being arrested. I wasn't complaining about that, I just knew it would only be a matter of time. My trial for the D.U.I (Driving Under the Influence) was set for August. According to the parenting guidelines, Chad turned in his requested summer visitation and all of it seemed right to me. It was nice to have the schedule set like that so there was nothing that could be argued over. I signed and returned the summer visitation sheet to Chad's attorney and all was good.

Bree was still having issues with Jade, but, for the most part, there were a few breaks from all the drama where Jade would stop focusing on using Bree to hurt me. Then it all went downhill. I thought it was going to be over my arrest, but I was wrong. All of a sudden, Jade and Chad came at me full force about how I was making Bree use my last name in school. I don't know why, and I couldn't believe the way they were both acting about it. I hadn't even thought about it since Bree and I had talked. I had so much more going on to even think it would have been an issue.

Somehow they seriously thought I had dropped Chad's last name to somehow hurt or affect Chad. I tried to explain what happened; that it was just easier for Bree. Chad and Jade didn't care. They both went up to her school and threw such a fit that Bree was required, for the rest of the school year, to write out her entire last name. I went to the school when I found out and tried to have them just go by Chad's last name, but the school was reluctant. They said because of the way Chad and Jade had behaved about the matter, they wanted to go by her full legal last name. It was only an issue for the few months of school that was left because, for the rest of Bree's school years, she has gone by my last name. She now begs me to have Chad's last name dropped, but I refuse. I tell her when she is 18 she can have the name changed if she still wants to.

When Jade and Chad found out about my D.U.I. (Driving Under the Influence), I knew it would be trouble, but I never imagined they would move from Tennessee to Indiana. They moved back to Jade's hometown, which, again, was only half an hour from where we were living. They were so focused on taking my daughter from me I don't think anything else mattered to either of them. When I found out they moved to Indiana, it just made me even more cautious of everyone around me. Now my biggest haters were pretty much right around the corner from me.

I tried not to let it show that it bothered me on the outside, but inside I wanted to pull my hair out from frustration. Ian and I were doing good, and Bree was even going with Bud and his mom for occasional sleepovers. Bud's mom also had a baby girl that Bree adored. Ian's ex was so cool and it was always about what was best for the children when it came to her. I respected her a great deal for that. We all got along really good and she even allowed her daughter to come stay with us for sleepovers.

After recovering from my surgery, Ian and I decided that it would be better if I quit my CNC position and start getting way more involved in Kirby. Our goal was to open our own office by July and we were on a great pace to do so. I was honestly tired of seeing Ian go to work in suits and bringing home twice as much as me while I was doing heavy manual labor, covered in steel dust every day and making way less money. We both agreed that, with Ian's income, we would be fine and things would level back out once I started at the office.

Also in March I was excited because I was able to take Bree to her very first concert and it was so much fun. We jammed to Christian music a lot and Bree was a huge fan of the BarlowGirl and Rebecca St. James. I happen to be blessed enough to buy a couple of tickets to a show that both of them were touring on. It was so much fun watching Bree's face light up when BarlowGirl hit the stage. She quickly made a friend with a girl her age that was sitting next to us. They both had a blast dancing and singing together. It was moments like this that made me feel encouraged that I wasn't as bad of a mom as Jade continued to try and prove to everyone, including my daughter. It took me a long time to realize that the mother I was and am with Bree didn't and doesn't need to prove anything to anyone, especially Jade. I knew in my heart I was doing my best with my daughter even though she didn't come with an instruction manual.

In April, Ian and I were headed to Gatlinburg, Tennessee for another trip that Ian had qualified for. We spent three days in this two-story amazing log cabin. The view was astonishing, there was a hot tub on the balcony and a pool table in the cabin. It was an incredible trip and the area was just, wow, gorgeous. We ended up going indoor skydiving and walking around a lot. We also rode on the back of a monster truck, which was very cool. We didn't have any boring moments on that trip. We rode go-carts and some of the rides that were there. It was a much needed relaxing trip that allowed me to clear my mind for a moment. There was always so much going on it was hard to keep up sometimes. I was now working as a secretary to the Director of Human Resources in our office. I, myself, was starting to qualify for things and get numbers in for my name in the same company Ian was excelling at. I loved the job. I was wearing makeup, suits, and heels and had my nails done. I felt so accomplished when I worked for Kirby.

In May, Ian asked me to marry him and I said yes. I was emotionally struggling to pull myself back into check since the surgery. It was at this time I got off the hormone medication and was finally leveling out. Even though things were going good, I was still always on the edge of my chair just waiting to see what Jade and Chad might do next. I was beyond excited about getting married, but we decided to do it quickly and quietly. I just wanted to be settled and thought Ian was the one. On May 11, 2006, Ian and I walked down the aisle and were married. We had our wedding at the church I loved and Bree dressed up in the most gorgeous little gown. Ian had his best man and I had my maid of honor plus Bree. It was an extremely small and quick wedding.

By July Ian and I were able to get incorporated and opened our own office as we had dreamed about. I can't explain how good it felt to be a successful family with our own business. I was convinced everything was going to finally be balanced out. Although Ian was still taking his pain pills, he really seemed to have it under control and handling himself well. I was really ignorant to the power of pill addiction, plus with everything else that was going on I think a part of me didn't want to see what was happening. How many times do you block out the bad because all you want to see is the good?

Between balancing the task of opening our office, working and parenting our children, Ian and I stayed pretty busy. The kids were happy and, even with our hectic schedules, we were able to make time to do things together. It may have been one day a week, but Ian made sure to be home to spend the day with the kids and me.

On July 11th my beautiful baby girl turned seven years old. I was blessed enough to be the one to teach her how to ride her bicycle without training wheels that day. I admit, it didn't take much teaching as Bree caught on pretty quick. The day was so fun and she enjoyed her birthday party. All of Ian's family came and we had a small cook out. Ian had gone out and purchased Bree's very first pair of diamond earrings. He didn't even tell me. Her smile was so adorable when she saw them. I thank God we had our camera back then because I can look at the moment of that adorable smile anytime I want now.

July 18th, the day before I was to pick Bree up from the police department in Jade's hometown, I unexpectedly found myself on the phone with Jade. She called me in the afternoon and was telling me she was concerned about the way Bree was behaving. She said she thought Ian was touching or doing something to Bree. I can't express how bad I wanted to jump through that phone and slap the shit right out of that woman right then and there. Jade had a way of making me feel that way about her a lot. I said, "Look, I don't know if something happened to you as a child, if your daddy touched you or what, but you really need to get some help" and then hung up. Those were my words verbatim. Later that night, Jade called me back and said I could have Chad and she hoped we were happy. I was lost and figured they were just fighting again. I responded with, "I have a husband and my hands are full, but thanks anyway."

On July 19th I went to pick my child up from her father and took a woman, my secretary at the time, with me. Chad was standing in the parking lot of the police station when I pulled in. The police station became the only place I was willing to meet because of Jade's constant outbursts during our transfers. When I got out of my car, Chad approached me aggressively. He was accusing me of saying that Jade's dad molested her. I kept looking around for Bree and told Chad that was not what I said. I finally spotted Bree across the street at the park. Jade was holding her hand and pulled her back when she went to run to me because she saw me too.

I explained to Chad he better back off and allow Bree to come over to me. Jade continued holding my daughter's hand and began screaming at me. She was calling me every name in the book and trying to call me out to fight her. I just replied with, "Get us in a cage match where it's legal and then I will fight you." What I would have given to legally be allowed to beat that woman during this time in my life; however, I was still trying to show Bree it is better to be the bigger woman and walk away.

It was always stupid, simple things that Jade used to hurt Bree. That poor baby girl felt so isolated when she was at her dad and Jade's house. One incident that occurred, before I asked Jade and Chad to stop sending things home with Bree, was she was allowed to wear a pair of her shoes home they had passed down to Bree from Jade's older daughter. They told Bree, not me, the stipulation for her was that she had to wear them back every time she went to their house. She really liked the shoes and wanted to wear them for school, so I did my best to remind her to wear them when it was time to go for her visit. It worked for a while until one day things were really busy for me and it was time to go. Bree and I had jumped into the car and she went for her weekend visit. When she came home that Sunday, she said she had to stay in her room almost the entire weekend because she didn't wear the right shoes to their house. What the hell? Did they really think that any pair of shoes or clothes they sent with Bree would somehow benefit me? It wasn't like they were my size and I was wearing them. Why couldn't anyone see how much stupid things like this was hurting Bree?

Back at the police station, as I tried to talk to Chad, Jade continued yelling all her vulgar normal words at me from across the street. Jade finally focused on only me and had let Bree's hand go so my secretary was able to get across the street and get Bree. Jade just kept going, yelling things like how she was a way better mother because she had a clean record and how I was such a stupid bitch. It was nothing shocking or new. I honestly found it funny how she used my criminal record against me. You and I could stand hand in hand, stretched out as far as we could and we still wouldn't be the length of her own husband's drug charges and criminal record.

Then it happened. Jade said, "There is a hit out on your ass. You're sure as dead. My dad is going to take care of you." That was it. My heart skipped a beat and my anger levels were all over the place. I grabbed my daughter's hand and my emotions were so high that I actually asked Bree if she heard that Jade was going to have me killed. I wish more than anything that I hadn't done that, but I just wasn't thinking straight at all. It was obvious this woman was never going to back down from trying to hurt me. I really thought all this was going to come to an end now that Jade had actually threatened there was a hit out on me and she was going to have me killed. I went into the police station and made my complaint. An officer came out and talked to me, then went to talk with Jade. I am just going to share with you what was in the police report and is public record.

The officer wrote his report as follows:
"When I arrived I spoke with Zara. Zara advised me that they have been having custodial problems for 2 years now and that her ex-husband's, new wife, Jade, just threatened her by stating she had a HIT out on her and that her father was going to take care of her. I then went and spoke with Jade. Jade advised that she did not say that and that she did say that if she kept accusing people of molesting kids that someone would put a hit out on her. I then went back and spoke with Zara again. Zara then pulled a tape recorder out of the pocket and on the tape was Jade making the treat that she did have a HIT on her and that her father was going to take care of the hit. I made contact with Prosecutor and he agreed with the decision to arrest Jade for Intimidation "D" Felony. I then went back over to the park to speak to Jade and advised her that Zara did have a tape recording of her conversation and that it is clear on the tape that she threatened Zara and she was being placed under arrest for Intimidation "D" Felony."

I had been carrying my tape recorder for transfers, but I could never get a clear recording of Jade yelling at me. She would usually be too far for my recorder to pick it up. This day somehow, even with being across the street at a park yelling at me, her threat was clear as day on my recorder. I had forgotten I had the recorder until my secretary asked me if I had turned it on when the officer went to talk to Jade. Chad and Jade both lied to the Courts and everyone involved from day one. I really thought this was finally the day all of this came to an end. Surely with the tape recording the Courts, Mrs. Mayor and everyone involved would see how crazy Jade really was.

It was later that night, once I had gotten home and reached in the back of my car to grab my briefcase, that I saw it. There it was, a folded up letter lying on the floor in the back of my car. I was shocked once I opened it and realized it was from Jade. She or Chad had thrown it in my car during the transfer. There it was, dated and signed with permission to do with the letter what I wanted. I proceeded to read this very lost, demon filled, bitter woman's letter. I unfolded the papers and read as follows;

> *"The problems I have had with you are these:*
> *1. You have used you daughter as a pawn on numerous occasions against her father. (Like if you get mad at him or myself you have kept Bree from seeing or talking to him.)"*

At that moment I felt this sickening feeling in my stomach and folded the letter back up. I just couldn't bring myself to read the rest of it, not yet. I put it in with all my court papers and proceeded upstairs. After everything that happened that day, Ian and I were leaving for Las Vegas that night. Before Ian and I were able to open our own office, he had qualified for a free trip to Las Vegas and we weren't passing that up.

With Bree safely at Ian's mother's house, we were on our way. Again, Ian and I weren't alone, we left with one of the funnest group of professional, yet crazy people I've ever been blessed enough to work with. I can't describe how good it felt when the plane left the ground. What a crazy day it had been. As the plane began to take off, I admit that on the inside I did giggle a little at the fact that the woman trying to destroy my life and my daughter's life was actually sitting in jail.

Ian and I left for Las Vegas on July 19th and returned on the 23rd. Our trip was one I will never forget. We had the opportunity to walk around and enjoy all of the casinos. Our room had the perfect view of the Bellagio Fountains. It was incredible, and I definitely hope to go back someday. Our boss ended up renting a Hummer limousine and took all of us out to a very popular club in Vegas. After we hung out there for a short time, we headed to the Stratosphere Hotel and Casino.

The Stratosphere Hotel and Casino is a skyscraper in Las Vegas that has rides on top of it. We ended up riding the one called, "The Stratosphere Insanity." The name fit, it was insane. This ride took us off the skyscraper and hung us over the side as it spun us. It was so much fun. Our company award show was wonderful and it was always nice to hang out with everyone outside of work. How many times do you get to wear a prom dress or gorgeous gown in a lifetime? Most of us women would say twice. Once for prom and once for our wedding day. This was now the third gown I had purchased and got to wear in less than a year and I was loving the life.

When we returned from Las Vegas, Ian and I picked up Bree, went home and settled down for the night. It didn't take me long to get everything unpacked and laundry started. As soon as I sat down to relax, unfortunately I remembered the letter that Jade had wrote to me. I thought about waiting, but I decided to go ahead and finish reading it. The letter continued exactly as such:

"2. Bree (without questioning) told her dad while I was sitting next to her about helping you & Bob pick seeds out of cigarettes that you two were making and taking the seeds out to the cornfield to see if they would make corn grow. I could never look at anyone who would allow this to happen as a fit parent."

My first thought was why would I ever claim pot seeds helped corn grow? I didn't even lie to my child about Santa Claus, why would I allow her to be ignorantly educated about anything? Also, I hadn't lived near a cornfield since Chad and I lived in his childhood home. Chad and I smoked pot all the time, even with Bob, but I don't recall anything like that ever happening with Bree or with Bob.

What I had found funny was the fact that social media was and is available. I had already printed pictures from Jade's profile on Facebook for Court. I had pictures of the kid's playroom in their basement having a pot leaf bead door on it. I knew Jade and Chad were smoking pot, and Lord knows what else. How this woman felt justified in her accusations and actions is still beyond me. Her entire social media was covered in support of marijuana. There were pictures of her wearing a hat covered in pot leaves and pictures of biker rallies where Jade really should have been wearing more clothes. Plus, of course, there was alcohol on hand throughout almost all of them. Truth be told, it was obvious that Jade and Chad partied and were living life the way they pleased all while trying to persecute and tear me down.

"3. You have tried to erase Chad from her life by not letting her use her real last name (....-....) It's not just Banks. You don't allow him to be involved in her school and extracurricular life. You, yourself admitted in front of his lawyer that you have warned the school about not letting Chad contact them concerning Bree. With joint custody he has as much right in this way as yourself."

"4. You have told Bree all about Chad being in jail. (Think about who that hurts.) You seem to forget easily that you have also been in jail since he has been out."

"5. You have said many false statements about myself. Like being abusive to your daughter. (Even questioning her about this and when she says I hadn't you told her you still think I do this came from Bree also)"

This woman was seriously insane. It made me question even more what the hell she was really capable of doing to my daughter. She was actually taking things she was doing to my daughter and writing about it as if I was doing it. I never questioned Bree about things that happened at their visits. I knew that it would hurt my daughter and, perhaps, shut her down from sharing with me what she did. I just simply couldn't believe this woman even felt like she had any right to write this letter to me to begin with. It really made me sick to my stomach.

Chad rarely ever called Bree after her fifth birthday. If he did call, I never stopped him from talking to our daughter. I always assumed he didn't call because Jade didn't want Chad and I talking. I would, however, call Bree when she stayed at their house for over three days. It was not as often as Jade made it out to be because it was rare that Bree was there for more than a weekend visit. It's ironic how Jade would hang up on me and deny me access to Bree over the phone and, at the same time, claiming I was doing that to Chad.

Jade and Chad had already been to Bree's school. She wasn't even in anything extra-curricular yet. I couldn't figure out what Jade was even talking about. Not to mention the fact that I never told Bree about her dad going to jail. It was just crazy how Jade claimed to have so many stories that Bree supposedly told her, yet she found it important to continue to mention it was "without questioning Bree."

> *"6. Bree talk about you having her get you beer out of your fridge & after you drink sometimes you drive with her. If you want to kill yourself driving this way do it but please keep her out of your car after you have drank.*
>
> *There are so many more points I can make like how you have kept Bree from Chad for months and yet when he has her for 2 days you call our house. The sickest and most twisted thing you have done though is accused my father of molesting me. When you made that statement that showed me that you are the most hopeless person I have ever met. I am making a copy*

of this letter so you can't add or take away from this for court purposes. Also here is my ex-husbands # call him & see how a mother who puts her kid's well-being first does it."

Needless to say, the violent visuals of what I wanted to do to Jade only got worse. I wasn't afraid of her or her biker gang or her dad, I just wanted to cause her physical and emotional pain for what she was doing to my daughter and me. I didn't even drink when my daughter was home. I was far beyond too busy running an office and dealing with my husband. I am not claiming that I was perfect, but I was not doing what Jade was claiming.

I didn't know exactly what to do, but with the supposed 'hit' out on me I went straight to the courthouse once they were open. I filed a restraining order against Jade to protect not only me, but Bree also. I typed up and filed an Emergency Petition for Termination of Visitation, which explained what happened during the last transfer. I then decided again to refuse any visitation until we let the court decide what should be done.

Now, Court for the Restraining Order was scheduled for August 17th. Jade's attorney filed his notice of appearance on July 25th, which happened to be the same day I signed a recommendation for my plea agreement to be entered into the Court in regard to my D.U.I. that had occurred December 2005. The agreement had me serving eight days in jail, one year of house arrest and one year of probation. I knew then that I deserved whatever my sentencing was going to be. Drinking and driving is no joke and is extremely wrong, not to mention dangerous to everyone around you, including yourself.

The only thing I was worried about was Jade and Chad finding out that I had to serve the eight days. I knew if they found out I was in jail for even an hour they would be filing something to try to take my daughter away. It was very confusing to me because Jade was horrible to Bree. Now with Jade and Chad being only half an hour from my home, it truly sucked. I had completely closed myself off from getting to really know other people and from making friends. In the end, I just didn't want to waste my time trying to figure out if new people in my life were hired by Jade or if I was just losing my mind. For a long time, because of this custody case, I didn't allow anyone to get too close to me.

I didn't tell anyone about the plea agreement because I didn't want it getting back to Jade and Chad. Plus, it wasn't final yet. The Court date for my plea agreement was set for August 28th. The Court date for my Petition for Termination of Visitation was set for September 21st. I was actually balancing all of this on top of running the office Ian and I now owned and operated. Ian was really acting different. At this time in my life I had no idea nor even considered that he would mess around with more than just his prescribed pain pills.

I knew something was really wrong with Ian, but I didn't take the time to notice what it was. I had so much going on I just kept convincing myself everything would be okay. Ian and I cleared a five number gross the first month our business was open. Granted, most of it had to go back into the business, but we were doing good. Jade's attorney requested that the Restraining Order court date be continued, which was granted and ended up being scheduled for September 14th. The Judge did grant the Restraining Order until further notice and it was official, Jade was not legally allowed near me or Bree.

On August 17th Chad and his attorney filed another Contempt Citation on me, which was scheduled for the same day as the Termination of Visitation I had filed. The Contempt was filled with all the same stuff; Chad was asking that I be placed in jail and pay all of his attorney fees. On the 18th I signed my official plea agreement and was required to report for house arrest in October. With all the stress of taking care of our office, making sure arrangements were made for Bree, preparing to serve the eight days in jail and get out before Jade and Chad could find out, plus getting ready to have an ankle bracelet on for a year, you could say I was beyond stretched emotionally.

On top of all of that, I had been in a constant battle with Ian. We were making good money and he started trying to take money out of our business accounts without me knowing. I kept all bookkeeping and was very aware of our finances. Everything to do with our office was mainly in my name. I had to keep accurate records because we were incorporated and had to file two separate tax returns. I wasn't about to take on an audit or do anything illegal at this point in my life, I was in enough trouble on my own. Ian, though, was going down a worse path than I even realized.

On August 28th I reported to the jail to serve my eight day sentence. I was released on my 28th birthday, September 5, 2006. I was in the clear. Jade and Chad had no idea I went to jail. I had made arrangements for Bree to be somewhere I knew she was safe and no one could or would hurt her. My husband was supposed to be focused on and taking care of our business while I was gone. When I got out, however, I found our bank accounts empty and our business going downhill fast.

My experience in jail was interesting, but it was nothing like the three days I spent in the other jail for Chad's paraphernalia (marijuana pipe). After booking and being processed, I was placed in general population. I was never afraid. Seriously, at this point, what the hell could anyone else do to me? I wasn't a tiny girl, either. I was still well built and covered in tattoos so I intimidated most women just by appearance. On the second day, the biggest woman in the jail and the one all the girls called "Momma," walked over and sat down next to me. She looked me up and down and asked me what I was in for. I explained I was there for a D.U.I. I told her I only had seven more days left and then I would be out. I started asking her questions about herself and her life. We talked for a few hours. We really got along well and she even gave me shampoo and some shower shoes because I didn't have any. Even though I could handle myself, she really looked out for me and I was grateful.

My cell mate, or Bunkie, was a lesbian whose girlfriend's cell was located right below ours. It was a strange and sad love with them both being locked up and all. My Bunkie would sing to her girlfriend every night through the vents in our cells. She really wasn't all that bad. I think the strangest thing I witnessed was how some of the girls were taking grease off of the door frame and using it as eyeliner. Desperate times call for desperate measures, I suppose. When I finally got out, I ended up putting a little money on the 'mommas' books (jail account) as soon as I could. It just felt like the right thing to do.

Once I was home, nothing was ever the same. It was September 12th, one week exactly since my release from jail, and Ian came stumbling up the front stairs to our home at 4 am. I stepped outside because Bree was sleeping and I didn't want to wake her. We had been fighting for days because of Ian's actions while I was gone. He was very strung out. I didn't realize until that moment my husband had a very serious drug addiction. I felt bad that I had just brushed off all the incidents that were actually signs of what was happening. I was so caught up in everything else, I didn't notice what my husband was doing to himself.

I had no idea what to do next. I knew I was not willing to lose my daughter over his drug habits. I approached him and he started crying. He told me he needed help. He then admitted that he had been doing a lot of cocaine and didn't think he could stop. I embraced him and proceeded to make a few phone calls. I found an inpatient treatment center nearby and they told me they had room for him. I was told to take him to the emergency room and he would be evaluated there.

By this time it was about 6 am. Ian agreed to check himself into the treatment center and get off the drugs. I carried Bree down to the car and we headed to the hospital. When we got there, Ian was processed and the people from the center were on their way to get him. It was then Ian started to back away from the plan. He started talking about getting help somewhere else and he didn't want to stay there.

I told him if he didn't stay I was going to file for a divorce. I didn't want Bree exposed to drugs, the poor baby was exposed to enough. I also couldn't risk Jade and Chad using this man's addiction against me, and I knew they would. I thank God that Bree was sleeping almost the entire time. In the end, Ian refused to stay and we got in the car to head home.

Ian started crying and told me he just didn't want to stay there. He said he would go somewhere else, but I told him I couldn't and wouldn't risk losing my daughter for him. Ian got so upset he slammed his fist into my windshield twice putting a huge crack in it. I instantly pulled over and got Bree out of the car because I didn't feel like we were safe. Ian just sat in the car crying, and I called the police.

This was the first time Bree had seen anything like that with me. She had never seen Ian get that upset, either. He was always loving and kind to her. I felt horrible and questioned whether I was even worthy to be Bree's mom because I couldn't get anything right. It felt like everything was just crashing around me. A police report was made and Ian calmed down. Once Ian was calm, I agreed to take all of us home.

I knew I had to start making a plan: Either Ian got the help he needed or I was going to have to kick him out. I had a child, and I took care of everything in our home, so I wasn't going anywhere and neither was Bree. Everything in the house was also in my name, including all utilities, cable, plus our internet. I promised myself when I moved into the house that I wasn't going to make Bree move again until she graduated, and I intended to keep that promise.

Two days after that incident Ian stayed out all night again doing drugs. When he finally came home, this time he found everything he owned in the front yard. I called the police when Ian showed up. They told him to collect his things and hit the road. I wasn't going to allow anyone, including my husband, to hurt my daughter or my custody case in any way. Lord knows I did enough stupid things on my own that were being used against me. The decision was extremely hard because I did love Ian, but it was for the best interest of my daughter. Bree didn't need a drugged-up stepfather in her life, and I wasn't allowing one.

Once we adjusted to having the house to ourselves, I realized that Jade's attorney was playing games with the Court but didn't understand why. He requested yet another continuance on the Restraining Order Petition. So our court date was now set for October 26th. Chad and I had our hearing on September 21st for the Termination of Visitation and Contempt Citation. I went in ready for whatever they could use against me. I was always prepared and thought Jade's death threat was going to end the fight. Again, we all met in the Judge's chambers with all the same people as the first time.

Chad's attorney announced they were not backing down in pursuing custody and requested a Custodial Evaluation. Chad and Jade were even more determined to take me down now that I had Jade arrested. The fact I had the restraining order in place against her made them both pretty angry. I presented all of my evidence to the Judge, including the letter Jade had written me.

On September 26th the Judge made his ruling and the Provisional Order was released. It stated we were ordered to go through a Custodial Evaluation and Bree was to start therapy right away. It also stated that everyone involved was to participate in the evaluation and therapy, none of which I had a problem with. As I kept reading, the third and last provision was as follows:

> *"Father shall have immediate and meaningful visitation and access with Bree in accordance with a schedule to be recommended by the guardian ad litem herein. The court notes that the parties have, this date, reached their own mutual agreement regarding visitation and access between father and daughter. **Any and all visitations between father and daughter shall occur in the absence of Jade, father's present wife.**"*

It was also ordered that Chad and I communicate only through email with the Guardian Ad Litem as a supervisor of the emails. I can't express my relief when I read the order. I thought everything was going to be okay for Bree from here on out. I was thinking, now that Jade wasn't allowed to be near Bree during visits, there was no way she could hurt Bree anymore. I couldn't believe it had taken so long for the courts to actually take action and I was happy with the order.

The same day the order come in, I was able to get Bree her first appointment with a therapist, Mrs. Deb Green. She was one of the best child psychologists in our area, and I knew Bree needed help with what she had been put through. Mrs. Green was 100% for Bree from day one. She ended up being so much help for Bree and offered some of the best advice to help me become a better mother. Right from the beginning, Jade started off lying to Mrs. Green. But Mrs. Green was different from the rest, she actually saw through the lies and knew how to talk to Bree and get the truth from her.

Mrs. Green also saw the evidence and knew we had to make changes with the transfers. There was a new program that had been recently designed called the Carousel Program. It was held at a local church and designed to provide a safe place for the children of divorced and fighting parents to transfer their children with supervision. If Chad was picking up Bree, I was required to be there with her 15 minutes early and we were put in the back room. When Chad would arrive, someone would come get Bree. After he would leave, I would then be allowed to leave. I was extremely happy with this program. There was no more verbal abuse during transfers. Chad couldn't be late anymore and I didn't even have to look at him. Bree was very comfortable with Mrs. Green and the new transfer program. We both grew a love for Mrs. Green throughout the many years Bree was with her. To this day, Mrs. Green checks on Bree and me here and there even though she is now retired.

In October I filed for divorce from Ian. It crushed me, and I wasn't sure how I would bounce back from it. What I knew for a fact was I wasn't willing to risk losing my daughter for a man that wasn't even willing to help himself. I didn't see him much during October and November, but he was talking to me here and there. I was in the process of closing our business and all the bank accounts. I was also placed on house arrest and had to wear a bracelet on my ankle for a year. I had so much on my plate at all times, but I kept my head up.

On October 20th Jade's charges for intimidation from July were dismissed. It was right then I realized why her attorney had requested two continuances for the Restraining Order court date. When I called to find out why, I was told they "Misplaced the original copy of the tape with the recording of the incident on it." I had gone and purchased a copy of the original from the prosecutor's office when I returned from Las Vegas. It was so bad you couldn't hear hardly anything on it. It was a little odd to me that she was able to get her charges dropped in her hometown and the tape was now gone. Seemed a little too convenient to me, but that's just my opinion.

When the death threat did happen and the officer asked for the tape, I was crying when I handed it over to him. I even begged the officer not to lose it. I explained to him that Jade was very wealthy and we were in her hometown. The officer assured me it would be taken care of, but apparently it wasn't. Of course, when we went to court for the Restraining order, Jade's attorney used the fact that her charges were dropped in the Intimidation case. On October 26th, representing myself again, my motion for the Restraining order was granted and extended for one complete year.

Even with all the craziness going on, I was trying to keep Bree out of it. I enrolled her in Girl Scouts and became a volunteer leader. I really enjoyed helping with all the kids, and Bree loved being a part of it. We were doing okay until the second visit Bree had with her dad; Jade was present the entire weekend. Jade was ordered by the Judge to stay away from Bree, not only in a Restraining order, but also by the Judge of our custody case. I wrote the Ad Litem and she acted like it was no big deal. I still have every single email. Mrs. Mayor said I needed to file for contempt because there was nothing she could do. So, on November 13th, I filed for contempt because Jade was around Bree when she was ordered not to.

I believe part of the problem was that our Ad Litem, Mrs. Mayor, had too many cases to focus on the specifics of ours. Emails between Chad and Jade, the Ad Litem and I were horrible and confusing. Mrs. Mayor was no help at all and, at times, made things worse for Bree by being involved. She even asked me on November 15th to write a letter to Mrs.

Green giving my permission for Jade to be involved with therapy. I didn't want to, but I did it to please the Ad Litem. She was appointed by the courts, and I didn't think I could really argue with her even though it made no sense to me.

Ian kept trying to convince me to at least celebrate Thanksgiving with him and see how it went. On November 21st Ian disappeared and was nowhere to be found. His mom called me looking for him, but I had no idea where he was. This was only two days before Thanksgiving, and I wasn't sure what he was doing. The very next day, the 22nd, I received a call from Ian. When I answered, I had no idea what to expect. Ian claimed he was stuck in Ohio with his van, he was out of gas and had no money. He told me he was robbed at gunpoint and needed me to bring him some gas money. Now, Ohio was only about an hour and a half away from my home, but I had been through enough. I wasn't about to just jump and run to Ian. He had destroyed everything we worked for.

I ended up calling the police, asking that they go to the motel Ian claimed to be at to check on him. Reading the police report still makes my stomach turn. In short, the police report states Ian admitted he goes to Ohio to buy crack cocaine and admitted he was an addict. I was done with all of it.

His son, Bud, eventually ended up graduating from a Christian school and is now pursuing becoming a missionary. He loves the Lord and it was a huge blessing to be a part of his life. We stay in touch with him when we get the chance. I am very blessed to say I was that boy's stepmother at one point.

The custodial evaluation was now set for March 9th and 16th of 2007. When Chad's attorney requested this evaluation he stated Chad was willing to pay for all expenses of the evaluation, which cost $7,500. It always amazed me how willing Chad and Jade were to spend money on attorneys and fighting to take Bree away, but threw a fit over a pair of shoes. Chad also only paid his 50 in support when he felt like it. Child support was never something I could count on to help me with Bree because it was always so unreliable.

A court date was set for a hearing on Contempt when Jade was involved in Bree's visits in February. The Ad Litem acted as if it was no big deal, I was just stirring issues up. On one of Bree's visits to her father, I finally had time alone to breath and just sit to think. I ended up on the floor crying and confused. On my knees, I prayed harder than I ever had and begged God to make a change in me. I begged him to take all the pain and nightmares away from me. To please just stop the violent thoughts and the hate that was built up inside of me. I cried and screamed asking God if I would ever get a break; would things ever just be okay for me? As hurt as I was and as empty as I felt, I continued to lean towards God begging him to bring me comfort; begging him to just help me. I questioned why everything was always a constant struggle. Did other people suffer and struggle like this? Was I doing right by Bree as her mother? I felt so lost, and I just couldn't pull it together.

I called Paul and he talked to me for hours. He prayed with me and continued to tell me that the Lord would lift me if I just have faith. It only took about two days after I spoke with Paul that he purchased and shipped a VHS series, a seminar called, "The Bondage Breaker", by Dr. Neil Anderson. Paul made me promise him that I would watch it.

I continued to work but, since our office was closed, I went back to the main office. This time I was the Director of Human Resources. Ian was off somewhere doing whatever it is he did. He wasn't my concern anymore. I wouldn't claim that I am a religious person just because I believe that Jesus Christ died for my sins or for believing that the Bible does have the answers most of us seek for this life. Let's be real about it, we aren't going to find any answers if we don't seek them. That doesn't mean sit and read the Bible front to back and you can expect all the answers to just come to you and make perfect sense. I don't have any special answers; but, for me, when I read my Bible, I do it to honor my Heavenly Father. I pray that he educates my spirit, even if my mind doesn't always make sense of what I'm reading. It takes faith to take steps forward when we are surrounded by nothing but darkness. I was really hoping that the seminar Paul sent was going to help me better understand how to handle the things I was going through and it really did.

The day the seminar arrived, once Bree was down for the night, I began watching it. I didn't know what to expect. I was so lost and hurt. The business was gone, my husband was gone, Bree wasn't emotionally safe and I was covered in shame, guilt and hate. Not to ever forget the fact I was also in full-blown menopause, an emotional mess and spiritually broken. Once Dr. Neil Anderson began speaking, I felt a sense of comfort. I can't even explain it now.

I wasn't sure how to let everything inside of me out or how to express what I was feeling. I felt like I was failing at everything in life. Bree had no clue of the war inside of me because she was only seven years old. Again, all I wanted was for her to enjoy every part of being a kid. I was angry because she was battling her own war with Jade and my hands were tied. All I wanted from the time Bree was born is for her to be safe and not under attack and I couldn't even make that happen. It wasn't long into the seminar video that I pressed pause and started crying.

I soon found myself with a notebook and paper sitting in front of my T.V. taking notes. I was connecting with and understanding everything that Dr. Anderson was saying. We are in a spiritual battle and demons can latch onto us. They can even be passed down from generations. They can drag us down, give us nightmares and convince us something is wrong with us. Many of us get depressed. We fight all kinds of things in this world, but our approach is usually always physical and of this world. When we live in the flesh and not the spirit, we tend to be deflected from the truth. We look at things physically and not spiritually. Dr. Neil Anderson was explaining how to go into battle spiritually. I couldn't believe how much the seminar made sense. Dr. Anderson went on to say, "You are not saved by how you behave, but by how you believe. Hard work doesn't set you free. The truth sets you free. God is bigger than your past." Once I had completed the entire seminar, which took several hours, I did everything wholeheartedly as Dr. Anderson said to do.

Dr. Neil Anderson had me get on my knees and ask God to forgive me for all the men I had sex with in my past; forgiveness for all my sins and my mistakes that I had made. The next step was one of the hardest things I have ever done. Dr. Anderson requested that I actually, wholeheartedly forgive Frank, Carl and Joe for what they had done to me. Once I decided to fully commit to forgiving all three of them, I proceeded to ask God to forgive them also. Each beat of my heart was filled with nothing but pure pain. I purely, and with all sincerity, asked God to forgive me and them. After that night, I have never again suffered from another nightmare about Frank or Carl. To this day I am not ashamed, not blaming or resentful toward either of them. The same goes for Joe, it never bothered me again. I haven't forgotten what they did; however, the hold that demon had on me is no longer there. I begged God to open my heart and help me to forgive Chad and Jade also. Once I was done, I felt a lot of weight lifted off of my heart.

By the time Christmas came, Bree and I did our usual decorations, including hanging up our upside down Christmas tree and our extravagant sugar cookies. We really had so much fun and even got into a huge flour fight while we were baking. The kitchen was a mess and so were we, but that memory is one that we have laughed and talked about for years and probably always will. We went all out every year with every color of frosting you can imagine, plus had all the fun glittery stuff to make the cookies shine. Bree and I decorated our entire house with snowmen decorations and Christmas lights. We even started baking a birthday cake each year to celebrate our Savior's birth.

It was also around Christmas that Paul ended up showing up to visit and surprise us. We used to tease him so much because, when he would be asleep on the couch, we could both hear him snoring upstairs. I swear he made the floors shake. Paul's visit was short, but comforting. We talked about everything that had been happening and he was amazed I was still standing strong. Paul told me I was one of the strongest women he knew and that just gave me a bit more strength.

After Christmas was over, I sat back wondering what was going to happen in the New Year. No matter what happened, I swore to myself I would keep my head held high.

"Once a man was asked, "what did you gain by regularly praying to God?" The man replied, 'nothing…. but let me tell you what I lost: Anger, ego, greed, depression, insecurity, and fear of death.' Sometimes, the answer to our prayers is not gaining but losing; which ultimately is the gain."
- UNKNOWN

Chapter EIGHTEEN

2007: On January 4th I filed a **Motion for a Final Hearing** for my second divorce. The 60-day wait from the first filing was over and the divorce could proceed. I also filed for a Restraining Order against Ian. I wasn't worried he would hurt me or Bree physically, but I knew it was safer to have physical proof of everything and anything that was going on in my life. I learned quickly from Jade and Chad that I needed evidence of everything in order to protect myself from their constant attacks.

Soon after, my divorce was granted and a date was set for the Restraining Order against Ian. I was hustling at work and ended up becoming a traveling DPS, which meant I went to different offices in Indiana and took over their Human Resource Department in order to help improve their office. I was in charge of interviews, hiring, training and several other things. I worked for the main office, but was sent to several locations to help. I honestly enjoyed my job, but I continued to keep people at a distance as far as friendship went. I went from a woman who loved meeting new people and making friends to isolating myself from others unless it had to do with work.

On January 17th Jade's attorney withdrew from the Restraining Order case, which was approved on the 22nd of January. On the 25th of the same month, the Restraining Order against Ian was found substantial and granted for two years of protection for Bree and me both. I felt heartbroken about my divorce because I loved Ian so very much, but I knew I was doing what was right. Again, I had to make sure I was taking care of everything legally and had evidence of such if it was ever needed.

I may not have been able to prove that Jade was crazy, but I could prove I wasn't everything her and Chad continued to claim. I was doing very well at Kirby and making enough money that bills were paid; but, our extra activities were over. I was determined not to lose our beautiful home no matter what I had to do. I wanted, more than anything, for Bree to continue to feel secure and to never worry we would have to move again. She never knew how hard things were for me because that was my weight to carry. I very firmly believe as parents we need to allow our children to be kids and not worry about adult issues that we should be taking care of.

In February, Chad's attorney started pursuing a deposition from me. That's where I am required to go into Chad's attorney's office, he could ask me anything he wanted and it was all on record. His attorney filed a Notice to Appear and a Subpoena against me. Transfers were still going smooth with the Carousel Program in place; however, Chad and Jade began emailing Mrs. Mayor complaining about driving the half hour to the program for the transfers. I did end up losing my license from the 2005 charge and everyone in the case was made aware of that fact. I believe wholeheartedly that is exactly why they were complaining about the program. Jade and Chad wanted to have me forced in a corner and be told I had to figure out how to get Bree to them. I couldn't fathom it being because of them running out of gas money for their Hummer or their Cadillac, just saying.

At one point Jade even said her mom, who was a Sunday school teacher, was going to start the same Carousel program at her church. In Jade and Chad's emails to the Ad Litem, they tried to convince her I should be required to drive to their town for transfers. Somehow, and I seriously have no idea how, they almost had her convinced. Once I spoke with Mrs. Green and explained what was going on, she stepped up quickly. Mrs. Green put a stop to all of that real fast.

I wanted the Ad Litem removed from our case so bad as she was not in it for the best interests of Bree and really didn't seem to care about our case at all. Truth be told, I think Mrs. Mayor was just tired of all the stupid fighting that continued to go on. I know I was beyond over it myself. I'll admit, I did wonder sometimes if she was being paid by Jade toward the end of her time on the case. Some of the things Mrs. Mayor said and did just didn't seem right and didn't seem to be in Bree's best interest. Jade and Chad were always trying hard to prove I couldn't provide sufficiently for Bree and had no intention of making anything easy for me. First of all, Mrs. Green was not happy about this and knew transfers could not be outside of the Carousel Program for Bree's sake. Second, Jade's mother supervising our transfers was in no way good for Bree's or my sake in any way, shape or form. Mrs. Green's very strong, direct recommendations in the matter are what stopped Mrs. Mayor from considering the idea.

The moment that Mrs. Green started seeing Bree, Bree knew she wasn't alone in this fight. Chad and Jade continued to sit Bree down and question her. It was two adults on one child and the odds were far from fair. Bree would tell them what she felt they wanted to hear just to get them to back off of her. Mrs. Green was working hard with Bree on how to not be afraid to speak the truth to her father. Even with the positive progress Mrs. Green was making with Bree, Bree was still very intimidated by Chad.

When Jade and Chad did do things with Bree, it didn't seem to be for her to have fun, but came across like Jade was trying to get to me and using the time Bree did have with her dad to do it. They would print off all the pictures of their trips to the dinner and show, museum or the park and then send them home with Bree, including an 8x10 picture of their whole family. There they were - Jade, Chad, her two kids and Bree. I would listen to Bree talk about their trips and how much she enjoyed it. Those visits made me so happy for Bree; however, I would simply return the pictures the next time Bree would go for a visit. I just explained to Bree they were really good pictures, but it seemed like they should be hung up in her room at her daddy's house. I knew it was just another way Jade was trying to stir things up. Pictures of Bree and her dad were always hanging up in Bree's bedroom at our home. Hanging pictures of Jade in my house; however, was happening as fast as pictures of me were going up on Jade's walls in her house. It was constant stupid things like that I found petty and ridiculous. Unfortunately, I should have just put the pictures up in a closet for when Bree got older. In the end, it just fueled the fire when I would send them back because it then turned into me not allowing Bree to have pictures of her dad and how wrong I was for that, according to Jade.

On February 25th I went to pick Bree up at the Carousel program. When I walked in, the ladies that volunteered let me know they had taken a requested statement down from Chad. Any notes or statements that were documented at Carousel were not private and I was allowed to obtain copies of all of them. On this particular statement, Chad had one of the ladies write:

> *"Talked to Bree Fri - withdrawn, wouldn't eat Stepdad & Zara doing drugs in front of her Mom tells her dad's trying to take her away and they wouldn't be able to see each other. He talked with Bree to reassure her - she told him she had told Mrs. Green about it and he was not informed. He will be talking with his lawyer on Monday."*

I couldn't believe this. It was just never going to end with those two. Ian hadn't even lived with us since September of 2006, and I wasn't even talking to him at this time. There was even a Restraining Order in place, which I am so glad I had when this happened, plus it was embarrassing. The women at the Carousel Program were only volunteers and they couldn't do anything except write the statement down at Chad's request.

When we left, Bree sat in the backseat very quiet all the way home. I didn't say anything about what the statement said because I knew it wasn't true and it wasn't important. I always gave Bree time to talk to me about her weekends on her own terms and when she was ready or wanted to. Even Mrs. Green reassured me I was doing as I should when it came to that. When we pulled up to our house, my friend that drove for me got out and went across the street to her house. Bree and I sat in the car for a minute and I said, "We're home baby girl." When I turned around to look at Bree, she instantly started crying. When I asked her what was wrong, she said her dad and Jade had sat her down during the weekend and told her she needed to say I was doing drugs in front of her. I got out quickly and rushed to the back seat. I just held her. We both ended up crying and all I could do was tell her how sorry I was. I assured her that everything was going to be okay and to remember the truth is what sets us free. I ended up carrying her seven year old butt in the house that day. That baby girl suffered so much at the hands of people hiding behind their lies. God knows the truth of what happened in that house and so does Bree.

I was so tired of what Bree was being put through and, even though Mrs. Green was great for Bree, I felt like she should have been pulling Bree out of that situation and stopping all visits with Chad and Jade. The delay was Mrs. Green had to make sure that Bree was really being emotionally abused by Jade and it was not just us adults continuing to argue and making things up. I can't even begin to describe my anger and frustration at the entire situation. Why did they want to spend so much time trying to destroy me at the expense of a beautiful young child? None of it made sense to me. All I could do was love and support my daughter. I just continued to keep things as normal as possible for Bree.

The 25th was a Sunday. The next day I scheduled an emergency appointment for Bree with Mrs. Green. When I went into Bree's school to pick her up for the appointment, the secretary said she was glad I came in. She explained Bree was in a room down the hall with Mr. Miller and he was with CPS (Child Protective Services). I just smiled at her and said, "It's okay, Bree's dad is just trying to cause more trouble." The secretary grinned and rolled her eyes. By this time the school had dealt with Chad and Jade a couple of times and their behavior was not forgotten or appreciated.

I waited in the office and it didn't take long before Mr. Miller came in and introduced himself. He asked me to follow him to a room down the hall, and I was more than happy to. We sat down and, right off the bat, he said, "Listen, after talking to Bree, I know this is a false report, but I have to investigate it according to the law." With that said, I just smiled and explained the craziness of the past three years. As Mr. Miller wrote a few things down, he asked me about Ian smoking marijuana in front of Bree. I laughed and explained Ian and I separated last September and were officially divorced in January. Mr. Miller rolled his eyes and just shook his head when I also mentioned the Restraining Order that was in place. He told me that I needed to take a drug screening within the next 24 hours, but he didn't see this going anywhere. I did as required and, of course, passed the drug test just fine. I asked Mr. Miller if he would come to the house just so he could put it in the report, but he told me it wasn't necessary. I strongly insisted, and he finally agreed to come by when he got the chance.

I ended up calling and talking with the Ad Litem and Mrs. Green about the fact Chad and Jade were continuing to harass me and now trying to pressure Bree into telling lies. It was just out of control. To this day it bothers me I was continually viewed as overreacting. I even ended up writing a letter that explained if anything ever happened to me the police needed to take a serious look at Chad and Jade. I sent it to two people I trusted just in case. Again, I was never sure what Jade and Chad were going to pull next.

On March 5th I wrote a letter to Chad's attorney and explained I was not attending a Deposition without an attorney and, once I hired one, I would have him contact the Courts. Paul and I were talking almost every day on the phone. Things were getting so hard on me emotionally. I was fighting to stay positive and keep things consistent for Bree, but after bedtime prayers and Bree was asleep my mind wouldn't shut down no matter what I did.

I was still constantly consumed by violent thoughts of hurting Jade. I wanted more than anything for her to suffer and feel the same way she was making me feel. I knew it wasn't right, but no matter what I did I just couldn't stop the visuals and thoughts from continuing in my mind. Paul would pray with me and really tried to support me. He agreed with me when I said the case was getting to be more than I could handle. Paul said I needed to find another attorney and he would pay for it. He said

I didn't need to represent myself in such a tough case and he was there for me always.

When Paul offered to help me with an attorney, I didn't hesitate. It didn't take long for my search to begin. I was determined to find someone that believed me when I explained what was happening and was willing to fight for my daughter. I had already done all of the footwork for the case. All of my Court papers from the case were and are in order and kept organized, even to this day. I met with two attorneys and the second one won me over. He had an attitude and convinced me he was willing to do what it took.

I just handed him the case and asked if he thought he could do what Bree and I needed done. After a few days of reviewing the paperwork, the attorney said he was willing to represent me. On March 9th Paul came up from Georgia where he was living to make sure Bree and I made it safely to the custodial evaluation. Dakota was also staying with us at this time, so he also came to help me with Bree while we were at the evaluation.

Everyone was there; Jade, Chad, Jade's kids and even Stacy and Tracy. I hadn't spoken to either of them in a long time. It was the most emotionally draining two days of my life. It felt like they made us go through every psychological test there is. It was crazy because, on some of it, I wasn't sure how to answer the questions. An example would be when I had to answer if I felt like somebody was watching me. Well at that time there were several people keeping eyes on me for Jade and Chad, but if I answered yes that would mean my results would come back with me being schizophrenic or paranoid or something.

I will and do fully admit that I lied to the psychologist about two things. I did it out of complete fear of the entire process and my custody case. My attorney explained the results of the evaluation were going to have a huge effect on the final decision of the court so I didn't tell the truth about the sexual abuse when I was younger and I denied ever using cocaine. To be honest, I knew the opinion and outcome of this evaluation was going to determine my daughter's future. I didn't lie or hold anything else back except those two facts.

Soon after the custodial evaluation, Mrs. Mayor emailed me and was requiring that I now allow Wednesday visits to Chad. It was according to the Parenting Time Guidelines, but we never exercised it because Chad lived in Tennessee. Now he wanted his Wednesday time with Bree. To me, I thought it was something that Chad's attorney suggested because it showed Chad was trying to get all the time he could. I still believe that is why he did it. I really felt like Mrs. Mayor had no clue what the hell she was doing. How was I going to tell Bree that after everything she now had to spend more time there? My heart was so hurt, but I was trying to do what the Court required.

While all of this was going on, I was able to get myself through GED classes and obtained my GED Certificate. My next goal was to get into college so that I could provide better for Bree and me. It didn't matter how many times Chad and Jade tried to knock me down because each time made me strive to do better for myself and for Bree. Chad and Jade wrote a long letter to the Ad Litem on March 31st about how excited Chad was about Wednesday visits starting. It also went on to talk about how he just wanted a healthy relationship with Bree. Of course, there were a few criticizing remarks about me, but I didn't care. At this time we were all still waiting for the evaluation results, which seemed to take forever.

Dakota stayed with us for a while, and I have to say he really helped me emotionally. Just by having him around I didn't feel like I was so alone. One day out of the blue Ian called me and told me Jade had gotten a hold of him. He said that Jade offered to pay him to testify on their behalf and say I that was doing drugs all of the time. Ian and I both knew I had proof he was the one who did drugs and I didn't, but I still thanked Ian after he told me that his response was, "No way." Ian and I weren't enemies and when he turned Jade down I was thankful.

It was around this time a neighbor came to me and told me she had gone to school with Jade. My neighbor was a friend of mine and confessed to me that Jade had gotten ahold of her also and offered $5,000 for her to take a picture of me drinking beer with Bree near me. I couldn't believe they were so desperate they were turning to hiring others to commit perjury with them. I really laughed at that. It was all so ridiculous and embarrassing to be a part of.

Paul stood by his word, as he always did, and hired the attorney I wanted and had agreed to take the case. Although my attorney was talking to me and giving me advice, he wasn't doing anything legally until his retainer was paid in full. When Paul was finally able to take care of the fees, my attorney was ready to be let loose and get to work. The first thing he filed was his Appearance, followed with another Contempt Citation based on the fact that Jade had been involved with visits despite the order given by the Judge in 2006. Both of those Petitions were filed on May 2nd. On May 17th the Ad Litem emailed me. The email went as follows:

Mrs. Mayor, 5-17-07; *"Zara, when did Mrs. Green recommend that Jade could be in the visits with Bree?"*

Me, 5-17-07; *"Mrs. Green never said a word about it to me, Jade has been involved in the visits since the second time Bree went; after the Judge ordered she was not to be involved with Bree's visits."*

Mrs. Mayor, 5-18-07; *"Then the Court order has been violated and you have not told anyone, it just started happening?"*

I just decided to give it a couple days before responding because I had to calm down. This woman has to be kidding me, right? I have, to this day, copies of all our emails and everything that occurred throughout this custody battle. I responded with;

Me, 5-20-07; *"Mrs. Mayor, I filed a contempt on my own and called you in November; the second visit Bree went, Jade was there the whole weekend. I just wrote down the wrong date for the trial date, I filed the contempt in November and the Court date was set for February, I didn't make it because I had the date mixed up. I did call you though, you told me the only thing to do was file the contempt, that is what I did. It has simply continued and nothing has been done. You don't recall me talking to you about this???"*

Mrs. Mayor, 5-21-07; *"Zara, I talked to Mrs. Green upon your suggestion after she met Jade and the child, she set up the holiday schedule. This is an issue as always between you and Jade not your child and her. It would be crazy to go backwards now........."*

Words cannot describe how angry and tired I was of defending the fact that the events my daughter was being put through were real and not just adults bickering back and forth. I was emotionally worn out and waiting for the results from the evaluation was like torture. I knew that it was going to make a huge impact on the Judge's final decision and I couldn't wait. My nerves were all over the place during this time and sleep was continually eluding for me.

The Court had already ordered the only people allowed to read and review the results of the evaluation were both attorneys, the Judge and the Ad Litem. It was my understanding the reason behind that is so the psychologist could conduct the evaluation with no concern of repercussions from either party. I will never forget the day my attorney called me and said that the evaluation was in.

The results pretty much revealed we were all messed up in our own way and none of us were perfect. Even though I wasn't allowed to read the results, my attorney told me that, in the end, it stated it was the psychologist's recommendation that Bree stay in my custody. This meant that all this stupid fighting was over with, right? I was hopeful that, now this was out of the way, perhaps someone would start taking notice of the real issues and everyone would stop giving so much attention to all the lies and distractions that Chad and Jade kept using. I was also hopeful that the harassment would stop.

Court was still a ways off and life had to go on. Bree wanted to be on the soccer team through our local YMCA. I was all about her getting into anything extracurricular to keep her mind busy so I went to sign her up. Bree and I were members of the YMCA already and we knew a few people that worked there. I asked about volunteering to be a coach to help out. I was always volunteering for Bree's school and I loved being involved with Girl Scouts when Bree was in it.

I did explain I was on house arrest and why because I didn't want to sign up and not be able to help because of that. The woman at the YMCA told me she didn't see it being a problem, I just had to pass the background check and a D.U.I. shouldn't affect the decision as long as none of the other parents complained. I thought that wouldn't be a problem at all because very few people even knew I was on house arrest. It wasn't something I was proud of or told people.

Everything was set up, background check went through and I was given the volunteer package for coaching, including all the children's names and numbers that were on my team. Dakota and I were looking up all kinds of things about soccer because the truth is I don't know much about soccer at all. I had already spoken with a few of the parents about our first practice and Bree was so excited I was going to be her coach.

I did have to let Jade and Chad know Bree was going to be starting because they were responsible to get her to her games if she was with them during those times. Then after one of Bree's visits to their house, I received a call that made Bree and I both cry. 'Someone' had called the YMCA and complained I was on house arrest and shouldn't be coaching any children. I was then asked to pass the position of coaching on and I did so with no problem. I was so embarrassed and ashamed. After all, it was ultimately my mistake that placed me in that position. I knew Jade and Chad had made the call, it just sucked because Bree, again, was the one it hurt. She didn't even want to play soccer after that and I didn't make her.

Believe it or not, Ezra still lingered in my heart and my mind quite often. I wondered how he was and if he ever thought about me. What was he doing? Did he have any kids yet? I daydreamed about getting on a Harley Davidson and just riding until I could find him. I fantasized about winning Ezra back and growing old with him. One day I was on Myspace messing around and decided to see if I could find Ezra on there. I can't even begin to explain the feeling the moment I saw his picture. I couldn't believe that I had actually found him.

I began writing Ezra a letter every single day on Myspace. I told him how sorry I was and begged him to please just forgive me for what I had done. I was honest about what happened back then and I was a train wreck after it was all said and done. I even confessed that he was the man of my dreams, literally. He haunted me. Confessions from me continued for many days. I apologized for how wrong I was to be so negative when he was deployed and of how lost I truly felt once he was gone.

I begged him to forgive me and told him I was going to continue to write, at least until he responded. I left my phone number for him and told him he could call me anytime. Hell, I even confessed how I was still looking for him in every man I met. I missed Ezra and what we had shared. I told him about Bree and how awesome she was. I bragged about being her mother and the letters just went on and on.

On July 4th I was sitting on my porch visiting with one of my dearest friends when my phone rang. It was a call from California. Now I knew people from all over, but no one from California. I answered it out of pure curiosity because I usually never answered calls from numbers I didn't recognize. I about fainted when I realized it was Ezra. He told me he couldn't keep reading my letters and not call me. We talked for hours, catching up and sharing where life had taken us. This was when he told me what happened with his mother's house being robbed by the house sitter they had hired. I was so happy to hear his voice, it had been so long. That night Ezra told me he forgave me.

What a release that was. I no longer felt like I had to find Ezra in every man, and I felt free from all the guilt I had about what happened. I was freed by Ezra's forgiveness. We did talk back and forth for a couple months, even about him coming to visit or me going there. I wanted to see where things could go for us now our past was just that, in the past. We emailed, sent texts and talked on the phone often but, one day, Ezra just stopped responding. I assume he got a girlfriend, but the truth is I haven't spoken with him since. I was just thankful to him for forgiving me and giving me the freedom I never thought I would have. It's amazing how the simple words "I forgive you" can take away so much pain when the words are truly sincere.

In September my attorney requested answers from the prosecutor's office in Jade's hometown with regard to the missing tape from the death threat in July 2006. The prosecutor's office actually tried to claim I had the original. I couldn't believe what they were saying. I was convinced Jade had them on her payroll. This case made me think of the craziest things because I just didn't put anything past Jade or Chad because they were getting away with everything for so long. My attorney was also struggling to get Chad's financial declaration completed. I had completed mine as soon as I obtained my attorney.

It took threatening contempt and months of half-filled out declarations to actually get the completed declaration form from Chad. This was a financial declaration, which showed all of Chad and Jade's finances. It showed a six figure income, college funds set up for Jade's children, owning two homes, a Cadillac, a Hummer and a custom built chopper. It was no wonder Chad stayed with Jade. It was crazy but, even though Chad was living large, he was still behind on his child support.

This was the year that Bree threw a fit about her Halloween visit. She did not want to go to her dad's. They were really big on decorating with all the normal scary stuff, and I never really celebrated Halloween much. I didn't know it, but the last time Bree had spent Halloween with Chad I guess someone scared her really bad and she didn't want to go to their house at all. I talked to Mrs. Green. I even tried to get Chad to consider exchanging our visits, but that wasn't happening. Mrs. Green even tried to talk to Bree about being honest with her dad and telling him how she felt, but Bree refused.

Bree was genuinely afraid to tell Chad how she felt because she was always accused of lying about everything. It was so sad that Bree didn't even feel comfortable talking with her own father, especially about how she felt. It broke my heart that my child was exposed to so much hatred at such a young age. Bree was so upset and she begged me not to make her go, but again, my hands were tied and there was nothing I could do.

Bree did have to go for the visit, but it was one of her good visits and she ended up having a good time. I truly believe Jade convinced and manipulated Chad into honestly believing I was the one hurting our daughter. That man really has no idea what he allowed to happen to his own daughter. Someday he will realize the money he chose will never buy the time he has missed nor fix the damage he not only allowed but also caused to our daughter. That will be what he has to answer for some day, not me. I do pray that Bree forgives him some day. In October I was also taken off of house arrest and placed on my year of probation.

On another visit to Jade and Chad's, Bree ended up calling me on a phone Paul had bought her. Paul got it for Bree so Jade couldn't stop us from talking to one another when Bree was there. Once she had that phone, we talked all the time when she was there. There was only a few times they took it away from her when they caught her talking to me. So they wouldn't take her phone from her, there was a point when Bree was actually sneaking her phone with her so she could call me. She even snuck a shirt home one time and didn't understand when I explained she had to take it back because it wasn't right. She just kept saying, "But mom, it's my shirt." I made her take it back and told her she could wear it when she was there. I told her we weren't thieves and it was like stealing because she didn't have permission from her dad to take it out of their house.

On this particular day, when Bree called me we talked for over four hours. She explained her dad had been on a bike run the night before and didn't get home until, "The morning time." That same morning, Jade loaded up her children and a couple of their friends and told Bree she had to stay there. Bree said they were going to King's Island, but she wasn't allowed to go. She was so upset. Of course, Chad was sleeping almost

296

the entire day. I got so frustrated because I had to talk her into going in their kitchen just to get something to eat for herself. She kept telling me she was hungry, but she didn't want to wake her dad because she was afraid he would get mad at her.

These are the types of things that happened, and I really thought Mrs. Green would do more than just talk to Jade and Chad about it. Mrs. Green was really trying to make things work for Bree and Chad rather than stopping visits, but Bree was always the one hurting from the stupid things they continued to do. With the results of custodial evaluation, the pre-trial for the custody case was set for January 3, 2008 and the trial was set for February 8, 2008.

With Bree no longer in Girl Scouts or soccer, I still wanted her to be involved in some kind of extracurricular activity. Mrs. Green and I both agreed it would be good for Bree to be involved with a team. After talking to Bree about it, she ended up picking the YMCA basketball team to join. I'll be point blank about it, she did not enjoy it once she got involved, but I made her follow through and finish out the season. I explained to her that she was part of a team and she already committed so she couldn't quit on her teammates.

Chad would bring Bree for her games, as he was required. At one game, Chad and his mom, Tracy, came. We stayed on opposite sides of the basketball court and didn't even speak a word to one another, which was what we normally did. I had agreed to the arrangements that Chad's mother could drop Bree off at my house rather than meeting at the Carousel program and, when she did, we reconnected. Tracy and I started talking and we decided to stay in one another's lives for Bree's sake. I explained to her I didn't talk to her for so long because of everything that Jade and Chad had been doing. I didn't know who I could trust and who I couldn't; but, truth is, I had missed Tracy. I never wanted her to stay out of Bree's life and hated that I had pushed her away so much.

Near Thanksgiving, here was Stacy and Tracy sitting in my living room celebrating the holiday with Bree and me. What I was told was, the day Tracy went to the basketball game with Chad, Jade went ballistic. I guess she accused Tracy of trying to get Chad and I back together. A part of me laughed because I knew that Jade was crazy. Tracy and Stacy were then given the ultimatum to choose Chad and Jade or Bree and I. They were told if they spoke to me they weren't welcome to speak with Jade and Chad anymore.

It's my understanding that Tracy told them she was a grown woman and I was the mother of her grandchild. She told them I had been a part of the family for years and she wouldn't stop talking to me. It was from this point on that Chad's sister and mother began celebrating all holidays with Bree and me. We spent Christmas, birthdays, all of it, and continued to spend them together for several years.

During all of this time, Paul was such a blessing and was always trying to lift me up. He encouraged me to be strong and hold onto my faith. I told Paul I didn't know what more I could do. I eventually had to quit my job because transportation out of town was becoming too difficult, and I was stressing because I didn't know what I was going to do. Paul proceeded to ask about the cost of all my bills and started doing some budgeting. He ended up taking care of Bree and me and paid all of our bills for me. He told me the only thing I needed to worry about was being Bree's mother. There were so many times I would have never made it without Paul. He truly had a heart of gold <u>always</u>. Paul came up at least once a month to visit, and I was so thankful to have him in our life.

On one occasion, while Bree was at Jade and Chad's, Paul ended up taking me to Alabama. He took me right back to the mountain we had stayed on so many years earlier. Paul asked me if I remembered the time I locked the keys in our trailer and how he treated me. I told him I remembered and it wasn't something to easily forget. Paul started crying and apologizing deeply to me. He told me all he wanted was to just be my husband. I still don't know why I never said yes to him. He truly did love me and he loved Bree so much, too. I told Paul I forgave him and, as our time visiting in Alabama went on, I ended up telling Paul about talking to Ezra during the summer. I explained we weren't talking anymore, but

I felt free from Ezra forgiving me for the past. Paul got really upset and claimed I would always love Ezra and never love him.

Even though I was beyond thankful for Paul being in my life, for some reason I just couldn't bring myself to commit to him. Paul helped me when no one else would. I didn't have the pressure of bills or worrying about losing our home and he took so much stress off of me. Paul wasn't a rich man by far. He was living in Georgia and owned and operated a small handyman business. Paul was always a workaholic, but he was dedicated to Bree and me. Although Paul's role in our lives wasn't what he wanted, he loved Bree and I unconditionally. I don't think he ever realized how much I truly did love him even though I wouldn't marry him.

On December 19th Chad's attorney wrote my attorney and stated Chad was willing to withdraw all his petitions for custody and all of his contempt citations. On this same day, Mrs. Green wrote to the Judge and stated that Bree should continue to see her, but Chad and I were not required to attend unless needed. Mrs. Green also wrote, "I endorse and recommend that the custody of Bree not change." She strongly encouraged that we also continue all transfers at the Carousel Program.

I was relieved about dropping the Petitions and the promise that Chad wasn't pursuing custody anymore. I already knew their attorney had no argument in court because of the results of the custodial evaluation; however, Bree was still enduring all the drama and ridiculousness of Jade emotionally badgering her and yet, the visits were still ordered. I was angry that Mrs. Green wasn't recommending that the visits stop, but she felt things would get better for Bree now all the fighting about custody seemed to be over. I think Mrs. Green was convinced that Jade would stop hurting Bree once the case was closed. I didn't agree with Mrs. Green, but she was the therapist and I believed in her program.

Christmas was right around the corner and Bree was excited. Although I wasn't working, Paul provided me the opportunity to take Bree and one of her friend's to see Hannah Montana in concert. He bought the tickets and a friend of mine was willing to provide the ride for us. Now Bree may not want the world to know this, but she was the biggest Hannah Montana fan ever. I actually had started Christmas shopping earlier in the year and learned a very good lesson Christmas morning. Throughout the entire year, I had been purchasing gifts and hiding them in my closet. I really didn't realize how much I had hidden until Christmas Eve. I am talking about several of the Hannah dolls, the bus, the stage, the curtains and bedding. I even found a light switch cover with Hannah on it. If it had Hannah on it, you can bet it was wrapped and under our tree. On Christmas morning, the pile of presents was ridiculous. As excited as Bree was, it didn't take long until she actually got sick of opening gifts. That Christmas I learned it means more to have some gifts rather than a million gifts. We did have a wonderful holiday, and I had some good laughs because Bree ended up asking me to help her open her gifts. I felt silly for getting so many gifts, but playing with them and her most of the day was worth it. Bree and I didn't have a flour fight while baking our cookies this year, but we had a blast doing all of our normal traditions together. The New Year was approaching and I was ready for 2007 to be over.

Chapter NINETEEN

2008: Although Bree found a church she loved and attended regularly, I, myself, hadn't been attending church. I did do my own Bible studies at home. I had recently completed a Bible study in 1 Kings 3:16-28. It is about two women who were fighting over a child. The two women fought so much that they both took their problem to the king. Both of the women claimed the baby as their baby and neither would budge. When the king ordered the baby cut in half so both women could then have a part of the baby, the real mother spoke up. The woman spoke up and said the other woman could have the child. The woman was willing to freely give her child up rather than seeing the child perish. The king in the story knew then that the woman giving the child up freely was the real mother. In the end, he gave the child to her alive and well. I realized after reading the story how much I needed to surrender my daughter to God and allow him to work out the situation she was going through with Jade. It wasn't easy, and things were still hard for Bree, but with the agreement in the works it did seem to cool down for a while when Bree went for her visits. I prayed that God would change the situation and keep Bree safe. I didn't want to fight with Jade or Chad anymore, I just wanted Bree to be able to spend time with her father and not be put under so much pressure or be used to hurt me when she was there. Bree deserved to be happy and just enjoy being a kid. Truth is, there is not one child that deserves to be used against another parent at any point and no matter the situation.

I was finally found a good balance with exercise and keeping myself busy with projects around the house. The violent visuals of hurting Jade were not overtaking me as they had been and it seemed as if I was gaining more control over those thoughts. One night when I was talking to Paul,

301

I ended up telling him I would be willing to try and work things out with him as a couple. I even ended up writing a note to his oldest daughter who was mad at me and felt like I was just stringing Paul along. That was never my intention, and I prayed she realized that I truly loved her father.

Even though Paul and I committed to try and work out our relationship, he refused to come live in Indiana, especially in my home. He felt like the house could never be ours because I was very blunt about it being mine. I didn't want anyone to have the power to take the one thing I knew was keeping Bree and me secure and safe, and that was our home. I wasn't allowing anyone to take that away from us. Even though I knew Paul would never try to take our home, a part of me didn't want to take any chances.

In February Chad and I went to court and signed a visitation schedule, transfer and custody agreement. The only thing I wanted to ask for was my attorney's fees back. Paul spent well over $5,000.00 and I wanted to give it back to him. My attorney told me I didn't have a good chance of winning my fees back and it would be better just to settle. I still didn't feel right about it, but I was also ready for some peace; not only for Bree, but for me. That day Chad and I signed the agreement and the custody case was settled.

Things seemed to be easier for Bree now there was an agreement in place. Jade seemed to be backing off Bree, which made me happy. Of course, there were still little things that would happen. Like the time Bree asked if she could have a Facebook account and I told her no. I just didn't feel an eight year old should have a profile on any social media site, and I still feel that way. Soon after, Bree had a weekend visit with Jade and Chad. When she came home and told me they allowed her to have a Facebook account I was disappointed, and Bree knew it. When I asked her what the password was because I intended to delete the account, Bree explained to me Chad and Jade told her she wasn't allowed to have the password. They told her she was allowed to have a Facebook account, but her password would be changed whenever she came home. The rule was she was only allowed on it at their house. That was unacceptable for me, and I was upset, but there was nothing I could do. I wasn't okay with her having a profile to begin with, but now she had one that I couldn't even monitor or delete. I didn't trust Jade or Chad to monitor what she was doing or who was talking to her. I told Bree that even when she was at their house she was not allowed on it and when she was a few years older she could have her own account. Bree never got on that Facebook account again.

With my GED in hand and the custody case settled, I decided it was time to go to a local college and enroll for fall semester. I was so excited I was doing something to better myself. I spent so much time staying focused on the ridiculous custody war and my daughter's well-being that I needed to do this for me. The plan was to go for nursing but, once I was sitting in front of my adviser, I realized that psychology was what I wanted to study. I thought about how much I could learn and how I would be better equipped to help Bree with everything she had already faced. The plan was, once I graduated, I would be able to help other children that were going through similar abuse as Bree had been exposed to. Once I passed all of the pre-tests, I was enrolled as a psychology major and scheduled for fall semester.

Throughout the year Tracy and Stacy were still around a lot and I let Bree visit with them as much as possible. Stacy was pregnant and, when she was in the hospital, we went to see her. Stacy ended up giving birth to a beautiful baby boy. Bree enjoyed her time with her grandma, her aunt and now she was able to enjoy her cousin. Tracy and Stacy lived together and Stacy's husband was serving our country overseas during this time. Stacy and her husband were such a great couple and are still together to this day. In my opinion, it seemed like her husband and baby made Stacy a bit nicer and not so cold.

With basketball season over and my fall semester at college coming up, I thought it would be good to get Bree into something new. After Bree and I talked about it, I decided to enroll her in cheerleading. She completely loved it from day one. The dancing part of cheerleading was her favorite and she was good at it. I attended all of her practices and the girls all had a blast together. The only problem we ended up having was getting Chad to bring Bree to her games when she was with him.

For some reason, Chad and Jade always acted like I put Bree into extracurricular activities to go against them or cause them hardship in some way, but it had nothing to do with them. It seemed like anything I did they tried to somehow twist it into me trying to go against them somehow. That was never the case though. I just wanted Bree to have a normal, healthy childhood. I didn't understand why it was so hard to drive half an hour for Bree to be involved in the things she enjoyed. One time Chad even had Bree write a letter claiming she didn't want to go to her game; but, when she got home, she told me her dad just didn't want to go and had her write the letter. It was sad because, at one point, Jade and Chad even said they were going to put Bree in gymnastics. She was so excited about that, but for some reason they never followed through with their promise to her. Bree even cried to Mrs. Green about it, but it was just something else Bree had to accept and work through.

As for me, when Bree left for her visits I learned to enjoy my time alone. I always knew, though, there was a chance Bree had a bad visit and was always prepared to be there for her when she returned. I realized there was a chance that Bree would have to endure the emotional abuse from Jade until she was old enough to stand up for herself, and there were still occasions where Jade and Chad were sitting Bree down and asking her a bunch of questions. But, for the most part, Mrs. Green was on top of it. At one point it got so bad that Mrs. Green again told Jade and Chad to stop doing that and it was only hurting Bree. Mrs. Green explained that Bree was only telling them what they wanted to hear because two adults on one child like that only intimidates the child. They would ask her all kinds of questions about me, what I was doing and what was happening in our home. Bree was put under so much pressure when she was with Jade and Chad and it was never fair to her at all.

Once fall came, it was time to start school for both Bree and me. I was so excited and ready. I really never thought I would be in college at any point growing up so I was very proud of myself. I did great in school and got really good grades. I loved everything about psychology and enjoyed my studies. Jade and Chad tried to cause some issues through emails, but I just told them to stop harassing me. It didn't stop but, since Bree still had to go there, I did my best to keep the peace. I wasn't worried about their issues because I was taking care of business and bettering myself. I didn't have time to bicker with them over silly things that seemed to be repetitive.

It was so funny because I believe, in part, the only reason they would try to stir something was to get a rise out of me and I wasn't giving them the pleasure. Like at this one transfer when Chad left another note that said:

"Could you please start sending Bree down in some decent clothes? We are running out of the good clothes that we had bought her -Chad."

It made absolutely no sense at all and that claim was getting very old. We had already been through this same thing several times before. I didn't let it get to me, though, I just simply replied to the Carousel workers with:

"They always send Bree home in the same clothes she goes to them in!! So that makes NO sense."

It was petty things like this that continued, which were not a big deal to me. I had more important things going on than to have to worry about Jade or Chad's issues. There was one visit when I was in the middle of working on an essay when I had to take Bree to the Carousel Program for our transfer. I asked Bree to write a note for herself real quick to remind her dad one of her games were cancelled. I guess Bree just gave him the note because the next thing I knew there was a long email about how wrong I was for having her write the note. He felt I should have emailed him. I didn't realize it was such a big deal. Perhaps I should have emailed him, but I really didn't think it was a problem. They were great at trying to make big deals out of nothing.

Through the fall months, Bree and I both spent most of our time focused on our schooling. I helped her when she needed it, which wasn't often. Bree always did good in school. She has always gotten good grades and been that student with perfect attendance. She was always so positive, even in the midst of negativity. When Bree was home she was a happy and active child. I never had many issues with her at all. Bree truly is a great example to others how to pull through rough patches. Even at such a young age her strength was admirable.

On December 24th Mrs. Mayor was finally removed from our case and was replaced with Mrs. Callie. We may have had an agreement, but our communication was still being sent through the Ad Litem in emails. I felt bad for Mrs. Callie. What a case to have to take over. I believe it was a bit overwhelming for Mrs. Callie at first. We weren't her only new case and, trust me when I say, not her easiest by far. It was around this time I also let my attorney go. He filed his motion for withdrawal and it was all over, or so I thought.

Tracy and Stacy came down and spent the holidays with us. Stacy's new baby was so handsome and he was full of smiles and sunshine. I continued to stay focused on school and doing all I could to provide the love and support my daughter needed. Having her grandma and aunt around really helped Bree through this time in her life and I was beyond thankful for them being there for her. Bree needed as many positive people around her as she could get. Lifting Bree was always easy because she was such a bright, spirited child the Lord has always had his hands on. The year finally came to a close, and I had great thoughts about a better year to come. With custody established and things settling down more than not during Bree's visits, it seemed like things were going to get easier for us both.   ON TO THE NEXT YEAR...........

2009: Bree was still enjoying cheerleading so much and was such a beautiful cheerleader, too. Paul was also coming up and spending time with us about once a month. He was always so sweet to Bree and me. His love for us never stopped growing and we loved him. He was even sending me flowers once a week, which I loved.

With Paul taking care of the bills, it provided me with the opportunity to focus on school and just being Bree's mom. I was able to do all kinds of things with her and enjoy our time together with no stress. Life was coming together for us and things with Jade continued to stay calm for a while. The transfers were good because of the Carousal Program and Bree seemed to be excelling with Mrs. Green.

There were only a few issues throughout the year with Jade but, with Mrs. Green on the case, everything was squashed pretty fast. Unfortunately, Mrs. Callie was thrown off by the whole case. She was very nice, tried to listen and understand everything; but, thanks to Mrs. Mayor, I was portrayed as the ex who just didn't like the new wife. With all honestly, though, I just stopped caring about what everyone else thought and stayed consistent for Bree.

At one point even Chad's mother went with me to meet Mrs. Green. Tracy apologized for her son's behavior and told Mrs. Green that she never raised Chad to act the way he was. Bree still hated going there, but she knew she didn't have a choice. I supported her and did my best to make sure she knew that I believed in her. Jade had truly made Bree out to be known as a liar at their house. I believe a part of Bree shut down when she would go over to Jade and Chad's house.

Our Easter was an absolute blessing this year. Chad and Jade cut anyone off that was still a friend to me. Not only did this include his own mother and sister, but it also included his best friend, Aaron. For the first few years of our custody case, I didn't talk to anyone that was Chad's friend because I was afraid they were going to set me up or hurt me in some way. I wasn't taking any chances when it came to Bree. Aaron and I, however, had reconnected and began talking again. I was starting to feel like things were getting better and I wasn't as alone as I thought I was. Aaron ended up bringing his son, Stanley, down and they spent the entire weekend with Bree and me. We had the kids color their Easter eggs and, in the morning, had an Easter egg hunt for them. Of course, Stanley was much older by this time, but he still hunted eggs with Bree. It was so much fun. I loved and will always love Aaron and Stanley. They are very dear to my heart and to Bree.

As months went on, Paul and I began growing apart. He wanted to get married, but I didn't want to. Paul and I never had sex again after the first time we broke up. Even though he was coming up and staying once a month, he slept on my couch. For some reason I was afraid to cross that boundary with him. I wasn't ready and, when Paul started saying things like, "I'll let you stay in school for now" and "You can decorate for Christmas, but only for two weeks and I can't be in the house during that time," it freaked me out. Paul felt that Christmas was offensive to God and he wasn't celebrating it and I respected that. What I didn't understand is why he felt he could tell me what and for how long I could celebrate. Bree and I transformed our home during Christmas. It was our favorite holiday and it offended me when Paul told me what he did.

I wasn't handling his demands well and I didn't understand why he felt what he was saying was okay. I just couldn't wrap my head around what he was telling me and, in the end, it made me really mad. I was getting worried and stressed out about the way Paul was beginning to be demanding toward me, about how it was and would be for us. I started thinking about how I could take care of Bree without Paul's help. I knew if I took out student loans, Bree and I would be okay so, in the end, Paul and I ended up breaking up. Soon after I broke things off with Paul, one my friend's oldest daughters, Liza, came to my house to talk to me.

I had known Liza for about five years by this time. She was someone that ended up being a great blessing for Bree and me. Liza was a young mother to three beautiful children who, at this time, lived with their father. She wanted to fight to get her children back and asked if she could move in with Bree and me in order to get her life together. She needed my help and I needed all the help I could get, so I said yes.

The fact that Liza was trying to get her life together was something I found honorable. As I have said before, and I am sure you're aware, everybody in this world is battling something in their own lives. Who knows what their battle is or why. I feel like it's not our position to fix or judge anyone, but, if you have a chance to help someone you should.

> *"Let's get to the point where we enjoy giving and making other people happy so much that we actually look for opportunities to give"*
> *- Joyce Meyer Ministries*

During this same year, my mother came down to visit Bree and me. At one point she ended up saying something to Bree that was opposite of what I told Bree to do. I will never forget the look in my mother's eyes when I reprimanded her as if she was a child. I just continued to tell Bree what I expected and, after that day, my mother never tried to correct my parenting with Bree. I only saw my mother about once a year. Truth is, I still hadn't faced my anger issues with her. I couldn't be who she was or do as she did and act as if nothing had ever happened in the past and all was well. Mom was always so good at pretending like everything was fine and I wasn't as good at pretending.

Eventually, at some point when my mother was visiting I would end up drinking. I am not here to lie, there were even some visits that I don't remember her being there. I knew that drinking wasn't the answer but, when it came to dealing with my mother, I made the choice to be incoherent most of the time. My mother always talked about how she wanted my hair color, my build and how we should have been switched at our birth. She would always say she should have been born when I was and I should have been born when she was. Sometimes I felt like she was right about that.

It wasn't long after Liza moved in she found employment. I can't express what a breath of fresh air she was in the house. Bree and I were happy to have someone else to talk to and hang out with. We all got along really well. There were a few bumps, but living with someone else always takes some adjusting.

There were many weekends Bree would go and stay for a few days with Stacy and Tracy. When she stayed with them I would usually go stay at Aaron's and hang out with him. I also completed all of my probation and was finally out of all legal trouble. I hadn't been in trouble since 2005 and I knew I wanted it to stay that way. I just wanted life to balance out and things to come together for us. I did my best to keep a positive attitude and was ready to take on the New Year yet again. Bree and I did all of our normal traditions and spent our holidays with Tracy and Stacy. I really believed things were changing for the best. I was passing all of my classes and Bree seemed happy most of the time when she came home from her dad's. Things were really looking up for us and, before I knew it, the year was over and we were welcoming 2010 with open hearts.

Chapter TWENTY

2010: I was finally feeling positive about this New Year and where it was going to take me. College was opening my mind, and I was beginning to believe that things might actually work out. Although it wasn't as often, Bree was still dealing with the negative comments and isolation when at Jade and Chad's. Unfortunately, I believe she was going into survivor mode the moment she would leave for their house.

Mrs. Green and I talked about the things Jade and Chad were doing, but she still didn't feel that it was extreme enough for Bree to stop going. I again disagreed, but listened and followed all of Mrs. Green's advice and suggestions. I personally felt Bree shouldn't have ever been allowed to go there to begin with. Perhaps if someone would have paid more attention to what was happening, things would have been seen for what they were sooner. I still feel like, if I would have been looked at as Bree's concerned mother instead of just the ex, this entire case would have been settled sooner and Bree could have been saved from much of what she had to go through.

I had spoken to Paul often since the breakup. We always remained friends no matter what happened in our lives, whether together or not. Even though he always preferred to be more, he never hated me for not committing. Perhaps angry at me, but I don't think that man ever hated me. He loved me too much and was the kind of man that didn't have room in his heart for hate. That man would help me and did help me out with everything he could whether we were a couple or not. I can't express how or where I would be today without having Paul in my life. He ended up calling me early in the year and asked me if Bree and I could come down to see him in Georgia. I told him I would try to make a trip down in May and started making plans to do so. It wasn't long after Paul asked me to come down that I called him back just to talk for a bit and let him know we would be able to make it in May.

When I spoke to him, he began to explain to me he had been diagnosed with cancer. He told me the doctors were doing what they could, but he believed he would be healed through Jesus Christ. Dean, and Paul's youngest daughter, Ruby, were staying with him at this time. Samantha, Paul's oldest, went to visit as often as she could. Samantha had three children, a husband and lived in one state over by this time, so she had her hands full needless to say. After talking to Paul and the kids, I didn't think it sounded like it was so serious that Paul couldn't bounce back from it. They all spoke of healing and were very positive about the entire situation. I had no idea how serious things really were.

In April, when I received "the" call I felt like my world had been ripped apart worse than ever before. I didn't want to believe what I was being told. The pain was instantly overwhelming. Paul passed away April 21st, and I was completely unprepared. I think in a small way Paul knew his time was coming. A couple weeks prior, he had sent me a cassette tape with him talking to me on it for about two hours. With school and Bree I hadn't even had the chance to listen to it yet.

Bree and I loaded up and drove straight down. It was a huge risk because I didn't have my driver's license and I wasn't supposed to be behind the wheel of any vehicle. The risk was what it was. The kids needed me there just as much as I needed to be there. I listened to Paul talking to me on the tape he had recorded the entire way to Georgia. He was talking about everything from the day we met to the way things had happened and brought us to where we were now. I cried so much. I just couldn't bring myself to believe he was really gone.

Once Bree and I arrived, we were both very worn out. All of the kids were there and we all cried, laughed and cried some more. It was hard to believe Paul was gone. I remember asking one of the girls why no one told me it was so bad and she said they didn't want to speak life to the cancer. They believed that God would heal Paul. When I went to the back room where he stayed most of the time there was lipstick writing all over the mirror. The girls had wrote scriptures of healing all over the place for Paul. It made me cry, but I knew Paul had hope throughout his battle and his children did, too.

At one point, Samantha told me Paul had bought another engagement ring and she thought he was going to propose to me again. It just made my heart ache more than it already was. We all laughed about him proposing to me on his deathbed to get me to finally say yes, but deep inside I was honestly falling apart. I couldn't believe the one man, other than my father, who was always a rock for me was gone. The loss of Paul changed me forever.

I was so angry at God, and I didn't understand how or why he would take Paul. I tried so hard to put on this front as if I was okay. I just wanted to be strong for all of the kids. Bree was raised calling Samantha, Ruby and Dean sisters and brother. There may have been distance between us, there may have been ups and downs, but Paul and I loved all of the kids with every fiber in us. He loved Bree as his own, and I loved his children just as mine.

There was a woman that Paul had seen on and off no one really knew or had met but, out of respect, the girls wanted to let her know Paul had passed away. When they called her to tell her, she decided she wanted to come to the funeral. She lived in another state and jumped on a Greyhound to head down to Georgia. The girls didn't expect her to head down, and it made it a little uncomfortable for all of us, but it was the least of our worries. The woman had wanted to come down sooner, but it's my understanding Paul told her he didn't want her to come. Now here she was on her way and none of us knew what to expect.

I had drove all night and hadn't had any sleep yet. As the day went on, Dean and I had a couple beers together and reminisced about old times. All of us had been crying and our emotions were intense. I couldn't wrap my head around how grown the kids all were. It wasn't long and the girls were heading to the Greyhound station to pick up the woman Paul had once dated. When they arrived back at the house with her, she walked straight up to me and gave me a hug. She whispered to me I didn't need to be intimidated by her and I was welcome there. I just looked at the kids in dismay. I didn't know what to think or what to say. This woman's first impression left not only me, but the kids in complete confusion. Who the hell was this woman to tell me I was welcome to be there? And what in the world would make her think I was intimidated by her? It was so strange. I really just don't think she was all there, how some people say a few fries short of a Happy Meal. Yes, that would be the best way to describe her, but I am going to refer to her as the crazy lady.

A couple of the kids expressed they felt uncomfortable with her around and, unfortunately, things just got worse. She was walking through Paul's house trying to tell the kids what to do with Paul's things. She was overstepping boundaries she shouldn't have been, especially with none of us even knowing her. When the kids would come to me and tell me what she was saying, I was a little thrown off and not sure how to handle the situation. This woman was a complete stranger to all of us. I was getting angry that she was upsetting the kids, but I just tried my best to be as supportive as I could for the kids. They were facing enough with the funeral the next day and I didn't want them to have to worry about more than they already were.

At one point in the afternoon, when I was feeding Samantha's youngest baby, this woman started acting like I was doing something wrong. I was giving the baby a bottle, which isn't rocket science. She started saying I had drank too much and I was going to hurt the baby. She was really rude and I tried to be polite, but she was making it very hard.

For the kids' sake I did my best to keep my temper level at a low. However, when this woman started accusing me, saying I was going to hurt the baby, I couldn't take it anymore. She had already upset everyone in the house, friends and family, at least once if not more. I ended up handing the baby over to a friend sitting next to me and that was it. I stood up and it took all three of our kids to hold me back from beating that woman. It was insane how she came in and acted like she owned the place and not one of us even knew her.

What I thought was crazy is she was only there for a few hours and somehow managed to upset almost every one of us. The girls got her out of there and she stayed the rest of her visit in Georgia with a friend of Paul's. We all ended up joking about understanding why Paul might of told her he didn't want her to come down in the first place. Once the crazy lady was gone, the kids and I, with a few friends, spent the rest of the night together talking, laughing, crying and missing Paul deeply.

The funeral was really hard on all of us. It turned out really nice and I thank God for Paul's family. They took care of everything and made things much easier for the kids. Paul had touched so many lives and it was incredible to be a part of it for so long. Even Dean's mother came down from Michigan, and I will never forget the moment she came up to me. Dean's mom said to me that everyone knew I was the love of Paul's life. I told her thank you as I cried and we hugged one another. It was so hard to believe I would never see Paul again. I couldn't call him anymore. He was never going to just pop in and surprise Bree and me. I didn't want to accept he was gone. What was I going to do without Paul in my life? He was my best friend.

While at the funeral, the crazy lady was getting worse and upsetting everyone. I felt so bad for Paul's stepmother. She began to follow the woman around so she could stop her from upsetting the kids more than she already had. At one point, she began introducing herself as Paul's wife and Ruby got really mad. Ruby ended up coming to me about it. It was so heartbreaking. Ruby was so upset and said if anyone had a right to be called Paul's wife it was me.

I couldn't take that woman hurting the kids anymore. She had no right to behave the way she was and I knew I would have ended up hurting her. All I could do was comfort Ruby and tell her not to let it get to her. I went to Paul's stepmother about it but, by then, the damage and anger was already there. I tried my best to stay away and not pay attention to what the crazy lady was saying or doing, but she didn't make it easy for any of us at all.

After the viewing, Paul was cremated. He wouldn't have wanted an expensive, extravagant funeral. Paul was a simple man of God. Seeing Paul laying there was the hardest thing I have ever faced in my life. He didn't even look like the Paul I knew. It had been months since I had seen him, but we talked on the phone often. Standing there looking at him just crushed my entire heart. I never thought I would ever recover from that moment.

When the funeral was over, all of us headed over to one of Paul's friend's house. It was so strange to be known by some of Paul's friends without ever having met them before. They knew who I was from all the stories Paul had told them about me. What was beautiful is there were some people I knew from Paul sharing their stories with me but I had never met either.

The house was filled with tears and you could feel the love in the air. Dean had put together a CD with all his favorite songs that reminded him of his father. It was very beautiful and had been playing at the funeral home and now at the house. We all ended up in a circle and it was quite large. We went from one person to the next and took turns talking about Paul and our memories with him.

Bree was still acting unfazed by everything. I knew she was hurting. She was very close to Paul and I knew I needed to keep an eye on her. I was aware that Paul's death hadn't really registered with her yet. Paul played with Bree as if she was one of his children whenever he came around. Bree and Paul had an unbreakable bond from the time Bree was an infant. Paul was always spoiling Bree and sending new things to her. She knew if she wanted something she could call that man anytime, and she did. It brings me to tears now just looking through pictures of Paul and of all four of the kids. There's not many days that pass I don't think of Paul. He is missed dearly and daily.

As we all sat in the circle, it ended up being my turn. I tried to fight the tears, but there was no way of stopping them. When Paul passed I felt like a part of me went with him. After I spoke about some of my memories of Paul throughout the years, it moved onto the next person and then several more. Then the inevitable came, the woman that had caused so many problems had her turn to speak.

All of a sudden she turned off the CD that Dean made and said Paul liked it when she sang to him. Then out of the blue she just proceeded to start singing. It was like opera and in another language. It had to be one of the strangest things I had ever witnessed. Everyone was looking at one another in disbelief, but we were silent in order to be polite. Dean and a few others ended up getting so upset they just got up and walked out. I, too, joined that crowd. We were all outside and could still hear her singing. Some of the people were saying it was very rude of her, but we all had to handle Paul's death our own way, even the crazy lady. This was a hard day for all of us and we were trying to accept Paul was gone and not one of us could change that.

It was after the funeral and after the gathering at the friend's house when Bree and I pulled into Paul's driveway. I went to get out of the car, looked back at Bree and she bowed her little head down and started crying. Paul's death had finally hit her. It tore my heart up and I just held her as we cried together. It wasn't long until Samantha, Ruby and Dean were surrounding the car and comforting Bree. It was so sad we had lost Paul, but seeing all the kids pulling together was beautiful. They truly pulled together to comfort one another and I knew Paul would have been proud of every one of them just as I, myself, was.

Paul strongly believed in and had been preparing for the end times. He had made each one of us our own survival backpacks and they were loaded and ready to go. He believed in running to the mountains and was prepared to do so. Paul had made all four of the kids a survival pack, plus one for him and one for me. After the kids gave Bree and me our survival packs, they also gave me some of Paul's things I wanted to hold onto. Once everything was finally settled, I tried to spend as much time with everyone as I could.

After a couple of days, Bree and I were headed back to Indiana. Somewhere in that trip from Georgia to Indiana I lost myself within. It felt like my world was over. I wanted to give in and call it quits more than I had any other time in my life. My heart was so filled with pain that I could barely breathe. I kept fighting the tears as much as I could and I became even more angry with God. I was so lost I even said I hated God.

On May 5th my neighbor's sister, Lori, saw me sitting on my porch and asked if I wanted to go for a quick ride to the store down the road. I didn't know her real well, but we had spoke several times throughout the years. Dakota was staying with us again at this time, so I figured why not. I really didn't have many friends because of Jade's games but, after losing Paul, I was just walking around numb all the time. Bree had been at her friends most of the day and, as we pulled down the street, I saw the girls playing outside. When we rolled past them, I let Bree know I would be back in 15 minutes, and Dakota had just walked to the corner store so he would be back in just a few. I had no intention of being gone for too long either way.

After we were done at the store, Lori said she needed to make a quick stop at her friend's house. I told her that was cool, but to please be quick because I had to get back to the house for Bree. She said that was no problem and, before I knew it, she was back in the car. When she turned the corner, she ended up pulling over real quick and then shut the car off. I had no idea what was going on. When I asked her what she was doing, Lori said she saw an undercover cop car in the alley. I kept looking back, but I didn't see anything when we had passed the alley. I honestly started to think maybe she was on something. She refused to drive any further and kept asking me to drive. She said she didn't have a license. I explained to her that I didn't either. The longer we sat there, the more I felt like I shouldn't have even came. I finally said I would drive us the few blocks we had left to get to my house and we switched seats.

As soon as I pulled up to the stop sign, out of the blue came the under-cover car behind us. I knew I was in trouble and that I was making a huge mistake, but I was already in the driver's seat and going. By the time the lights came on and I pulled over, I was actually at my house. I don't know why, but I jumped out of the car instantly with my hands in the air. I just kept explaining that this was my home and I was just trying to get home to my daughter. I was instantly placed in handcuffs and sat in my own yard. Dakota and Bree were just a few feet from me and Bree was crying. I couldn't do anything but put my head down in shame. I reassured Bree everything would be okay and told Dakota to please get her in the house. Lord knows she didn't need to see that. After the officer ran my name, of course, I came back as a suspended driver and I was then placed under arrest. I guess the license plates on the car were stolen or something, but Lori admitted that the car was her boyfriend's and gave the officers permission to search the car. When the officer came back to me he asked if I owned what was in the car and I said no. I told him I had no clue what was even in the car. I again tried to explain what happened; that I was just along for the ride with Lori and only got behind the wheel so I could get home because Lori wouldn't drive.

Apparently they found a needle in the car when they searched it. I couldn't believe it and began explaining over and over that I was just along for the ride and it was the first time I had ever even been in that car. When the officer went to Lori and asked her if the items belonged to her, she freaking denied it. In the end, I was charged as a Habitual Traffic Violator, plus Lori and I were both charged with possession of paraphernalia because neither of us would claim the needle that was in her car. At least I thought that was all they found.

Once we were placed in the holding tank, I really started to get ner-vous. I knew the longer I was in jail the worse things would be for me with Jade and Chad. God knew they would have to call this out against me. After a few hours and no sign of someone coming with bail money, Lori and I were processed and placed in another cell. I was astonished by what I was seeing. On the small table in the jail cell there were pills crushed up the girls were snorting. One of the women rolled up several pieces of paper to form a long funnel, she shoved a baggie of pills in the center so they were secure and proceeded to stick it in the toilet. The damn thing actually reached the other cell behind the wall through the toilet. You could hear them hollering when it came through on their side. I just couldn't believe all of it was happening right there in the jail.

We didn't have to stay the entire night. Dakota and my neighbor came up with the money and bailed us both out. I can't express how happy I was to see Dakota that night. That jail was dirty, and I saw more drugs in there then I did on the street. Okay, perhaps that's an exaggeration, but it was really bad. When I got home, Bree was already in bed and Dakota, Liza and I sat up talking. I asked him if Bree was okay after seeing me get arrested and what Dakota said threw me off a bit. He said the only thing Bree was afraid of and had asked him was if this meant she had to go live with her dad and Jade. Dakota said once he told her everything was going to be okay she calmed right down and told him she just didn't want to have to go live there. The next day, as soon as I woke up, I typed up two petitions: one for a dismissal of the paraphernalia charge and the second begging the court to drop the habitual charge down to a misdemeanor because it was filed as a felony. I already knew all of this was just going to cause more issues with Jade and Chad.

My court date was scheduled for October and, honestly, at that point, I emotionally shut down. I gave up. Also, in May, Liza's ex was arrested and she was granted custody of all three of her young children. At this point I pretty much just let Liza, Dakota plus all of the kids take over my house while I stayed in my room. There were about two months I didn't even come out of my bedroom. I started drinking a fifth of Southern Comfort a day and some days even more.

I thank God they were all there to bring life to the house and to be with Bree when I couldn't be. I wasn't okay at all, and I definitely wasn't okay for Bree during this time. I just laid in bed and cried all the time. I drank to drown my sorrows in every bottle I got my hands on. I cussed at God and told him how mad I was at him. I continually replayed the tape Paul made me and listened to him talking to me all the time. I couldn't stop thinking about Paul and questioning why everything was always so hard. I wanted to die so bad, but then I would think of Bree. There were so many times I wished I could just drink myself to death, and there were some days I probably should have died with how much I drank.

Most of the summer was a complete blur to me. I stayed in my room a lot of it so that none of the children saw me drunk. I was just getting drunk and passing out over and over every single day. My mother says she came down for about a week, but I don't even remember her being there. I was so out of it at all times and I didn't care anymore. I had failed my finals, had been placed on probationary status with my college, and I just couldn't get a grip on anything.

I felt like my life was worthless and there was no point to me even being here. I thought about allowing Chad and Jade to take Bree because I didn't believe I would ever be okay again. But every time the thought would come to mind, my heart would kick it out quickly. I knew Bree wasn't better off over there no matter how much more money they had. She was abused half the time she was there. I just didn't know what to do. I missed Paul and I missed my dad. I felt like I was all alone and the world was always going to be against me.

Bree wasn't too phased by my behavior only because she didn't see me very often. Everyone hung out downstairs, and I stayed away from them in my room. I can't express it enough -- My gratitude and thankfulness for Dakota and Liza being there and, with the kids there, Bree was far from alone. I couldn't have pulled through any of it without them. It would have been extremely unhealthy for Bree to have had to deal with me one-on-one. I just didn't want to be strong anymore and didn't feel like I could be.

Dakota tried so hard to help me and get me to stop drinking, but I was too far gone emotionally. There wasn't a day that went by I wasn't drinking. I was trying to drown myself and all the pain. I was so ashamed of how I was behaving and handling Paul's death, but I felt so lost. I knew I wasn't being a good example for Bree, and it was killing me, but I couldn't stop. The pain just felt too heavy to carry.

I had notified the Ad Litem, Mrs. Callie, and Mrs. Green about my arrest. They both seemed to feel like it wasn't too big of a deal and pretty much told me to stay out of trouble. By September I was starting to slow down on drinking when I first woke up and I was coming out of my room more often. On my birthday Jade and Chad manipulated our visitation schedule and made it so I couldn't get Bree as I was supposed to. Although it was their weekend, Bree was supposed to spend my birthday with me according to the Parenting Guidelines, but that didn't happen as it should have. I planned to take the day and just spend time with Bree for my birthday. I was honestly trying to pull myself together and out of the darkness I had been drowning in.

I got so upset when Jade and Chad refused my visit I ended up at a girlfriend's house. My one and only gift was a fifth of 100 proof Southern Comfort. I just carried my bottle around my friend's house and got really drunk. Somehow I ended up wrestling someone in the front yard, but a neighbor thought it was more than just playing around and the cops were called. I was then arrested for disorderly conduct and public intoxication. Those charges were all dropped in October when I talked to the prosecutor. He actually looked at me and said he felt I already had enough on my plate so there was no need to pursue the charges. I was so thankful for that prosecutor.

When Jade and Chad found out about my arrests in September they sat Bree down and questioned her again. Two adults on one child, which seemed to be the way they liked to do it. I was so over the two of them and didn't even think I could pull through another custody battle, but then it happened. On September 20th Chad and Jade hired another attorney and filed a Petition to Modify Parenting Time and Support.

Even though I was leveling out and slowly pulling out of the depression, Bree had been affected by all the circumstances that had happened. It could have been the mix of me being so far gone and Jade and Chad starting crap again, but, either way, her grades weren't the best and she actually brought home the first and only F she has ever had. I did give her a spanking and, yes, it was with a belt. The times my child has been spanked can be counted on one hand. It wasn't normal for Bree to get in any trouble because she was truly a good kid. Bree received her spanking on a Friday which just happened to be a weekend she went to her dad's.

That Sunday, Bree was supposed to come home. It was about an hour before I needed to go pick her up and there was a knock at the door. It was an officer who said my daughter was at the police station with her dad and he was claiming I was abusing Bree physically and doing drugs in front of her. I just shook my head and invited the officer in the house to look around. We talked for a while. I explained why I spanked Bree and he said he would have done the same thing with his child. The officer did tell me the next time I needed or wanted to spank Bree, I needed to do it with only my hand and not a belt. He then explained I can spank my daughter with my hand, but using an object such as a belt is considered abuse. I just apologized and he ended up leaving. When Bree and I got home, she fell into my arms crying as she continually apologized to me as if she had done something wrong. I held her and explained that everything was okay and she didn't do anything wrong. I told her she deserved her spanking, but if she ever got another one it would be with my hand and not a belt. After a short time I got her laughing and calmed down and everything was okay.

Jade and Chad were asking the court to grant them physical custody of Bree and for me to be required to exercise the Parenting Time Guidelines. I had been doing really good and picking myself up, but this made me finally straighten up. I stood up, brushed myself off and stopped drinking so much. Again, if it weren't for Jade and Chad attacking me, I am not sure I would have pulled through this time in my life. With the custody case in full force again, it made me realize I had to at least try to get myself together for Bree.

I was extremely emotionally weak, but looking at me you couldn't tell how bad it was on the inside. I was also back in school and trying to complete another semester. With being on a probationary period, my grades were being watched and I didn't want to fail out. But no matter how hard I tried, I couldn't stay focused on the homework. By the end of it all, I did fail out of college with only 1.5 credits shy of my associates in psychology. I was doing much better about not drinking during the day, but I just waited until night after all the kids were in bed. I am not claiming there weren't any days I was able to hide my drinking from my daughter. For the first time in her life she saw me very drunk a few times. I tried not to expose her to what I was going through, but I will not sit here and claim I hid it well at all times because I didn't.

I had some rough days and struggled, but I was trying my best to keep it together and bounce back. On October 11th I was placed on probation for the driving as a habitual charge. The possession charge was rightfully dropped. On October 13th Jade and Chad's new attorney filed an emergency Petition for Custody and Petition for an Emergency Hearing. I couldn't believe they were starting this all over again. In the Petition, Chad's lawyer wrote:

> *"Father's Petition to Modify Parenting Time And Support was initiated when he learned that mother was charged with a Class D felony of Operating a Vehicle as a Habitual Traffic Violator and with an A misdemeanor of Possession of Paraphernalia. At the time of her arrest for such charge, the arresting officer found in mother's possession, in the center console of the vehicle which she was driving, a silver metallic spoon which contained charring on the underside, a used hypodermic needle, and copper scouring pads which are commonly used as a filter for the smoking of illegal narcotics."*

I didn't have a clue about the officer's finding the "Copper scouring pads or the spoon", but, then again, I had no idea what was in that car to begin with. If you read the Petition I filed the day after my arrest requesting to have the charge dismissed, you would read that I call out the hypodermic needle and nothing else because that was all I thought they found at first. In my Petition I expressed I am not a diabetic and don't even need needles for anything. I didn't know what was found in the car until after I had filed my Petition and ended up requesting a copy of the police report for my records.

The Petition Jade and Chad were filing went on to claim that now, because I didn't have a driver's license, I couldn't properly care for Bree and should be placed on supervised visitation. I just couldn't get a break and things were never going to be easy for me, at least I didn't feel like it. I hadn't had my license for almost two years before I was pulled over in May; but now, all of a sudden, it would hinder me from taking care of Bree. It was just insane the way Jade and Chad would not give up and used everything against me. I was on probation and my case was done, yet here they were.

Our court date was set for November 8th. Truth is, there is only one reason I made it through all of the harassment Chad and Jade were putting me through on top of dealing with everything else going on in my life - The Lord never left me. Even when I felt like He had, even when I was cussing and yelling at Him, He was always there with me, it just took me time to realize it. I knew that, when I went to court, I had enough evidence to prove Jade and Chad were just aiming bullets at a dismissed drug charge and I was not a drug addict as they claimed. If you know me or just look at me, you can see that the only needles that go into my body are the ones found inside a tattoo gun.

Also, in October I was taking care of Liza's three children plus Bree during the day while Liza was at work. She had two toddlers and one in school during the day like Bree, so the house was never empty and being around the babies really helped me to stay sober throughout the day. Once the kids were in bed and adult time began, I started finding myself lonely and sitting at my computer drinking my vodka.

I don't know why, but for some reason I decided to start getting on an online dating site. It wasn't long before this young 24-year-old, very handsome man ended up emailing me. I thought he was playing with me at first because he was eight years younger than me, no kids and living in

Ohio. I ignored his efforts to connect with me at first, but then he sent me an email. It was very sweet and stood out to me. He complimented my beauty and said he would feel blessed to know me. The email continued to draw me in and seemed sincere. I ended up emailing him back and we talked for a while. We even ended up connecting on Facebook.

His name was Ty. He seemed to say all the right things and made me feel better about myself. I really loved his smile and his companionship. We video chatted and talked to one another often. Talking to Ty seemed to take my mind off of everything. When we would talk he made me feel like I had someone who was just there for me. I looked forward to hearing from him and found myself very attracted to him. By this time, I was about 40 pounds overweight, my self-esteem was low, but, when I talked to Ty, I felt like I was the only one he wanted. It felt good to feel wanted.

On November 8th we went to court and it was ordered we have Mrs. Callie as our continued Guardian Ad Litem. We were ordered to also have a mediation to try to settle our disagreements without having to go to trial. The court stated this was not deemed an emergency and it would proceed at a normal fashion if we could not work things out. Mrs. Callie was directed by the court to conduct a full investigation and we were ordered to continue communication through her. Jade was throwing a fit. She felt I should have been locked up and was just getting slapped on the wrist. Thank the good Lord she wasn't and isn't my judge.

It wasn't long after court that Jade and Chad called CPS (Child Protective Services) on me again. It was the same as the last time and they were claiming I was doing drugs in front of Bree. When Bree talked to Mrs. Green and Mr. Miller, the man from CPS, regarding what was being claimed, it would always come out that Jade and Chad were trying to pressure her into telling them I did drugs. It was insane and the visits for Bree started to get real bad for her because she wouldn't tell people what they wanted her to. I thought Bree had been through enough in the past, but I never imagined it would get as bad as it ended up getting. Emotionally and spiritually I was still lost and didn't even care to be found. For Bree's sake, I tried my best to hide the emptiness I was feeling. She was already being put through hell at her dad's and I didn't want to add to her stress.

During the holidays I tried to play this role of the mom that had it all together for my daughter. The kids really enjoyed themselves and everyone was happy with their gifts. Tracy, Stacy and Stacy's son came to spend the holidays with us again. We still spent every holiday we could together. It was nice, but I felt like I was faking everything: Being happy, my smile, my joy, it was all a front. I was struggling inside, but one thing I knew for sure was the fact I was still Bree's mother and I needed to behave as such. I started to realize there was no way I could allow myself to ever give up. If I choose to give up, it meant I was giving up on Bree, too, and there was no amount of pain in the world that was going to tear me down and bring me to that level. The only thing I found that did bring me comfort was talking with Ty. Even through all the pain he seemed to make me smile. He was always complimenting me and the conversations we had made me feel like he really cared about me.

Bree was miserable when she went to her dad's, and she was being treated as if she was an outcast when she was there. I had to fight for myself to get right. I had to pull it back together. I had to be there for my daughter because she needed me. Bree was counting on me to always be there for her and I intended to be. New Year's was just another night. I was leery of things getting better, so I looked at the New Year and figured it was best to just take it one day at a time.

Chapter TWENTY-ONE

2011: Once the New Year had passed, I tried to get myself right with God. I knew it wasn't right to be so angry and begged God for forgiveness for being so mad at him. Things for Bree got much worse. Now, because she wouldn't tell other people that I was a drug addict, she was isolated physically. For a long time she felt isolated and alone at Jade and Chad's, but now she was told she wasn't even allowed to hang out with the other kids, her stepbrother and stepsister. Jade and Chad told Bree she was a liar, manipulator and dangerous to the other children because she might claim one of them touched her. They told her no one could trust her.

Since she would only tell Jade and Chad what they wanted to hear when they were two adults intimidating her, she was now fully isolated from everyone when she went over there. I don't know why it was so hard for me to accept Chad was allowing so much to happen to our daughter. He is pure evidence that sometimes money can blind weak people. I continued to contact Mrs. Green and Mrs. Callie right away, but, again, they seemed to only look at me as the ex-wife that was overreacting.

I continued to emotionally support Bree when she would come home, but all I could do was hold her. I can't tell you how many times Bree would come home and just cry. I would constantly tell her everything was going to be okay. I was still emotionally unstable myself, but on the outside you couldn't tell. I had quit drinking during the day unless Bree was at her dad's. As much as I tried to hide the pain, we all know kids are smart. Bree knew mommy wasn't well after Paul passed away, but I was starting to come around.

I had gained a lot of weight and had no self-esteem, but Ty was always building me up and making me feel good about myself. He always seemed to say the right things to me. In February, Bree and I ended up going to stay with Stacy and Tracy for a couple nights. I gave Bree time with her grandma and aunt and would go hang with Aaron. We had a great weekend. Once home, Ty and I continued to talk to one another but, by this time, we were talking every day. Ty didn't mind our age difference even though it bothered me at first. He really seemed like a guy who had his head on straight. He knew I couldn't have children and said it didn't bother him. Ty made me feel like he accepted me as I was. His Facebook was always covered with praises to God and I convinced myself that he could be the one to lead us as a family.

At the end of February, when Ty and I were having our normal video chat, I asked him, "Why don't you just come to visit me?" The next thing I knew he was sitting in front of his video camera with his credit card in hand. He booked a trip to Indiana that night and it was done. I was always drinking heavily at night, so when I woke up I only remembered glimpses of our conversation. I ran downstairs and jumped on my computer to see if perhaps I was just dreaming, but there was his itinerary in my email. He was really coming down. I couldn't believe that he was really coming to see me. We were actually going to stand in front of one another for the first time.

Ty and I had been speaking for months and I was nervous about meeting him. I questioned myself, but I was so lonely and Ty always said everything so right to make me feel better. I just wanted to be touched so bad. I wanted to be wanted and to just be loved. I kept trying to talk myself out of letting him come down, but Liza would calm me down and say it was okay for me to do something for myself. Liza was one of the few people that knew what I was going through. She kept telling me I deserved to be happy and, Lord knows, I wanted to be.

I wasn't nervous about meeting Ty as if I thought something bad would occur, I was nervous because over the last few months I grew a very strong like for Ty. I can't explain how nice it was to have someone that wanted to listen to me. I told Ty a lot about what was going on in my life, but never how lost I felt inside. That was one thing I tried to keep from everyone. Ty was so sweet, he listened and had no problem telling me things would be okay. He brought me a sense of comfort that no one else seemed to.

I wanted to believe everything that man said for some reason. I wanted to be somewhere I belonged and I had no idea where that was. The day Ty was supposed get on the bus there was a really bad snow storm and his bus was delayed for three hours. Ty and I just texted and talked the entire time he was waiting. He said he was as nervous as I was, but Ty was saying things like, "I hope you never ask me to leave." I should have known better and run away right then.

Ty was nothing I expected or saw coming. He was from Nigeria, dark, gorgeous, young and intelligent. I was swept off my feet before I even had a chance to understand what was happening. Liza took me to pick Ty up and, when I walked into the hotel where the bus had dropped him off, I walked up to him and asked, "Hey, do you need a ride?" He smiled and that was it, I fell head over heels. He was gorgeous. His full lips, his perfect smile and his accent took my breath away. When we finally arrived at my house he was shocked. From appearance, I had all my shit together. I had a huge, beautiful home and was helping Liza until she got on her feet. I was the perfect target for what Ty needed from that point on and I was clueless to the game.

Ty came down on a Friday when Bree was at her dad's and was supposed to leave that Sunday. The first night together we drank and I got pretty hammered. We even had sex. I didn't remember any of it, but I wasn't upset when I woke up next to his sexy body. All of my friends, which weren't many, kept warning me about him and telling me about how guys like Ty used women. I refused to believe Ty was that kind of man. He brought me so much comfort and made me feel loved, which was what I was seeking. He was providing me with everything I desperately needed, but the problem was I should have been seeking it from the Lord and not a man. The weekend was like a dream. Ty was right on with every word he said and I thought we had fallen in love. When Sunday came, I asked Ty to stay with me and just be with me. Of course, he agreed.

Bree was having to deal with some horrific visits at her father's. Jade was on the attack of Bree worse than she had ever been in the past. They kept tearing her down when she would go, and Jade had no issue trying to convince the world what a liar my daughter was. At night my nightmares of hurting Jade weren't haunting me as often. I knew and accepted that all I could do was support and encourage Bree because, legally, my hands were always tied.

Ty and I seemed good together and he was very smooth. When he first came down, I knew he didn't smoke cigarettes, but, since I did, I tried hard not to let my smoke bother him by moving away from him when I lit up. He would say things like, "It is okay baby, if I want to be with you I'll have to get used to it." I kept thinking this could be it and he kept convincing me it was. Ty and Bree got along well. She had spoken to him several times throughout the months when we were video chatting. By the time he arrived he didn't seem like a stranger to any of us. By this time, Liza and the kids were working on getting their own place and Dakota was in and out of the house. Dakota has always had a home wherever I was and he always will.

Things with Ty seemed amazing and like a dream. The sex was good and we really seemed to connect well. Ty would drink with me at night and it was not a big issue. We would get drunk and have sex, it was what we did. I will never forget the night Ty had a good buzz and started telling me he was younger than what he had told me. When I started to ask more questions about it, he instantly withdrew and changed the subject. I asked him several times after that, but he would get offended and tell me he never said that. He continues to claim to this day that it never happened. Like most things that he got upset about, I just dropped it. It wasn't worth a fight to me and I really didn't care, so I let it go.

Ty was so smooth and everything he said intrigued me. One night when Ty and I were alone he played this song by P-Square, called 'I love you,

I love you'. He started dancing around the table, eyes locked only on me and began singing it to me. I was almost in tears the way he proclaimed his love for me. He made me feel like he truly loved me. It had been so long since I was touched with so much passion. He said everything every woman dreams of hearing better than the guys in the romance movies do and I believed every word. I fell into his arms as if he was the only person in the world that could hold me up and make me feel okay again. I wanted to do nothing but make things work out with Ty, and Ty had me completely convinced that he wanted nothing but the same.

I didn't have a lot of money or anything Ty could steal from me, so when everyone would warn me about him using me I would think they were crazy. What could he use me for? I didn't want to believe Ty could or would use me for his citizenship. That just seemed crazy to me. He made me happy and I needed that. I was convinced that I needed him in my life.

In March, Bree was doing so much better in school and even tried out for the Math Bowl Team. She had tried out over the past two years and never made it, but this was her year. She qualified for the team and I couldn't have been more proud of her. I was always so amazed how well she did in the subject of math. Truthfully, she had to have gotten that from her father because I am not good in math at all. She really enjoyed being on the team and actually earned a scholarship through it.

It didn't take long until Ty and I went to Ohio and picked up all of his things, which was just a big duffel bag of clothes. He ended up giving me $200 to help me with the bills, but, because he wasn't a citizen, he couldn't work. With Ty there was so much he had never done and I wanted to be the one to do everything with him for his first time. I took him to the casino, bowling and Buffalo Wild Wings, which for a sports fanatic like Ty was like Heaven. I loved watching his head bobble like a bobble-head doll as he tried to catch what was on each television. One day Bree and I even took him to the Basketball Hall of Fame and he really seemed to enjoy that. It felt so good to be doing things together. I had craved the feeling of family for so long that I swore I would never let that go. I decided early on I would do whatever it took to make our relationship work. I was convinced Ty was the man I had been waiting for, my other half.

By May things were out of hand at Jade and Chad's house. Bree came home the first weekend in May and she was crushed. She fell into my arms, literally, and just cried harder than she ever had. When she was strong enough, she began to explain that Jade had told her that her dad was thinking about killing himself. She asked this 11-year-old child how Bree would feel walking into a funeral home seeing her dad dead and knowing it was her fault. Bree was a mess. I didn't think her tears were ever going to stop and it just broke my heart. I had had enough. This woman had gotten away with so much, but this was it. That Monday I began blowing up Mrs. Green and Mrs. Callie with emails. I wanted someone to help Bree or I was going to seriously hurt Jade. She couldn't keep getting away with tearing this beautiful child down. Mrs. Green and Mrs. Callie both wanted me to bring Bree in so they could talk to her and I did.

By the time both women spoke to Bree it didn't take long before there was an emergency order to place Chad on supervised visitation. I don't know everything Jade said to Bree that weekend and still don't. I thought the whole dad killing himself thing was bad enough; however, when Mrs. Callie, our Ad Litem, walked out of the interview with Bree she looked directly at me and said, "That woman is the true definition of an evil stepmom." She went on to explain this case was the only case that had actually given her nightmares. When I asked her what else was said to Bree, Mrs. Callie told me she couldn't disclose that information.

To this day Bree claims she doesn't remember exactly what else was said, and I don't pressure her on the subject. I picture her locking it up in her own treasure chest and throwing the key and chest back in her mind separately just as I had done so many years earlier. It was that Petition that put a stop to my daughter having to go over to that nightmare Jade and Chad called a home. Jade and Chad gave up. They said they would see Bree when she was 18 years old. Bree has never had to go back to that house again. It was really over and Bree was finally safe from Jade's emotional abuse. Praise God!

Ty was so different than anyone else I had ever been with. At first he would spend hours upstairs walking around our room singing and praying to God. I loved how much he showed his love for God and wanted the same relationship with the Lord. It was honestly one of the biggest things that attracted me to him because I was coming out of the depression and needed God more than ever. I thought God was so far away from me. I never realized God was carrying me the entire time.

Ty was really stressed a few months after he came my house. He had received a letter stating his temporary citizenship was expiring and needed to return to Africa. I wasn't willing to lose the man I loved, and I was convinced I couldn't be right without Ty. I told him we would get through it together. I explained to him I was willing to help him in any way I could. I believed with my entire being that I loved him and he loved me.

Ty and I drank together, but sometimes he would get upset if I got too drunk. He kept telling me I was better than the alcohol and the way it made me act. We had a few fights where Ty would start packing and threatening to leave, but I would literally get on my knees and beg him to stay. I would be covered in tears and it felt like my world was crashing when he threatened to leave me. One time I just started packing with him. When he asked what I was doing I told him he wasn't leaving me behind and I was going with him. He left several times the very first year we were together. Actually, every year we were together. I had been drinking heavily for over a year. Although Ty and I stopped drinking every single day, it was obvious I was blacking out at certain times when we did drink. I knew I had to get a grip on my behavior, but it was almost as if I couldn't.

In June Stacy gave birth to her second son. Bree and I were able to go to the hospital and visit, but we couldn't stay too long. Even Stacy and Tracy accepted Ty. It was a great feeling to be a part of Stacy's children's lives. They were and are both very good kids. We were all still doing everything together as often as we could. We either went to Stacy and Tracy's or they came to our house at least once a month. Stacy and Tracy also believed in Bree and lifted her up with support, which she desperately needed.

In August Bree was invited to the courthouse for a small ceremony. Ty went with us and it was really exciting to watch the Judge honor all the children by presenting them with their scholarship. She was so proud of herself, and she had every right to be. Bree was growing so fast and, even now when I look at her, I can't figure out where all the time has gone.

I was trying to pull close to God again because all I did was push him away after Paul died. Ty and I even tried praying together for some time, but our style of prayers were extremely different and it faded quickly. Ty tried to make me want to stay sober. He would make me feel so bad that I started to question myself, which at that time I needed to do. It wasn't the best or a real effective approach, but I made the decision to change for him and not for myself, which never worked.

Even though Bree didn't have to go to her father's anymore, Jade and Chad still found ways to hurt Bree. They would send cards and presents. The cards would be filled with things like, "I am always here for you. I love you. I miss you." It would take me 20 minutes holding Bree while she cried. Bree would say, "It doesn't make sense mom." She didn't understand why her father didn't want to see her and, even though she was happy she didn't have to see Jade, it crushed her that she wasn't seeing her dad. Even with everything that happened, Bree has always and always will love her dad. I stopped giving her the things they sent and started putting them into a closet for when Bree got older.

This was the year that I received an unexpected phone call from Ina. Her and the boys were in Indiana and wanted to come see us. We hadn't seen them in years, and Bree and I were so excited. Jeremy and Luke had grown up so much. They ended up staying with us for a couple weeks and we had a blast. By this time, Ina had married and had another baby. Ina had a girl and she was so precious. I have always accepted and loved her as if she were my niece. Bree loves her very much, too. It was a blessing to have the kids together again. Ina and I agreed we wouldn't go so long without staying in touch and we never have.

I was always desperately searching for where I belonged and I felt like I found my place with Ty by my side. Money was really tight, and I ended up getting a job at Walmart working in the pharmacy. I thought it was crazy because, due to my record, I couldn't work at Applebee's and serve beer but I could work in a pharmacy and hand out drugs and needles all day. Truth is, I really enjoyed the job and things were going well for us.

In October Ty asked me to marry him and I said yes. I was determined that this marriage was going to be forever and Ty and I would grow old together. We married on October 25th. It was stupid and I should have never even gotten with Ty, but the fog had settled and I was on cloud nine. I was blind to the underlying purpose of our marriage. For me, it was because I loved Ty. With him, it was for an entirely different reason. Once we were married, it didn't take long at all when Ty began pursuing his citizenship with the financial help of his family. His personality also began to change a lot. He seemed to distance himself from me, and I was so blind I didn't understand why.

I had spoken and met several of Ty's friends and family by this time. Anytime Ty and I would get into an argument I would usually call his friend that lived in the states or his brother who lived in Ireland. They would always talk me down and tell me things were going to be okay, then they would call Ty and he would come back apologizing for being an ass or I would apologize to him. Things were slowly changing though. My smoking was now a problem and Ty seemed to just pick fights when he could. I would do my best to keep Ty happy. I even had our cable turned on just so he had his sports channels and could watch his soccer games.

I never knew what Ty's family or friends would tell him, but, because he would come home and make things right, I never thought twice about it. I thought Ty was actually helping me pick up the pieces and giving me the desire to get myself back on track. Liza and the kids finally found their own place and it was just Dakota, Bree, Ty and me for a while. It's funny looking back on it, all the signs were there and I just didn't want to see them.

A good example would be the day I was using Ty's computer and his Facebook was open. Being the nosy bitch I am, I started looking through it to see what he had going on with his profile. I couldn't believe what I found in his archived messages. My heart dropped and I felt so stupid. It was filled with no less than 80 letters, all to women. He had wrote them all the same letter and it was the same letter he had captured my attention with. You know, the one that claimed how beautiful I was and what a blessing it would be to know me. Yup, that one. I felt like such an ass, but I didn't want to accept what I was seeing. I didn't want to believe I had fallen for a trick and this wasn't real. This man was holding me and telling me he loved me. He made love to me and promised to never leave me. I needed him. I refused to accept -- no, could not accept what we had wasn't real. I didn't want to see the obvious. I was married for the third time, and I definitely didn't want a third divorce. I wanted to prove to the world Ty was not using me. The truth was, Ty had a plan before he ever even came to my house.

To ease my discomfort and confusion, Ty ended up giving me the passwords to his Facebook and his email. I also gave him mine. He always came up with some of the best excuses, and I wanted to believe in him with all that I was. Ty convinced me I had to trust him. What's a relationship without trust, right? I begged Ty to tell me if he was just using me for his citizenship, but he always claimed it had nothing to do with our love.

I was doing much better with my drinking, or at least I thought so. I was working and taking care of all of our bills. I wasn't the drunk who woke up with a bottle in her hand, I was the functioning alcoholic that would work my ass off, take care of all my responsibilities and then proceed to enjoy drinking at the end of the day. Sometimes Ty would criticize me really bad when we would drink together and the alcohol would hit me harder than him. I am not sure if he believed his name calling would help me quit or if he even cared, but it just really tore me down and made me feel belittled. It also made me think about alcohol and drinking more than I ever had.

Fighting with Ty was the one thing I hated the most. He was such a baby when he got upset about something. I was always tiptoeing around him making sure not to say anything to upset him. It wasn't hard to make him mad. Simple things, like not agreeing with his opinion, would set him off. If I would say something that offended him, he would go to our bedroom and literally not talk to me for two or three days. It would crush me so bad when I would sit in front of him crying while trying to apologize and half the time I didn't even feel like I should be apologizing. He would just ignore me, walk away from me and not even acknowledge me talking to him.

When Ty would get over his anger, or whatever it was that made him mad, he would continually apologize for treating me that way. I just wanted to push through and make it work, so I would just leave it in the past and move on. My biggest excuse for his behavior was always "He's from another country, it's different there". I tried harder with Ty than I had with any man I had ever been with. I wanted to make things work between us more than I cared about myself. I was trying to change who I was to make Ty happy. In the end it made me feel lost and miserable.

My weight was starting to bother me more and more. I weighed the same as when I delivered Bree and that was the biggest I had ever been. My mother was always really big and I'll never forget her telling me as a child that, "You're going to grow up and look just like me." I was determined to never allow that to happen so I dedicated my New Year to losing weight. After watching a lot of episodes of the Ellen DeGeneres show, I decided I would dedicate the journey to Ellen. It was in hopes that perhaps she would help pay a year of rent or just help us out. I was still the only one working and I was struggling financially. Ellen is always so loving and giving to people in need that I thought we could maybe get her attention. Bree and I thought making a video diary was a great idea, and Ty did, too.

During the holidays Stacy and Tracy were down and, again, we spent the holidays together. I was happy that even though Bree wasn't seeing her dad she was at least around Chad's family. Even though I was happy Bree didn't have to go over to Jade and Chad's anymore, it still sucked she lost her dad. Throughout everything I have been through, I still feel family is important, but not if it is a family that is tearing you down. Sometimes it is the family we choose that is more supportive than the family we are born into.

Ty was starting to shut down and be quiet a lot of the time. It was crazy how fast things changed once we were married. I always came up with reasons why it was okay for a grown man to act like such a child. I let a lot of things go, apologized for things I shouldn't of and made excuses where there shouldn't have been any made, all the while fighting to convince myself I was happy even though inside I was a mess. Ty was very judgmental after we married. He got so much worse on criticizing me and tearing me down. I knew that being just 'some drunk', like Ty called me, wasn't what I wanted in my life. I knew I was better than that. Somehow I allowed Ty to convince me I was nothing more than what he called me.

I bounced from feeling loved to feeling like I wasn't worth a thing. Ty was so good at lifting me up, but he was also very good at tearing me down. He knew exactly what to say and how to say it to make me feel like everything wrong with our marriage was my fault. It was crazy how hard I tried to make him happy. I would do everything from cooking, cleaning, laundry, to writing love letters on the mirrors with lipstick for him. I did everything I wished someone would do for me. I would surprise him with cards that expressed my love, small gifts, anything I could to make sure he knew my love was true and pure. I supported us financially and, even when things were tight, I did what I could to get us out of the house. It was hard for me financially, but somehow I made it work.

After Christmas, of course, the New Year began……..

Chapter TWENTY-TWO

2012: After the New Year I began dedicating every day I worked to making a video for Ellen DeGeneres. I worked at Walmart, which was a little over four and a half miles from our home. My plan was to walk to work every day I was scheduled and to make a dedication video to Ellen when I would do it. At first it took me an hour and 15 minutes to get there, but by the end I could walk the four and a half miles in 45 minutes.

I spent the entire year making video after video. I would upload them to Facebook and YouTube daily. Whether rain, snow or sun, I walked. I was shocked by the support I was receiving. People would even come up to me in the store and ask if I was the woman walking in the mornings. One time a woman came up to me and told me I was such an inspiration and that my dedication was honorable. It almost brought me to tears.

The videos were awesome and fun to make. Bree and Ty even got in on a few of them and talked to Ellen. We watched the show every day and all of us felt like we had a chance that she would call. I don't know if you ever watched Ellen DeGeneres, but she is such a funny and loving person. It was crazy because, although Ellen never did get a hold of us, she inspired me to do better every day. I was walking in the snow, rain, I didn't care. I was dedicated and wanted to do this for myself, but even more for my family.

Bree was so excited about the smallest chance of Ellen calling us there was no way I could quit. I even had people from all over supporting my videos. A published author, who is a friend of mine, wrote a small article for the local paper and, although it didn't get published, it was so cool to have that kind of support. It was no less than three times a week someone new was coming up to me and telling me how I was inspiring them to do better. I was honestly amazed by the reaction and support I was receiving. It made me feel like I was making some difference in my life.

Bree was really big into choir during this year. She absolutely loved it and wanted to be involved in every activity that had to do with choir. I supported her 100%. I was so glad she found something she really enjoyed. She ended up being in 'Circle the State with Song' and received a plaque for her participation two years in a row. I never understood how I was able to raise such a wonderful little girl. She had been through a lot, but I was always shocked at how little she allowed it to tear her down. Not only the things Jade had done, but I was far from some perfect mother. I made mistakes and just kept doing the best I could for Bree.

I had a surprise visit in April by one of my old carnie friends. He was actually one of the men that trained me in the Circle of Science and had been a dear friend to Paul also. He is a pretty amazing guy and it was really good to see him. Now my friend may have been in his late forties and looking like life had really taken its toll on him, but his energy and spirit were as young as it was years ago when I first met him. It made me reflect a lot on Paul and, although it was tough, I was thankful for his visit. We had a lot of fun reminiscing on the old days and the way things used to be. It was wonderful to have that connection from so long ago. I still keep that connection with not only him, but his son also.

During the same time I was making the videos to Ellen DeGeneres, Ty and I ended up in another fight. He said it was only the drinking that tore us apart. I ended up talking to one of his family members who told me in Nigeria they don't see alcoholism as prominent as it is here in the states. Ty felt I should just stop drinking, no big deal. That was fine for during the day; however, the war within me began at night when I was sitting at home and everything needing taken care of was taken care of.

I would have one hell of a time getting alcohol off my mind after the day was done. I would just get bored and convince myself, because I had taken care of all my responsibilities, it wasn't a big deal to drink. I usually always asked Ty if it was okay if we got a bottle and he rarely was against it, yet, he would usually get mad and go off on me by the time we were done drinking the bottle. I would end up in tears, begging for his forgiveness for whatever it was I did to set him off. Half the time I didn't even understand why he was upset.

The truth is, I was starting to suffer more frequently from blackouts. It was as if the alcohol was going straight through me. I believe my liver may not have been the best, it wasn't able to process the alcohol properly and that's what caused me to get so drunk so fast. It was only when my mother came down I really hit the bottle hard with the purpose to get drunk. I didn't go out to bars and had no interest in running around on Ty. When I was drinking, it would be at home and my husband was drinking with me.

If I had blacked out I would wake up confused and with Ty mad at me. He would claim I did something to hurt him or offend him. It was a vicious cycle of me feeling guilty and begging Ty to forgive me even when I had no clue what he was talking about. I had partied for years – a redhead, woman in menopause that had ran and worked a bar. Not at one point was I ever violent or turned violent on anyone. I hadn't even been in a fist fight since I lived in New Mexico. However, for some reason with Ty, I would throw things at him and go crazy when I blacked out. I didn't realize then, when I was drunk, Ty would start calling me names and yelling at me. Ty threatened to leave me again and I begged him to stay.

In order to convince Ty to stay with me this time and not give up on us, I told him I would go to the doctor and ask to be put on Antabuse (a drug that makes you extremely sick if you drink). I had considered going on it before and had already talked with the pharmacist, plus done some research online about it. Ty and I both went to the doctor and I began six months of sobriety. I didn't drink a drop. That is what Ty wanted, so I did it for him. While at the doctors, I also asked about my memory issues. I was forgetting things more often, even sober, and it scared me to think there was a chance I could end up with Alzheimer's like my father had.

The doctor wasn't very encouraging on helping me with my memory. He just said menopause could be what was causing my problem and there wasn't much we could do about that.

Bree was turning 13 years old soon. I wanted to do something really special for her, so I started preparing early and made all the plans plus ordered all the things I needed for her surprise. Our upstairs had three bedrooms, one master bedroom and two others that were connected to each other by a door between them. I took off the door in between the rooms in order to connect them both. I had Bree go stay with one of her friends for a few days and got started. I remodeled Bree's room, along with the spare room. I painted the walls blue and green, her favorite colors at the time, and decorated it with black bubbles. I made the spare room into her own personal teen zone. I got her a flat screen T.V., a Wii, a PlayStation, a small blow up couch and a play table that was an all-in-one. The play table went from air hockey to pool table to several other games. I also got her a dartboard and a small basketball hoop. It was the first girl/boy party she was allowed to have and she was so excited. The turnout was awesome and seeing her face when she went upstairs to her new teen zone and bedroom was priceless.

As I have said before, I have always been pretty strict with Bree. I know some of the time she thinks it is because I'm just being a bitch, but, the truth is, I strive to always do the best I can for her. I do not claim in any way I am perfect or have some great answers to things in life, but I do promise to always be honest and real. I know there is a lot I have overcome and, it may seem like I should be in a straightjacket, perhaps locked away in a room with cushioned walls; however, God has always renewed me. He gives me strength when I am weak. And when I feel void of that strength, I hold my head up and rely on the truth that He is still with me. I never won a battle on my own. God was and is always there. Even during the times it was my choices that made things harder for me, He never abandoned me and it took me a long time to realize that.

We weren't created to be or demonstrate perfection. Every single one of us make mistakes. I think it is in those moments we can grow and learn the most. Each day is a new day and a new opportunity to make better choices. It is hard when you are under constant attack and it's coming from all directions, especially for those who are trying to be better and their past is held against them all of the time. I believe we are in a daily spiritual battle and most of us spend it focused on ourselves. How can I fix me? How about focusing on becoming more spiritual than mental? Meaning we are in a spiritual war so why do most of us fight physically? Have you ever felt like your mind was hurting you worse than someone else was, like when my mind continued to be haunted by visuals of hurting Jade?

Even after I was begging God to take the violent bloody visuals away from me, they stayed for years. It was only when I referred back to Dr. Neil Anderson and his seminar, "The Bondage Breaker," that I was truly free from that demon's hold. The war in my mind never had anything to do with my dislike for Jade because of the way she treated Bree, it was my own mind I was battling. Until I realized I was in a spiritual battle, I was always wandering around in the dark, afraid to share what I was really thinking because I thought something was wrong with me. I can't hide now. I'm keeping no secrets. Here I am, the real me. The bare and true me is right here in your hands. I had to forgive Jade in order to be free. I have learned not to hold onto my anger and pain because it just makes it grow and become worse.

Now, Dakota had left for a while, but he came back to the house out of the blue one day. After visiting, I made steaks and noticed Dakota wasn't eating. It was not normal at all for my little brother to pass on a steak. As we talked a little longer, Dakota told us he was having trouble with some stuff called 'Spice'. It isn't marijuana, but looked like it. Spice was actually supposed to be used as an air freshener like potpourri.

Dakota and his buddies had been smoking it for a while and it was making Dakota sick. He was puking blood and couldn't eat anything. I took the little bag that he had and flushed it down the toilet. Ty and I agreed Dakota needed to stay with us for a little while till he got on his feet. Ty was still unable to work at this time because he was waiting on his temporary residency to be approved. After a couple months with both Dakota and Ty at home, I began crying one day. I explained to them I couldn't keep taking care of things on my own. The money I was making didn't cover all the bills. I don't know how we made it as long as we did, honestly.

Ty started doing the best he could to help. He got a few odd jobs that paid under the table, but it didn't last long. Dakota ended up getting a job at the store with me and things worked out good. Bree was doing her thing and just loving life. She was enjoying having her uncle around, and even started calling Ty dad by her own choice. It was going well, and I wasn't drinking a drop. Ty and I still fought on and off, but it wasn't about drinking. I almost believed he enjoyed being mad at me, but I continued to do what I could to keep the peace with him and try to make him happy.

I started to realize Ty was going up to the library almost every day, and I knew it was for the Internet. I am not sure why, but it just started to seem strange to me. I felt like he was hiding something. One day I started digging in his computer again and found some dating sites that were being visited frequently. When I questioned Ty about the dating sites, he told me he had met some Mexican guy at the library and was letting him use the laptop. He swore to me it wasn't him on those sites. I didn't believe him and it didn't even make sense why he would let anyone else use his laptop. It hurt me and I just couldn't let it go. The next day, after I got home from work, I waited till Ty fell asleep, grabbed his laptop and began searching it again. As I dug deeper, I found that Ty was pretending to be a 50-some year old white guy. He was talking to and hitting on women through these random dating sites. I couldn't believe it and, when I confronted Ty, he broke down and started crying. He said he was just trying to get money out of random women so he could, "help me" with the bills. I looked right in his eyes and said, "How can we be blessed by God while you are trying to steal from others?" He agreed to never do that again, and I just didn't know what to do. As most of the crazy things he did, I again ended up letting it go and moving on despite the hurt and pain it caused me.

I chose to remain blind to the obvious signs because I enjoyed the love I thought Ty was providing me. I even began to hate telling people Ty was from Nigeria because the first thing they would do is respond with 'oh be careful' or 'watch out for that guy'. I knew Ty had his issues, but so did I. He put up with a lot from me so I convinced myself that, if together, we could get through anything. Ty was really complicated to adjust to and the first and only man I tried to change for. It wasn't healthy for me in any way. I would think carefully before speaking to him because he would get upset so easily. He was never violent, but his judgments on me were clear and defined by his silence and arrogant behavior.

Ty was the kind of man that if I said the sky was a beautiful blue, he would then google it and say it was a light blue. He had to be right about everything at all times and it was so hard to try to please a man that was like that.

I did end up asking him for a divorce on a few occasions, but he would actually start to cry. He would convince me something was wrong with him and tell me how he was going to change. He would tell me he was going to work on himself and make things better. Things would be good for about a month or so. He would be loving and communicate like when he first came, but it would always go back to silence and no communication. It was always an emotional roller coaster, but I was dedicated to the ride. Eventually, our problems would go back to being all my fault.

Ty had handled all of his applications for his citizenship on his own without an attorney. He was finally granted a two-year Temporary Residency and was able to get a job. That made us both extremely happy, but he was different with money then I was used to. We fought over money for a long time and we finally just agreed on what amount he would give me to help pay the bills. The other chunk of his money he would claim he was sending home to his mom or sister. He had several bank accounts, but he was very secretive about his money and banking. I found it strange, but it was easier to just ignore it then fight with him over it.

Ty had to have his Temporary Residency for two years before he could receive his Green Card, which provided him with a ten-year citizenship. We even had to go to an interview and take our wedding pictures with us. I truly believed this man loved me and was in this for the long haul, but I had moments I doubted him because of how withdrawn he would become. When I would ask him if he was just using me and explain that I would still help him, he was always smooth to quickly reassure me it was just me. He would convince me he was here for good and I was wrong for thinking he could ever use me. It's insane how blind and stupid we can be when it comes to love and wanting it.

Ty knew from day one I couldn't have kids and, looking back on it now, I realize it was just another reason I was perfect for his hustle. He started making comments about how beautiful our children would be and how bad he wanted kids. I began to feel like something was wrong with me. I am a woman, having children is something I should be able to do, but with my partial hysterectomy it simply wasn't possible. I would go back and forth emotionally on why he was making those comments. Didn't he realize how much that actually hurt me? Honestly, I am not really sure if Ty ever really cared if he hurt me or not.

By the end of the year I had about 78 videos on YouTube dedicated to Ellen DeGeneres. I had also lost 60 pounds and was looking like my normal, well fit self. Ty was shocked at how good I looked and I loved his attention when he gave it. Although, it wasn't always good with Ty, the moments he did act like he cared were precious to me. I wanted him to be happy and I tried to do what I could to make sure he felt that way as often as possible.

The videos also brought people back in my life I hadn't spoken to in a long time, which included some of my Butterfield friends from New Mexico, cousins living in Florida and a few others. Everyone was encouraging me and saying the most positive things about my dedication. I still couldn't believe that people were taking notice and even trying to help me by sending the links of the videos to the Ellen DeGeneres show. It was amazing and felt good to have such overwhelming support, not only in the store I worked but online as well.

Jade was still trying to play her games and made a comment on one of my videos about how I was a liar and she hoped that Ellen looked into my story before helping me. It really cut right through me because the videos and losing weight had nothing to do with Jade in any way. She posted she was happy someone told her about what I was doing and how I was so pathetic. My biggest hater was watching all my videos, which was no shocking news to me; however, posting some comment full of her negativity and lies on my video just pissed me off. Ty talked me into deleting it and not even feeding Jade with a response, so I did. I had never been submissive to a man emotionally or physically in my life, by choice, but I was with Ty. I didn't feel like it was wrong because I had never done it before. I convinced myself, since I was never willing to change for anyone else, perhaps it was the answer to making my marriage work. Even Dakota questioned me and asked me why I let Ty treat me the way he did. Truth is, I just wanted to make things work when it came to Ty. But changing me to please him was never the right answer.

By the time I had met Ty I had two half sleeves and several other tattoos. I thought it would be cool to throw a Halloween party and have a tattooist come to give tattoos at the party. I didn't care for Halloween, but I wanted to build any positive memories I could with Ty. The party turned out great, but Ty ended up upset at me because I wanted to get more work done on my tattoos. He asked me not to get anymore, but I rebelled and ended up starting a piece that was to go from my ring finger, up my arm, then down my entire left side and then simply end on my toe. I wasn't backing down from my tattoos and my love for fresh ink. It was the one thing that I felt I could do for myself and he wasn't taking that away from me.

Close to Christmas a huge box appeared on my front porch. When I pulled the box in the house I had no clue what it was. I am so thankful that Bree was at school that day because it was a six foot tall teddy bear. One foot on this ginormous teddy bear was embroidered with the word 'Bree' and the other said, 'Love Dad'. How the hell was I going to stash a six foot tall teddy bear? I thought about how bad it would suck to have this thing daily remind Bree of all her pain and suffering. I felt that her having to look at it every day would remind her of her dad and the emptiness and anger she felt from what she had endured over the years. I was angry because I felt like Jade and Chad did it on purpose, obviously. After thinking about it and talking to Mrs. Green, I decided to make it a Christmas present from Ty. Bree had already been calling Ty dad for months and it was the only thing I could think to do other than throw it away.

Bree was still seeing Mrs. Green, but not at all as frequently. She was doing so well now she didn't have the stress and pressure of having to go to Chad and Jade's, plus, Stacy and Tracy were still coming and spending time and holidays. We didn't miss many birthdays or family events with them. I even asked what Tracy thought about the six foot tall teddy bear and she didn't seem to disagree about my decision to make it from Ty. Although Ty and Bree got along well, I always noticed Ty would keep his distance as far as doing things with Bree. I asked him to try to get more involved with her, but he didn't seem to care too. I didn't understand why, but let it go and figured they would work out their relationship in time.

I convinced myself Ty was still adjusting to life in America. He had only been in the U.S. since May of 2010, so when we started talking in October of the same year he hadn't been here long. Food was different for him and he really missed his native foods. At first, Ty acted like he liked most of my cooking and ate the food I cooked all the time. There were a few times he ended up with a bellyache from whole milk, but, all in all, we were on the same level as for what I cooked for our dinners. Ty and I always talked about going to the African grocery store in Indianapolis as soon as we financially could. I was anxious to see what food he ate and how different it was from ours.

Sitting here now, I realize more why I fell so hard for Ty in the beginning, he was intelligent and very good looking. But with that aside, when we first got together we were always talking and conversing. I was always asking him about Africa and how things were over there. I always had some question about something and tried to keep the conversations between us going. At one point, I even did some research on Nigeria and the role their women play. I just wanted to please Ty, but what I didn't realize was I was losing myself while doing it. I was always worried about how he felt or how he would react. I truly set myself aside when it came to Ty and he knew it. I thought if I approached this marriage differently and actually put in effort, then everything would work out.

It was about six months after I started the Antabuse and I hadn't drank anything with alcohol. Ty and I discussed it, both felt my drinking was now under control, so I stopped taking the medication. It didn't take long until Ty and I began drinking again. We didn't drink all of the time, but once Bree was down for bed we would have our adult alone time.

Christmas was great and all of the family, including Stacy, Tracy and the kids, really enjoyed themselves. I usually always held the holidays at my home because it was a bigger house and easier on me. Even one of Ty's friends came down from Michigan. I will never forget the moment when he walked in and his shirt said, "Trust me, I'm Nigerian!" It was so funny. He was the kind of man that had music going on in his head at all times. Ty's friend was always dancing and so full of energy. At one point, Dakota was sitting on the couch and Ty's friend came in the kitchen and asked us if Dakota was gay. We died laughing. See, while he kept dancing, Dakota couldn't help but stare at him because the way that he danced was so different. I didn't really like or trust Ty's friend and it wasn't because of his shirt. It was so obvious he was playing so many women on Facebook and trying to find one to marry him to get his citizenship. I believe he ended up paying a woman to marry him and fake their marriage, which is how he is a citizen now. The man had about four or five Facebook accounts and it was wrong to me the way he played with women's emotions. Amazing how it was so obvious to me what he was doing to other women, yet I couldn't see what was happening to myself.

By the holidays, Ty and I seemed to be getting better at communicating when we disagreed. Bree and I had talked to Ty's family on occasion and they seemed to care about us. I really thought with Bree and me being involved with Ty's family it would help bring all of us closer as a family. Ty's brother, in Ireland, even mailed Bree an Irish Flag for Christmas.

Once the holidays were over, it was that time of year again. I had no idea what was in store for us, but the year ended and the new began.....

Chapter TWENTY-THREE

2013: The New Year didn't start well for any of us. Early in January, Oscar, our step-father, passed away and Dakota didn't handle the news well. Dakota was very close to Oscar throughout the years, so for him it was like losing his dad all over again. Oscar really went downhill after he had his surgery. He had cancer in his mouth and had to have a muscle in his shoulder taken out and put in place of his tongue which was removed. It was hard to understand him and, when he would put a 40 oz. beer straight into his feeding tube, it was impossible for me to know what he was saying. My mom and Dakota always knew what he was saying because they had spent a lot of time with Oscar. With the news of his death, Dakota broke down for a bit. All we could do was pull together and be there for Dakota.

It was about two weeks after the news of Oscar's death we received the news of Ty's father unexpectedly passing away in Africa. I had a hard time understanding exactly what caused his death, but Ty didn't take it well at all. I actually stayed next to our bed for three days as Ty mourned the loss of his father. I sat on the floor next to him most of the time because I didn't want my movements to disturb him when he was able to sleep. I stayed by his side and was there for anything he asked for or needed. I wanted to be right there to make sure I could provide emotional support. We cried together and I felt so bad for his heartache.

The loss of Ty's father really changed Ty. He began to distance himself from prayer and from God after his father passed away. He shut something off inside of himself and I understood that more than I would have liked to admit. Ty felt guilty for not calling his father more often and it tore him apart. I knew and could relate with loss, especially that of a father. I wanted so bad to just take the pain away from Ty, but all I could do was hold him and be there every second he needed my embrace. I felt it was important that Ty knew he didn't have to go through that loss alone and he didn't.

Soon after all the bad news, I started to encourage Bree to get involved in a sport at school and she ended up in diving. She loved it and was actually really good at it. I would tease her, because being a loudmouth mother who hoots and hollers in complete support of her child, diving isn't something you can do that at. She would dive and everyone would do a simple quiet clap. I behaved, but Bree always laughed at me when she was done and we would be leaving because that is when I would jump her and start hooting and hollering. Stacy and Tracy also came up and watched a meet with us. Bree was still very involved in choir and participated in the 'Circle the State with Song' again. She was doing really good in school and finally had a somewhat normal life, whatever normal is exactly.

I was also able to petition my college during this year, because I had failed out when Paul died, to fight to be allowed back in. I did everything required and was accepted to start back for fall semester at a nearby University. I was excited to get back to school, but, truth is, it didn't last long. I ended up becoming full-time at work, and trying to balance work, life and school seemed impossible for me. I give so much credit and respect to those who balance full-time work with full-time college, plus full-time parenting. For me, doing that on top of taking care of my daughter was not working out and it didn't take long before I had to choose work over school.

With Ty, Dakota and I all finally working, things at the house were getting much easier for us. Ty and I talked and agreed, as long as I didn't get drunk, we didn't feel drinking was a problem for either of us anymore. We would both drink and get a little wild on nights that Bree stayed at her friends or with Stacy and Tracy. Dakota never had a problem finding a friend to stay with. He has always been a person that ends up with groups of friends around him.

Ty and I had so many fun nights of dancing in our living room together, plus our sex life was a lot of fun. I was not shy to dress up for my man. A lady in the street, but a freak in the sheets. I was dedicated to Ty and no other man could take my attention off of him. I tried to do whatever I could to please him, whether in the bedroom or just in and out of our daily lives. He was all I thought I wanted. We had worked through all the crazy fights and were actually getting so much better when we disagreed on things.

Another thing that really won me over with Ty was he could move. His style of dancing was so different and very attractive to me. I loved when he would just start dancing to the music out of the blue. He had the power to make my heart flutter just by smiling at me. I was actually starting to completely love being his wife. We really enjoyed one another and things seemed to be falling into place peacefully.

We weren't drinking often, but there were a few nights here and there I wouldn't be able to handle my alcohol when we did drink and Ty would get mad at me. I started to realize what was happening and tried to talk to Ty about it. See, when we would buy a fifth we would drink it shot for shot and we always drank the same amount; however, when my body would get intoxicated and Ty's wouldn't he would get mad at me for getting drunk. Ty would then begin calling me names while I was drunk and it would never end well. He wasn't nice about it, either. He would call me a worthless drunk and several other names that would send me into a violent rage. Most nights I blacked out as soon as our fighting began. I asked him to take note he couldn't come at me with anger and being mean to me if we were going to drink together and he agreed to stop, but he never did. I thought I could control the amount I drank with moderation. Truth is, though, once the bottle cracked open any idea of moderation was gone because we drank until the last shot was poured. Some nights were great and we had a blast, but the nights that alcohol hit me harder were hell.

In July Ty and I ended up going to Michigan for one of the most beautiful weddings I have ever been to. It was so different and held very late

355

at night. What they did was held a normal American wedding during the day then it was time for the African wedding that night. It was incredible how beautiful the dresses were and the colors were amazing. Everyone was celebrating and so happy. The room was filled with so much love, and I enjoyed myself a great deal. It was an amazing night spent with Ty's friends and we were thankful for the time we got to spend there.

The next day Ty and I went over to his friend's house where the celebrations were still going on. The ladies were all cooking and preparing food while some of the men were in the back just visiting. There was a barbeque and the food was incredible. I really enjoyed our time in Michigan.

While we were at the wedding, Bree actually got to spend some time with Ina and all the kids. Each summer we try to swap kids so all of us have time with one another.

The entire trip was wonderful and, on our way home, we stopped by my mother's. She was now living with her parents in their basement and had piles of things to give me. Mom always loaded me up or brought piles and bags upon bags of things when she would come to our house. Just things and usually nothing specific. It was stuff she purchased at yard sales or on discount. She loved thrift stores and the freebie items so it was always random things. I would go through everything and keep what I wanted then just give the rest away or donate it. This time was a little different. Once we got back home and we were done unloading everything, I sat down and began going through all the boxes and items my mother had given me. I just wanted to start crying. She had given me things before I didn't feel right about. I already had my baby books, things from my childhood and all the items of my father's. I even had all Dakota's baby books and most of his pictures. I really thought I already had everything a mom should keep and you shouldn't have until she passes away; however, I was wrong. My mom gave me things that Derek's kids should have. There were letters Derek wrote mom while he was in the Navy. All kinds of his things, including everything of mine and Dakota's baby items. She gave me all of our family photos still in the frames. She gave me all of it. I went through it with Dakota and we made a box for Luke and Jeremy for when they get older. Dakota asked me to hold onto his things until he was more settled, so I have a box for him put up also. It really hurt Dakota and me both, we just felt weird about having things we thought a mother would hold precious until the day she left this world.

It wasn't long after we were home we were loading up for a family camping trip. Ty wasn't real excited about the camping trip, but he had never been camping so there was no telling if he would like it or not. I know how to camp in style, and I brought everything we could possibly need. I love cooking on the fire and the smell of the woods. I have always loved the outdoors and was excited about this trip. So was Bree, she's the same as me when it comes to camping and being outdoors.

I personally feel Ty had decided that he wouldn't like the experience before we even went. He didn't enjoy the camping trip and we did get rained out almost the entire time. Ty and I had one fight the first night we stayed there because I had drank a little. I wasn't drunk and was just enjoying our time. In the morning we both apologized and moved past it. We ended up going to different places and I thought we really had a good time. Dakota even came out for a night and hung out with us.

On the occasions that Ty would get upset, most of the time it wouldn't make any sense to me. I felt like we had overcame so much so there was nothing we couldn't' get through. We fought about drinking or money. The rest of the fights were so petty I always swallowed my pride and apologized, again, even when I didn't feel I should have. What I thought was insane was I wouldn't drink unless Ty did. If we drank, it was always together. I didn't understand the problem. We weren't drinking daily, and I never wanted to again, but Ty always wanted to stir an issue where there wasn't one. It would confuse me and hurt me so much because I thought I was okay. I was at home, safe with my husband and we weren't getting too crazy or out of control. Ty would tell me he was afraid I was going to go back to drinking daily, yet had no problem bringing a bottle home for us to drink together. I tried to explain I only did that after Paul died and I wasn't trying to drink my life away anymore, but I felt like Ty only saw me as a drunk and he just couldn't see past that. I felt like I was good. I took care of our bills, my daughter and worked every day. I wasn't drinking when I had other responsibilities and was taking care of business. It was only when I would get drunk he would get angry and tell me I needed to have control; however, I was binge drinker -- I am a binge drinker. Once that bottle is open and I get that first shot in me, I want more. I could go months without drinking, but the moment I start again, well, I could drink for days.

When Ty came to me in February of 2011, he saw what other people didn't. I was drinking every single night when we got together. Actually, I had been drinking every single day after Paul died. At night, Ty saw me so wasted that there were even some nights I passed out during sex. I can't begin to tell you how many times Ty held my hair back while I got sick or how much blood I was puking during the first few months we were together. I was a mess, and I hid it well for a long time, but Ty saw me as I was. Truth is, my daughter and I have had to do a lot of healing. I've asked for her forgiveness because of my behavior and how it really did affect her. Even though she doesn't know everything I did she knew enough. She felt how off I was and how lost I was. I hurt my child then, and I can't express how bad I wanted to get a grip on myself but couldn't after Paul passed away. I am beyond thankful for Bree's forgiveness. I am also thankful that Ty helped me pull out of that place; but, he only saw me there in that place even though I wasn't in that place anymore.

At this time in my life I wasn't drinking to drown myself or hide from the world. Most of the time Ty and I were enjoying ourselves and there were even nights that drinking was Ty's idea. I felt like I had my shit together. I wasn't going to go backwards and drink my life away. I knew I didn't want to be that woman and knew I was better than to allow alcohol to control me. I didn't see anything wrong with drinking on occasions and enjoying ourselves. Ty, however, kept trying to make deals with me. One time we even talked about what we drank making a difference in how bad the alcohol would hit me. Again, he was good drinking with me, but not me getting drunk. Unfortunately, even though we weren't drinking every day, I began focusing on alcohol so much it was all I thought about at night once things were settled.

Ty convinced me I had a massive alcohol problem, even while bringing alcohol in front of me. I begged him on several occasions to look up alcoholism and how it works, but I don't think he ever did. It was so very confusing to me, and I didn't understand how he would be doing one thing and saying another. I would even tell myself I wasn't going to drink with him anymore so he couldn't get mad at me, but then another bottle would come in the house and we would drink. We both contributed to the problem and then he would just sit back and complain about how I had a problem. I did have a problem, but I wasn't with a person that was there to help me. I knew I had to help myself, but I didn't know how. I wanted to count on Ty to be there for me, but it was never his intention.

I began to just focus on work and trying to get my felonies dropped down to misdemeanors. Having felonies hurts you in so many ways. By this time, I wasn't even able to volunteer to help Bree with anything in school or any extracurricular activities. As for work, I was given a raise and promoted to a Department Manager. I set my goal at becoming a Store Manager within the next five years and even won an award for employee of the month. I didn't want to be known as a felon or defined by the mistakes of my past, I just wanted to get my life together and be successful at what I was doing.

I typed up my petitions and filed them with the Courts. It had been over seven years since I had gotten in trouble and received my first felony. The felony charge for driving as a Habitual was dropped without any problems and that left me one more to fight for. When I went to court, I was sure it would be dropped since it had been so long ago, but the prosecutor made a very lame argument about my other felony being dropped and it seeming suspicious. I was surprised when I saw the judge denied my request. So the only felony I still have is from 2005, ten years ago.

Ty and I continued to grow and work through our disagreements. There were no more days of him not talking to me and hiding in our bedroom.

He would actually take some time and then we would talk about whatever it was we didn't agree on, most of the time. There were a few days he would hold onto the fight, but we were finally at a point he wasn't going days ignoring me. I couldn't handle his anger and judgment against me because he held onto the anger for so long. I had never met anyone that would hold onto anger as long as he did. Almost every fight was my fault, so he claimed, and even begging him for his forgiveness would make no difference. If it was a bad fight, he would always threaten to leave or actually leave. One time he even had my friend take him to the bus stop, but he always came back. As I told you before, he left several times a year.

Even though things seemed to be getting better, I still felt alone a lot of the time with Ty. I felt like every time I would say I loved something about him he would take it away from me. I loved the way Ty danced and he danced so much when we first got together, but when I admitted that I loved watching him he stopped dancing as much. In the four years of our marriage, Ty purchased flowers for me three times. When I would ask him to be a little more romantic or show some passion, he would just close up and withdraw from me more. It was only when I would sit down and talk about how unhappy I was, or the few times I told him I wanted a divorce, that he would try to show passion and romance. It would last for that month or two then it would all go back to the way it was. I was trying to adjust to everything, convincing myself this man was from another country and that's why he was so different. I convinced myself of that a lot.

Due to Ty being on the dating site and withdrawing from me so much, I did go through his Facebook and email on rare occasions. There was one time I was looking through Ty's emails and found he was trying to keep some kind of record of our arguments in his email drafts. It was so funny because he wrote about me asking him to be romantic and how he just couldn't be romantic all the time. The same man that was dancing and singing "I love you, I love you" couldn't be romantic? The same man that did everything he could romantically to win me over and marry me couldn't show passion? I found it funny because I never asked him to be romantic all the time, but once in a while would have been really nice.

I continued to stay in constant confusion with Ty. I would feel a mix of what I thought was love and then complete anger from him. I didn't know how to feel half the time. It was insane how for several nights things would be fine and then we would have a free night, drink, dance and make wild love. Then another night we would repeat the same events and Ty would get upset at me. He would always end up leading me to believe everything was always my fault. At one point I believed him and thought I caused all the problems in our marriage. I think that is why I tried so hard with him. I truly loved him and thought I was in love with him. I didn't ever want to be the reason our marriage fell apart. There were some fights between Ty and I that I do remember and some I don't remember anything about. He used to call me a liar because I would explain to him I had no idea why he was so mad and I had blacked out.

When I tried to explain to Ty I was blacking out, he just continued to call me a liar. He knew exactly when I would get to a certain point when we drank together then start a fight with me. I would get so mad and my anger would cancel everything else out. Sometimes I thought he was doing it on purpose. Truth is, I really believe he was. A part of me feels like Ty kept that anger and distance between us so he could do exactly what he did in the end. It was around this time that I kept convincing myself if Ty stayed with me at least three months after he received his green card, his citizenship, then he truly loved me. It was an insane way to look at my marriage, but I bounced so much from feeling loved to feeling hated I didn't know what to think.

One night Ty started a fight with me and we weren't drinking or anything. It was over money, and I had no idea why or where he was coming from. The fight didn't make any sense to me. Honestly, he just seemed like he wanted to fight and I went to bed so mad at him. It was a fight that had no purpose or reason and he was just being an ass.

When I woke the next morning there were a dozen roses sitting on my dresser with a card. This was one of the three times he purchased flowers for me. The card actually read, "I'm sorry I started the fight with you. I just wanted you to appreciate your flowers more!" Seriously, this man started a fight with me to help me appreciate flowers? I began building a wall against Ty. I started questioning if he was just with me for his citizenship or if he even loved me at all.

It was getting old how we could enjoy one another and then, out of the blue, Ty would get upset and call me names. He was always threatening to leave me. It was confusing me so much I wasn't sure what to think about our marriage at all. His threats to leave came so often I was really growing tiresome of the threat. I actually ended up not caring if he left or not. At least I did my best to convince myself of that.

Ty had this way of twisting things so much I found myself always apologizing to him. I was just tired of fighting, honestly. I started reading more books about marriage and trying to make things work. Even during my six months of complete sobriety we fought. It just seemed like it was never ending, and I wasn't giving up on trying to make things better. Ty was very convincing, and I thought perhaps it was me so I continued to try very hard to change myself in order to please him.

Being with Ty was like being on a yo-yo; one minute things would be fine and the next he would be upset at me. He always aimed his anger at my drinking, but I knew it didn't matter. He would be loving and keep me in his grasp and, when I was secure and comfortable in our marriage, he would withdraw and spend months being cold towards me. Then I would come to him about being unhappy, he would make me feel better, and do the same thing over and over.

I was trying everything, even following all the advice that I was reading. I started leaving love letters in lipstick on the mirror and even love notes in his lunchbox because I tried to make his lunch every morning before I left for work. It became so repetitive that, only when I was finally over the neglect from him, he would provide me with the attention I needed. It was always a back and forth feeling and it was starting to really get to me. I continued to feel alone even with Ty next to me. He continued to make me feel like I was asking too much of his attention, but it was a fight just to get his attention to talk about anything.

I never knew a man could be addicted to ESPN and sports the way Ty was. If there was a soccer game or anything sports related on T.V., he wasn't listening to anyone around him. It was so annoying to compete with a television almost every single night. Ty also watched the shows that were about the famous and rich. You know, the reality shows that show the big houses and big money. He was almost obsessed with being rich and always talking about making more money from the day we had met.

Ty told me that in Nigeria everyone thinks money is so easy in America. He said that a lot of the people there picture America as if it were built with streets of gold. Ty was here long enough by this time to know it was a struggle and nothing as he imagined America to be. Did you know that they actually have a Lottery in Africa like our Powerball? If you play there, you have a chance to win a citizenship to America. I was just amazed by that. We play for millions of dollars here and they play for a fighting chance for their dreams to come true in America. Ironic right?

Even with all the fighting between Ty and me, Bree didn't see a lot of it. Not saying she didn't ever see us fight at all, big difference; however, I am a positive and motivated person. I am usually always in a good mood and, whether Ty and I were fighting and no matter the confusion in my heart, I was always happy to be around Bree. She was doing good in school and was pretty much happy all the time. We were always doing things together and she had many friends around our neighborhood. I was so blessed and will be forever blessed to be her momma. Ty always kept his distance from Bree and never got too close to her. I have no doubt he loved her, but looking back now I believe he knew what he was going to do and being close to Bree might have hindered his plans.

It was during late summer when a friend of mine from work won tickets to a Miranda Lambert concert and wasn't able to go. She asked me if I wanted the tickets and I was all about it. I thought that would be something fun to do with Ty since he had never even been to a concert. I knew it could get us out of the house, and I was trying to follow what all the books about healing and helping your marriage said. Everything I was reading said the more memories a couple built together, the longer their relationship lasted. So I tried to talk Ty into going with me, but he refused and claimed he didn't like concerts. I told him he had no idea whether he liked concerts or not since he had never been to one, but he had no interest. I just ended up going with a good friend of mine.

Money always seemed to be a fight on and off from the moment Ty had a job. If it wasn't my drinking that was his problem, it was the money. Ty really became an asshole every single time it came payday and he had to hand me money to help with bills. He wanted to keep his money for himself. I thought things would settle after we agreed to a set amount he would contribute to the house to help cover the bills, but I was wrong. That only lasted for a short time. I even began hating payday because of his attitude.

Ty was keeping over $600 plus of his money every month that didn't go to the bills. That was money that was not to be talked about or he would get upset. He would claim to send money home, but I knew he didn't send all of it home. He had control of all of it, and I didn't care as long as he gave me enough to pay the bills. The only thing that bothered me the most was how anal he would be, and I usually paid for everything, including going out for dinner, family trips, etc. It was strange to be in a relationship so opposite of together. Ty and I were anything but working together. Like I have said, it was like a yo-yo. He would embrace me then push me away. He kept me believing and hanging onto the idea we were going to always pull through our tough times, and I wanted to believe that more than anything.

At one point, Ty even started some business with one of his brothers still in Nigeria. I didn't have anything to do with it, but just let him do his own thing. He kept me at a good distance at all times when it came to his business and money. He was always wanting and talking about more money and being some huge success financially. Truth be told, for the first time in my life I was just happy with our family and beautiful home, but Ty wanted so much more. I wasn't against it. Who doesn't want to make more money? I was happy, however, with all we already had and it was obvious that Ty was not.

Ty was so good at making it all sound like he was doing everything for our family and for our future that I was willing to go with him wherever he wanted to go. Ty also started trying to help other Nigerians with the processing of their citizenship to come to the United States. He was trying to charge his friends in Nigeria a chunk of money to file and apply to colleges here, then guide them through the rest of the process and paperwork. He was never successful at it, but he came close once. If the people he was trying to help acted like him, I am honestly glad it didn't work out for him. I told him I thought it was wrong because he was next to robbing people he was calling friends. It's free and easy to apply to most colleges here. He was charging them and acting as if it was really hard to go through that process and, to me, it was wrong. When I voiced my opinion about it, Ty got so upset at me. I ended up apologizing and just letting it go.

I started to notice Bree was getting a bad attitude about things. It was really strange for her, and I wasn't sure why she was behaving the way she was. Bree was usually always happy, so I started to get worried about her. After I had a long talk with her, I came to realize she had a lot of anger built up inside that she didn't know what to do with. I thank God I happened to run into Mrs. Green at my store. See, by this time, Bree was no longer in therapy and Mrs. Green had retired. After explaining to Mrs. Green about Bree having an attitude and anger issues building up, she suggested Bree write a letter to her dad to express how she felt. She said it didn't matter if I mailed the letter to him or not, it was a way to help Bree get her feelings out.

So when I got home that day, I had Bree sit down and write a letter to her dad. I told her she could write it just as she felt and say whatever she wanted. I honestly never expected a four-page letter filled with so much pain and hurt. The anger Bree had toward her father for allowing Jade to cause her so much pain was immense. The fact that he never believed her when she would tell him what was happening hurt her more than I can express. The words my daughter wrote brought me to tears. It broke my heart that a child I swore to protect, my child, was hurting so much. After Bree finished the letter, it was like you could actually see a weight was lifted off of her shoulders. It didn't take long at all and she was back to normal, feeling better about herself and her attitude was so much more positive. The letter really helped Bree heal.

Things were calm and going well and I was at work one day when my Facebook notifications started blowing up. When I went on break, I was shocked and taken back a bit to see it was Jade all over Stacy's pictures of Bree. Jade was making comments as to how beautiful Bree was becoming and 'liking' all of the ones that had my daughter in them. I suppose I was tagged or had tagged Stacy and that is why my notifications were blowing up, but I instantly unfriended Stacy and Tracy. I was at work and didn't have time to figure out what was going on, but I didn't want to see Jade's name anywhere on my page.

Before I was even able to get home, Stacy was blowing me up and mad at me because I had unfriended her and her mom. Once I finally got home I tried talking to Stacy to figure out why Jade was on any of our Facebook accounts and it dawned on me that maybe Stacy and Tracy were reconnecting and talking with Chad and Jade again. I tried talking to Stacy about what was going on with Bree and how she had been having problems, but Stacy didn't want to hear any of it. I even sent her the letter Bree wrote to Chad about how she felt, but it was dismissed as if it wasn't important. Stacy asked to talk to Bree and I allowed it, but when Bree started crying I took the phone away to find out what was going on. Stacy was telling Bree she needed to talk to her dad and Bree told her she didn't want to.

Stacy was now convinced the things that happened throughout the years were over exaggerated and perhaps Bree wasn't telling the whole truth. Stacy told me she, herself, grew up without a dad and was fine so she didn't understand why Bree's behavior would have anything to do with Chad. She felt me saying Bree was acting out with an attitude didn't make any sense. When I asked Stacy why Jade was even able to be on her page and if they were talking with Chad and Jade again, Stacy said "Yes." It was at that moment I knew exactly what was going on. Stacy and Tracy had always supported and believed in Bree about

366

the things that had happened to her; Now they didn't?

At one point Stacy asked to speak with Bree again. I put the phone on speaker, but Stacy was convinced of whatever Jade and Chad had told her. I respected them talking to Chad, he was her brother and Tracy's son; however, when Stacy claimed that maybe Bree wasn't telling the full truth about the past, I knew right then I would have to do something about this entire family. Stacy even got rude with me and said I was wrong for not telling Bree about the presents Chad sent. I just laughed at her because by this time Bree knew he sent things, but I was putting some of them up for her. I would give her the gifts that came in, but I would usually wait a few days before I let her know who they were from. She took the news much better that way. The cards Chad sent I would just put away because the words in them hurt and confused Bree. Hell, by this time I had even told Bree about the six foot tall teddy bear being sent from Chad. Bree ended up throwing it away, but that was a decision she had the right to make. The way Stacy was acting really took me off guard. It was later that night that I saw all the posts Jade and Stacy had shared about me on Facebook. Stacy was bashing me, along with Jade, and the two of them were having fun doing it on social media. I just blocked all of them.

Jade was trying to convince people I had Delusions of Grandeur and was narcissistic because I had won the custody case. Won? Didn't that woman realize that no one won that case? My daughter has lost years with her father because of Jade's constant emotional abuse. Now here she was claiming I brainwashed my daughter into believing the things that happened and saying they never really happened. To this day, Jade claims she is some good-hearted person and I am a horrible role model for a parent causing Parental Alienation. That woman is straight crazy. Jade was never going to stop and I had already come to face that. It was just the same shit, but a different day when it came to Jade. Instead of responding or trying to fight with any of them, I ended up cutting them all off from Bree and me both. I needed answers to what to do and I had nowhere to turn. I ended up writing a long letter to The Dr. Phil Show and thought for sure if anyone could help me on how to handle this he could.

I blocked Stacy and Tracy from Bree's life and asked Bree to please give me time to pray about this and make sure I made the right decision with how to handle the situation. She was hurt and couldn't believe that her aunt was pretty much calling her a liar. It made Bree feel like none of them believed her, but it wasn't Bree's fault in any way. What happened to Bree was real and someday Jade will be the one to answer to our Heavenly Father for what she did. That's between Jade and our maker!

It was only about three weeks later when I ran into Mrs. Green again and asked her what I should do. I explained to her what happened and that I cut everyone out of Bree's life until I could get an answer on what was best for Bree. Mrs. Green looked at me and told me I was doing the right thing. She said that taking them out of Bree's life was probably the best thing I could do for Bree. Mrs. Green even expressed her disappointment with Tracy, Chad's mom, who she had met and talked to. We have never spent another holiday with any of them. Mrs. Green even said that writing The Dr. Phil Show was a great idea and he could definitely help if he picked up our story.

It wasn't long after I took all of them out of our lives that Bree was shining and smiling every day as she used to. She was healing and church was helping a lot with that. She was always telling me she was praying for me and for our family when she went to church. That child was truly and is truly a blessing. She has grown to be so smart and very dedicated to her beliefs in God. The thing that makes her stand out is her smile because Bree rose above what she has been through and her smile is an example of strength. God has always been watching over her and, even though she went through hell, she made it out.

Soon after all of this happened, I was at work and there was this handsome young man that started at our store as an Assistant Manager. We clicked really good right off the bat. He was so sweet and just an all-around good guy. His name was Dom. I was finding myself very attracted to him physically, but my heart was with Ty. Ty and I were back to the silent nights with conversations feeling like I was pulling teeth or forcing him to talk to me because all he wanted to ever do was watch television. Dom and I ended up becoming really good friends and we began hanging out a lot outside of work. He would even come to the house and hang out with Ty, Dakota, Bree and me. We all got along really well.

At first I thought Dom would make my husband jealous and Ty would pay more attention to me, but it didn't work. It was only about a month and a half later that Ty even said anything about Dom and me spending so much time together. Ty didn't even seem to care at first, but his simple comment about not liking the time I was spending with Dom made me think that perhaps he did love me. What a messed up way to look at the situation. Dom became a very dear friend and Bree loved him to death. Dom and Bree got along really well, and I enjoyed having him around because he talked to me all the time. We always had the best conversations and, since Dom was a deacon's son, talking about God was something we always did. It was as if Dom and I could always find something in common to talk about and it felt good to have a friend like that.

The holidays were good and we did all of our normal traditions we always did each year. Baking cookies, decorations, baking a cake for Jesus and all of it. We spent time with one another and enjoyed the holidays, plus the town parade. I always loved spending time with Bree and doing all we could. Ty was isolating himself more and more. He worked and came home, but getting him to go out with us and doing things was getting harder. He would claim he worked all day and was tired and just wanted to relax. So we let him. The Christmas parade was memorable for Bree and me. We got to walk around the town and look at all the decorations. We had a blast. I took a lot of pictures, as I usually did. Bree really enjoyed the walk and so did I. We have never really had a problem having fun together. Our Christmas and New Years were good, and I was ready to take on the New Year with a positive attitude about it.

And so it began......

Chapter TWENTY-FOUR

2014: The year started out really good. Ty was working and I was loving my job. Ty and I were finally at a good point in our marriage where there were more good times than bad. I still tried my best to make him happy. He was my husband and I wanted to please him. My brother and a few friends noticed I wasn't my normal self and told me I needed to make sure I was happy and not just trying to keep Ty happy. I thought if Ty was happy, I was happy.

I convinced myself that Ty could somehow complete me and that was never further from the truth. Dakota and a few friends kept riding me about how I was acting so different with Ty and I would, again, try to explain that a third divorce wasn't an option for me. I was in this marriage for the long haul and with this man. I would tell my brother I was actually trying with this marriage and that is why I was different. I thought I could somehow become the woman Ty wanted, not ever realizing I was just providing him with what he needed the entire time.

I didn't realize that standing on the outside everything was extremely obvious and, when someone would tell me I was being played, I would simply convince myself they were wrong. Things did get a lot better when I took my brother's advice and I stopped trying to please Ty so much. I actually started focusing on me and not him. I explained to Ty I was done with tiptoeing around him. I felt like he was too sensitive and angered over little things too quickly. He agreed, said he would work on that and it really seemed like he meant it. Things were good again for a couple months, but it all went back to the normal yo-yo effect. Wasn't long until Ty was back to being silent and withdrawn from me.

Before the winter break had ended last year, Bree was caught cheating on a test. I sat her down and we talked for a while about what was going on and why she had cheated. As I listened to her, I began to realize things at school were worse then I knew. Bree was talking about kids selling pills, marijuana and other drugs in the bathroom. She also told me about some girls who were bullying her. She was a freshman now so things were a lot different. Despite the attacks, Bree had already suffered at the hands of her own father and stepmother, I really wanted to protect her from being bullied and abused again.

Our conversation honestly made me reflect on when I was bullied in my youth. I began to realize that it didn't teach me any important lessons except to defend myself and fight back. I wanted Bree to know how to defend herself and fight back, but I didn't feel being pressured into it by a bully was the best way. Let me also mention the fact that things are not the same as they were years ago. Nowadays, there are more and more children out there taking their own lives because of bullying. All I can say about this is don't take your own life over some mean bullies picking on you. A bully is just another person facing their own issues. Yes, they suck and usually take things out on others, but they are not worth giving up your life for. There is a purpose for every single one of us. Trust me when I say to you that in just one day you can make a difference in this world. You have a purpose. It's what we do with our time that is our own choice. You can choose to believe and walk in faith. Accept the fact that, for most of us, change happens every day. Your situation today can change tomorrow. Sometimes it gets easier and sometimes it doesn't, but never give up.

I believe it is through our battles that we become the warriors we are meant to be. Stand tall, my friend, you are not alone. We aren't here to hurt each other and to continue tearing one another down, so make a choice to not be the bully. Take a stand and make a change for yourself. Love is a powerful essential in life. We can be broken, not shattered and still show love. The walls that most of us build in order to protect our hearts is not only keeping things out, but it's also holding things in. Let your walls down and fear not.

After a long talk with Bree about what was happening at school, I sat back and prayed on what to do for her. I kept coming back to the idea of homeschooling. I began to research some of the programs that were available and Bree ended up finishing her freshman and sophomore years in a great homeschooling program. She really enjoyed the freedom it gave her and she passed her classes without being bullied or dealing with drug dealers. What was crazy is the local newspaper ran an article soon after she started homeschooling. The entire article was about more security guards being placed in the high school. I pray it benefited that school.

Ty ended up losing his job and was very upset, but I tried to comfort him and explain that everything would be fine. I had supported Ty and our home on my own for a long time before he ever got his job so I knew as long as we stuck together we could make it. I wasn't making a lot of money, but I was able to keep us afloat. With Ty home he would clean to help contribute and, on occasion, make Bree and I his wonderful rice and stew. When Ty first came to the house, he would ask me to get him specific items when we went grocery shopping and I would. He had two recipes he would cook that were delicious. I always tried to make sure Ty had what he liked in the house at all times. It didn't take long before Ty began job hunting, but it took several months before he was able to find something.

Everything became so peaceful at the house and, even though Ty had lost his job, we were able to go out to do extra fun things here and there. It would take some persuasion, but Bree and I got Ty to go out too. One day Ty, Bree and I all loaded up and went to the apple orchard. We had a blast running around on the hay bales. We even took a bunch of family pictures and drank warm apple cider. It was so nice to just spend that time together. Ty and I ended up finally making it to the African store in Indianapolis. He was a bit disappointed in the selection, but all in all he was able to get some of his native food and was happy with that.

Out of the blue one night when we were all sitting in the living room my phone rang and I picked it up. The voice on the other end said, "Hello, I am -- and I am from the Dr. Phil Show." My stomach turned and I was excited that this was really happening. As we talked, the woman said she had never heard of a custody case lasting so long. I went on to explain the situation and what I had done back in November with cutting all of Chad and his family out of Bree's life. I also told her about speaking with Mrs. Green and what she had said. I explained that Bree was doing so good I didn't want to open those wounds for her again. In the end, the woman said it sounded like I was doing the right thing and, if anything else occurred, give the show a call. She told me she was going to put my letter on the shelf just in case. There have been a couple occasions Bree wishes I would have tried to get on the show. I think it's because she would feel safer being on the show when she talks to her dad for the first time. Perhaps I should have tried, but I thought I was making the best decision at the time.

It was always when I felt like things were going really good in our lives that Ty would start a huge fight and leave again. He always did it on a night we were drinking, and usually the issue was I got drunk and he got mad. It was always because I couldn't hold my liquor well. Shot for shot was an ignorant thing I did in my youth. I thought I was cool because I could out drink almost anyone when I was younger. Now, shot for shot straight blacks me out and I am not fun. Yet, that was how Ty and I would drink every time.

Before he only left for a few days or hours, but this time he was all the way in Ohio. Ty had his friend come pick him up and I had no idea about any of it until after he was gone. Come to find out, his friend told him he didn't even want to drive down to pick him up because he knew that Ty would come right back. I remember coming home from work that day to find Ty had left his wedding ring and was gone, again.

I didn't even cry when he left this time, but I still wanted him to come home. We were talking on the phone for hours at night and he kept claiming I was drinking too much and was going to start drinking every day. He even told me he thought I was going to drown myself in alcohol when he left, but was surprised to hear I wasn't. It was strange how when he was gone I didn't even think about drinking, yet, when he was home

I thought about drinking every night. He had been gone for a week and I was focused on work, fitness and Bree. I again begged him to look up alcoholism and what it is, but it didn't matter. Ty felt I was just weak or making excuses and having alcohol in the house shouldn't even matter.

I may not have cried when Ty left, but I didn't want to give up on our marriage and I continued to pursue him. I was always chasing Ty. I tried to explain to him I would quit drinking again. I told him our family was more important to me then alcohol. As usual, I didn't understand why he was so upset. He knew when I drank shot for shot it would mess me up. It would only take us about an hour and a half, if that, to finish a fifth between the two of us. He just felt like my alcohol addiction was something I should have complete control of. He would say that he didn't have a problem with drinking, I did, because I would get drunk when we would drink. I felt like he was overreacting and just trying to blame me for everything. It was confusing because we weren't even drinking weekly. We only drank a few times a month during this time. It never dawned on me he was actually feeding my addiction. He was supplying and encouraging the same thing he was always using against me, and I was letting him. I don't blame him for my drinking problem because, truth is, I could have said no or just not bought a bottle. He just wasn't helping either.

When I would say that drinking with me didn't help me, he would convince me I was out of control and not him. I explained to him that quitting all together was a decision I had to make and not one he could force me to make. I may have wanted, could say needed, my husband to encourage and support me, but the truth is tough. Overcoming things such as addiction can only begin when you yourself realize you have a problem. Only you yourself can decide to change that problem and actually make the change for yourself. Everyone around you can try to force you to quit, but you never will until you choose to get help and admit the truth to yourself.

I was confused because, when Ty would leave, I didn't drink anything or even have the urge to drink. I wasn't drinking daily, and I wasn't trying to hide from anything. I felt like I had some huge confusing drinking problem because Ty said I did. I honestly feel like Ty kept alcohol close and constant because it was his intent to use it as his out. Even when I was begging Ty to help me or help me find someone to help me, he always treated me as if I could and should just handle it by myself.

Ty would work so hard at convincing me I was the problem in our marriage and most of the time I believed him. Yet, he was withdrawn and unemotional toward me which always left me feeling lonely and unworthy. It was things like the night we were sitting in our living room and Ty said, "What do you want to do tonight?" I replied with, "Whatever you would like to do baby. You know my mind goes straight to let's get a bottle and, since we aren't drinking, why don't you come up with something." He didn't say a word for about ten minutes, he just sat there. Then out of the blue he got up and put his jacket on. I asked him where he was going and he said, "I am just going to get a bottle." SERIOUSLY? It was things like this that completely threw me off, but I would just go along with it.

Even though Ty was in Ohio, I still had access to his Facebook. I was talking to Ty's brother in Ireland about the fight, which I did often. I would talk to him and he would talk to Ty and we would work things out. It was after I would talk to his brother that Ty would usually call me and apologize. Something made me decide to see what the two of them were saying to one another. I wondered what it was that his brother always said to Ty to make him want to come home. When I got on Ty's Facebook, I was so hurt by what I was reading. I shouldn't have said anything and just filed for divorce right then.

Yet, I just couldn't bring myself to give up on my marriage. My love for Ty was always real even if his wasn't. The only thing his brother was saying to Ty was he needed to come home because he was so close to getting what he had been working for. What else could he have been talking about other than Ty's citizenship? He encouraged Ty to come back to me and "finish what he started." I was so broken. After all the time and everything we had shared and worked through, his brother was straightforward about what Ty was doing there. His brother and I have never talked much again after that.

After reading what Ty's brother had wrote, I called it out. I truly wanted to kick myself for choosing not to see what was right in front of me. Yet, somehow we ended up on the phone and Ty convinced me his brother was talking about something completely different. He convinced me his brother was talking about not giving up on our marriage. I knew better, and I knew what I had read, but I fell for it. I wanted to believe that Ty loved me. I wanted more than anything to make our marriage work. I convinced myself that if we just didn't give up on one another there was no way we could fail. Ty continued to promise me he would not to give up on our marriage. Even though it was so obvious that Ty was never there for us, I just couldn't grasp it.

After a week of talking on the phone with Ty, he said he was going to come home but wanted to spend a couple more weeks in Ohio. I got really upset because I had been the only one working for months and he needed to be home looking for a job. Plus we had worked things out with Bree being in homeschooling, so his leaving was already enough stress on me. Even though his answer to our disagreements always seemed to be running away from our marriage, we both agreed not to give up and he ended up coming home. Once he was home he promised me he would never leave again.

I already had my plate full being a mother, working full time and taking care of my house. I was also helping my little brother and dealing with all the other things life threw my way daily. I eventually gave up trying to figure out if Ty truly loved me or not. I convinced myself that, if he was going to be with me, he was. When he got his green card, his citizenship, if he left me then it was his loss. I may not be perfect, but I am a good woman that has been through a lot of crazy things and learned from them. I am educated and God is with me. I thought if that man felt life was so much better and easier somewhere else then I would wish him luck.

Things were back to normal when Ty returned. We didn't argue much because it wasn't worth the fight anymore. I didn't know how to take

Ty, so I just went along with things even when I didn't understand or sometimes even agree. Just like before, but now the only difference was his attitude didn't hurt my feelings as much. Ty ended up getting a good job as a correctional officer soon after he returned home, which was a good thing for us. Even though I didn't know how Ty truly felt, I knew I was still in love with him. My effort toward our marriage didn't change, but I wasn't as focused on pleasing him as I had in the past.

Even after walking four miles to work, working an eight hour shift, coming home to Bree and doing homework with her, I wanted to be the wife and mother I was meant to be. I loved cooking for my family and all of us eating together, which we did almost every single night. Some days were good, others were bad, but we were just living the best we could. It wasn't very long once Ty returned that his hateful and distant attitude came back out, especially after he got his job as a correctional officer which paid very well. Now Ty had more money to send home or stash and he loved that.

One night after Ty came home I had just finished cooking dinner. I liked to give him his food fresh and hot when he got out of work, so I always tried to time dinner appropriately. That night, Ty walked in the kitchen and moved all of my pots and pans out of his way, the same pots and pans that contained all our freshly cooked dinner. He began pulling out more pots and pans and decided to make himself a full meal because he didn't want to eat what I had cooked. I realized I was never going to understand this man. I did say something to him about it, but he got pretty upset at me. He said, "I'm a grown man and can eat what I want, can't I." I just agreed and said, "Of course."

I was really livid, but I tried not to let it show. I thought his behavior had nothing to do with some cultural difference, he was just being rude. I hated cooking for him after that and began hating cooking all together. When I was younger, if you didn't eat the meal that was cooked you didn't eat. At no point in my life had any man ever cooked a full meal after I had already cooked a full meal for us. I did still cook after that, but it wasn't as often at all.

Tracy called two times this entire year and I think Stacy may have called once. The first time Tracy called I told her, "I'm not letting you talk to Bree." I would let Bree know when they called, but they continued to claim I didn't tell Bree about their effort to reach her. The second time Tracy called I told Bree she needed to stand up for herself and speak. Bree was 15 years old and I felt it was time she stand up for herself. When I gave Bree the phone she told Tracy, through tears, she didn't know if she wanted to see her again. Tracy just hung up on Bree and neither Stacy nor Tracy ever called again the entire year.

My mother ended up coming down and Bree went on her first summer visit with my mom, which is something that will never happen again. It only took a week and Bree was calling me crying. Come to find out, one of the first things my mother said to Bree was, "What happens at Grandma's stays at Grandma's." Ironic because that is one of the first things I taught Bree was a sign of danger. If you can't talk about the truth then it won't set you free. We do not keep secrets from one another and it made me mad that my mom was encouraging just that.

While Bree was at my mom's, her and my grandparents were asking Bree to do their laundry, cleaning and pretty much be a live-in maid. They made her feel bad for not knowing how to properly set their dining room table, as if she should know, and little nitpicks like that. One time Bree called crying because my mother scolded her for eating her chili cheese fries with her fingers and not a fork. My mother always taught us good table manners and how to properly eat at a dining table. I had instilled the same in Bree, but I didn't ride her like that about it. I eat chili cheese fries with my fingers. I knew I had to get her out of my mom's, but I wasn't sure how. With our work schedules, I couldn't just come and get her. Ty and I were planning to make the trip and had taken time off work, but that was still two weeks away.

I decided to call Ina and found out that Derek was up from Florida. He was actually at her house for a short time. I begged her to please go pick up Bree and help get her away from my mom. I explained the visit wasn't going good at all for Bree. Ina and Derek went down and picked up Bree. Her visit up North was so much better after that. Unfortunately, by this time Ina's husband had passed away and she was a single mother with a lot on her plate, but she always made time for Bree and me.

I was thankful God provided some time for Bree to get to know Derek. It had been many years since they had been around one another. We had spent some time with him here and there throughout the years, but we really didn't know each other and we still don't. Bree did enjoy what time she had with her cousins Luke, Jeremy and, of course, Ina's beautiful little girl. I was just happy that Bree wasn't calling me crying anymore and that she was actually having fun. When she called she was laughing and I could hear the difference in her voice.

I know I am blessed and thankful for the Lord for helping me with my daughter. At 15 years old she still tells me she loves me every day. She calls on me for advice and tell me everything going on in her life daily. She doesn't do drugs, she talks about college and her career. She loves God and acknowledges Jesus Christ as her Savior. She really amazed me once she started her homeschooling. Bree's homeschooling had been a great decision and she was very self-sufficient. If needed, this girl can cook, clean and run some Algebra II all around you, while speaking a little Spanish. She is amazing to say the least.

Bree is very well-mannered and doesn't cuss in front of adults, not counting Dakota. He doesn't count as an adult to Bree because those two have been raised more like brother and sister. I am not trying to act like my daughter is the best kid in the world, however, to me she really is. She isn't perfect and she gets an attitude on occasion, but she is the most awesome teenager I know. This kid makes social media posts stating how she understands that life can bring you down, but she will always be there for anyone that needs support. It's things like that she does that warms my heart. She amazes me as each day passes, and I am sure that will never change.

Soon the time had come and Ty and I headed to Michigan to pick Bree up. We had a good trip and I did get to see Derek for a very short time.

Ina and Derek ended up leaving for a canoe trip the day after we arrived, so we got to spend the whole weekend with all the kids. Brandon and Sadie also ended up stopping by. We didn't get to visit long, but it was always good to see them both. Ty and I enjoyed the time we got to spend up north and we were both happy that Bree ended up enjoying her visit.

Ty, Bree and I ended up stopping at my mother and grandparent's house after we left Ina's house. My mother had a pile of items waiting for me to load in the truck, including a recliner my grandparents gave to me. None of us ever spoke about the things that happened in the past. Everyone in my family has perfected acting like nothing was ever wrong even when everything was. The trip was good and we loaded up and headed back home to Indiana. Once we arrived back in Indiana and unloaded everything, we settled down for the night.

Ty was still doing all kinds of business things with his brother in Nigeria. He was saving a lot of money and always claimed to be broke. I felt more comfortable asking a friend to loan me $20 than I did my own husband. On a couple of occasions I saw the numbers in his bank accounts, but he claimed it was never his money it was his brother's. I just simply continued to look the other way. Things between us were actually going good and there seemed to be a sense of peace between us.

Everything was going well for me at work and I really enjoyed my job. I was a Department Manager and continually trying to climb the ladder of success. I finally ended up getting an interview scheduled for an Assistant Manager position. I was so excited and thought I had the position locked down because the interview went so well. I loved my job, but I was tired of working in the store I had been in because we were now on our third Store Manager and he didn't seem to care for me too much. Then two days after my interview, I woke up and could barely move. My back was in so much pain, and I had no idea why or what I had done to hurt myself. I had a hard time walking and bending was next to impossible. I forced myself to go to work because I didn't want to take any chance of losing the Assistant Manager position that I had worked so hard for. After getting to work, my back only got worse. As I moved at the slowest pace possible, I knew there was no way I would be able to make it through the day. At first break I ended up calling a friend who came to pick me up and take me to the hospital. They weren't much help in identifying the problem. The nurse and doctor explained how much the cost of running a lot of tests would be and asked if I wanted to have them done. After asking a few more questions, they also explained that even with running the tests there was a chance they wouldn't find out what the true problem was.

My issue was that none of us were carrying health insurance yet. Of course, once Ty was past his required date at work, he did put Bree and me on his insurance, but that didn't help me then. I ended up on unpaid medical leave and was required to go to a physical therapist.

I was so thankful for my physical therapist. She not only worked with me on a payment plan, but this woman taught me new stretches and helped me better understand my spine. I was with her for a month and money was getting really tight. Ty and I had been discussing the idea of me quitting my job and just opening a small daycare at the house, but Ty was worried it would affect his money in some way. I had already lost the Assistant Manager Position and it was really bothering me. Even though I was tossing the idea around about the daycare, I knew I had to get back to work because I really didn't like the idea of counting on Ty's money. I asked my physical therapist to release me even though I knew I was pushing my body. She was reluctant to do so, but she did it and I was soon back to work.

On my first day back to work I knew I made a mistake going. I was in a lot of pain and pushed myself through the day. I ended up checking on my schedule before I left and wasn't scheduled to work for the entire next week. I wasn't upset at all. I ended up printing off my schedule and took the entire week to stretch my back. I was very cautious with my movements and took care of myself while I was off work. On Friday of the week I was not scheduled, I received a notice that I was a 'no call, no show' for the entire week and was fired. I filed for unemployment, which was granted.

I took getting fired as a sign and opened up a small daycare with the decision on a maximum of four children. I loved all the kids and we filled up fast. It honestly felt refreshing to be home full time with Bree and the other children. The laughter and little feet running around the house was wonderful. Even Ty enjoyed having the kids around. He was always so good with all kids. The only thing we fought about was the fact he made such good money and I felt he should support our home more. I had covered everything on and off for a long time by myself and it only seemed right that Ty step up. He hated the idea, but in the end began giving me $1,200 a month to cover our bills.

Ty remained distant as far as being active with Bree. There is this famous guy named, Taylor Caniff, that was coming to Indianapolis and Bree and her best friend wanted to go so bad to meet him. Ty could have taken the girls, but he refused, so Bree called Dom and he came right away. He even fixed his schedule so he could take Bree and her best friend to the event. I had to watch a few toddlers so there was no way I could go with them. It was so funny because, while they were there waiting, Dom texted me and said he was surrounded by thousands of teenage girls and ready to pull his hair out. Dom stood in line with Bree and her friend for over six hours so the girls could get five seconds next to Taylor. Dom was great with Bree and always has been. He was never afraid to do things with or for her. We are very thankful for him even to this day.

Ty always wanted children and, at one point, we researched In-Vitro Fertilization. I was considering the idea of having another baby. I felt bad at times because I couldn't give Ty any children and some of his comments really hurt me. My partial hysterectomy left me with my uterus, but I don't have ovaries. We discovered that, if we could find an egg donor, I would have actually been able to carry a child, but it was only something we discussed. I kept going back and forth because we were always so up and down. I eventually told Ty I didn't want any more kids. I am thankful as I sit back now and see where I am that we did not proceed. The Lord knows we didn't need any children together.

In October Ty and I decided to celebrate our wedding anniversary and headed to a Jacuzzi room with all our goodies with us. I paid for the room and we had food, drinks and each other. I made sure to pack everything so, if we didn't want to, there was no reason we even had to leave our room. I did end up purchasing tickets to a local comedy club also. Ty had never been to a comedy show and I still loved doing those first time things with him. When we arrived, we unpacked and got settled in.

We broke open one of our bottles and we took a few toasts to our anniversary. After a while I knew I had to get some sleep before our comedy show that night. While I was napping, Ty got upset that I had fallen asleep. I don't know what came over him. While I was sleeping he ended up dumping all the liquor we had bought out. When I woke up he was hateful and mean toward me. I kept trying to understand what was wrong and he said it was because I was drunk and I passed out. I argued with him, but I was so lost. I wasn't drunk at all when I went to sleep. What the hell was this man even talking about? I even told him I was going to take a nap. Ty treated me like shit the entire night, even at the comedy club. It wasn't until the next morning he apologized a million times and said he was wrong for treating me like he had. Ty kept saying he didn't know why he got so upset. He even took me to the bar next door and offered to pay for anything we got, which wasn't like him to offer to pay. The rest of our stay was nice; we just enjoyed our room, the jacuzzi and made love.

A part of me wanted to believe Ty wasn't lying about his money even after seeing the amounts he had put away. I wanted to believe everything that man said. Ty ended up talking his uncle into sending him money so he could purchase a car he found on craigslist. When I talked to Ty about it, he said he would pay his uncle back and didn't want to spend his money. I thought that was crazy, but Ty did as he pleased. It was an old beater stick shift, but it was worth the price and Ty now had his own vehicle.

In early December I asked Ty if I could do anything to please him more. He told me he wouldn't mind if I wore wigs and changed my hairstyle more often. I explained to him I didn't wear wigs, but, one day while he was at work, I took a pair of scissors and cut off all of my hair. It was down to my butt, long flowing beautiful red hair, and I chopped it all off. I ended up having to go to a salon and they gave me my first highlights and styled my hair better. When Ty saw it, he didn't have much of a reaction. When I asked him if he liked it he told me he didn't really care for it, but by that time it was too late. It hurt my feeling, but I grew to like the style. I did miss my hair and vowed to never cut it short again.

A couple of weeks before Christmas my mother made plans to come down and stay for a couple of days. As what Dakota and I had come to consider normal, the day she was to arrive we were off to the liquor store. By this time, Dakota had his own place right down the road from us and he came by often. Dakota and I both always seemed to drink heavily when our mom was around, but, truth be told, Dakota and I drank heavy whenever we drank together.

I didn't understand why I always wanted to drink when my mom was around until I began healing. I was angry at my mom and had never faced my issues with her. I blamed her for the things that happened to me as a child. I was angry at her for a long time. I hated that I really couldn't believe 90% of what she said either. I always told myself she was my mom and I couldn't just get another mom. I didn't realize that, by holding onto all that anger toward her, I was hurting myself spiritually and mentally until I faced it and forgave her.

The first night mom came down I ended up pretty drunk. Mom brought a bunch more stuff and, as I sat on the floor in the living room going through everything, I drank. All of us sat around and visited most of the evening. As the night went on, I had laid down and passed out on the floor between all the piles of clothes and other items mom brought. The next day I woke up and, while I was sitting in the kitchen talking to my mom, I explained to her how odd things were with Ty. I cried and explained about his several secret bank accounts. I told her about when he would drink with me how he would call me out for drinking. I just opened up and expressed to her I was afraid he was planning to leave and I didn't know what to do.

My mother, with all of her wisdom and great advice, looked at me and said, "Zara, you've had a drinking problem since you were a teen. I don't blame him for having a backup plan. I would if I were him." Meaning what? What was she talking about? Ty and I weren't drinking half as often as we had in the past and things weren't bad between us. We had been getting along fine for a while by this time.

As tears continued to roll down my face, I told my mom I didn't know what to do anymore or what was wrong with me. Why was it always about me drinking? Ty and I could go without drinking for several weeks, but the moment we would drink together I had a drinking problem because I would end up drunk. I told my mom I wanted to quit drinking altogether and went on to explain that Ty and I hadn't been fighting very much for months. We were actually doing pretty good despite the hidden secrets and plans Ty was making behind my back that I didn't know about. My mother looked completely past me. As she looked out the window she said, "I don't know what you're crying about, you have everything I have ever wanted."

I tried to stop crying in that exact moment. The first thing I thought was, "I will never treat my daughter or my grandchildren like this woman does, ever!" What mother says that to their child, and what exactly did I have that she always wanted? It was okay for my husband to have a plan to leave the family we had and hide things? My mother was someone I never looked up to in my life, but she seemed to look up to me which really hurt our relationship for a long time. After my mom finally left, I just sat everything aside again and went on with taking care of Bree and all the other kids. Cartoons and toddlers made for some fun days. It was easy to not think about everything Ty seemed to be hiding because he became loving toward me and that was all I wanted.

Ty seemed to really fit in at work and he enjoyed his position as a correctional officer. His personality and arrogance really helped him get far since the day he arrived in the United States. He even told me one time that everyone liked him because he is so likable. I personally feel he was just good at fitting in, deceiving, and it had nothing to do with him being likable or not. He is also very good at manipulating a situation.

    I thought we were starting to come together better. I started to notice the small loving changes in Ty that made me happy. He really seemed to be putting an effort into our marriage and that is what I convinced myself of. I actually began to think he was really dedicated to our marriage. Perhaps his bank accounts were just for our future or maybe he was planning a big surprise for our family. I started not to care so much because, as long as he was beside me, I felt like we were okay. He was talking more and seemed so much happier. We were really connecting and talking about bettering our marriage way more often. I was so optimistic or blind, whichever you would want to call it. My thoughts were, BRING ON THE NEW YEAR...I was convinced it could only get better from here for our family.....

Chapter TWENTY-FIVE

2015: As the New Year came and went, I realized I needed help with all that I had been going through with Ty, my mother, Jade and Chad, alcohol and life all together. I was confessing that I was an alcoholic and wanted help. I went to the one place I knew I could always turn to and that was church. I began attending every Sunday morning and even joined a women's Bible study on Wednesdays. Although Bree had attended another church for several years, she wanted to go with me and check out the one I was now attending. She ended up loving it, her best friend also attended the same church, so it was a true blessing. I tried to get Ty involved with going to church with us, but after attending once or twice he really had no interest in going. Although throughout the years I read my Bible and even tried to read with Ty on a few occasions, I felt like God had abandoned me. I decided I wasn't giving up and began reading my Bible every single day.

When I joined the women's group I felt like God was nowhere near me. Although there were times I could feel his presence, those moments were far and few between. In my women's Bible study I held nothing back about my drinking problem. I shared about the void I felt from my distance with God and even how I fell so far when Paul passed away. I almost thought that perhaps Jesus didn't want me because of all the anger I had toward him after Paul died. I couldn't have been further from the truth. He never left me. Even when I didn't feel him close he was there. The women of the group embraced me and prayed for me. Their support was beyond what I ever expected.

At the time, Ty and I were good in our relationship. Things were really going well between us and we were even communicating more than we ever had in our entire marriage. I bragged to the women in my group about how lucky I was to be married to my best friend. I truly believed, after pulling through so much and all the madness, that Ty and I were stronger than we had ever been in the past. I even ended up making a few friends from my bible study group. I have to say that one specific lady has been truly a blessing to me ever since we started talking. Her name is Angel and she was truly sent from God to be a part of my life at this time.

Angel was a single mother of four of the most wonderful children. She was exactly the support and loving sister I had always prayed the Lord would send me. Angel had a rough past, also, but we are two complete opposites. She didn't drink, smoke cigarettes or have a body full of tattoos. Angel was soft spoken and I am not. She was timid and worried about her looks and I was not and did not. Even with our different pasts and different personalities, we became best friends quickly. I am very thankful for Angel being in my life and for her support.

At the end of January Ty finally received his Green Card. He was officially a citizen of the United States for a ten year period now. We were both so excited and I was so happy for him. He really worked hard to get everything together and did the entire process without an attorney. We celebrated and had a good time that night. We even started to discuss what we should do for our fourth anniversary that was approaching. See, we celebrated our anniversary twice a year: Once for the day we were brought together in February of 2011 and once for the day we married. The anniversary approaching was the day we were brought together. Truth is, that one was just as important to me as was our wedding anniversary.

February was here and, as usual, Ty didn't get me anything for Valentine's Day. That was nothing new for him so, even though it did hurt my feelings, I didn't let it get to me too much. He was never a man that liked to spend money on anything. He never cared to spoil his woman, at least not this woman. Bree, however, was turning 16 in July and had her first boyfriend. He surprised her with a teddy bear half her size and candies. She made out like a bandit. It was so awesome to see her smile and enjoy her day.

At the end of February Tracy asked me if she could spend time with Bree. I'm not sure why I told her I would allow it if she came to our house alone, but I did. I showed Bree the message, and Bree asked me two times after that if I had heard anything else from Tracy, but Tracy never contacted me about it again. I was honestly glad because I shouldn't have said yes to begin with. Then in April Stacy instant messaged me and asked if Bree could come to their house for her first son's birthday party. I simply said no because I knew Chad and Jade were going to be there. Stacy criticized me for not letting Bree decide and for keeping Bree from them, but it didn't get to me. When I showed Bree the message, she said she didn't want to go and wouldn't go even if I had said yes. That was the very last time that Bree or I ever heard from Stacy or Tracy again.

I was doing really good with my Bible study group and with the support all the women provided. I was continuing to do my own Bible studies at home, and I was enjoying life more and more as each day passed. I started to feel like the Lord was with me. His presence brought peace and comfort to me. I felt like everything was going to be okay with the support I was now receiving, along with the prayers. I just truly felt lifted up. Now, don't think I am claiming I instantly conformed to some perfect woman because I will never be perfect. I struggle daily and continue to make mistakes, but I grow and learn as each day passes.

After the first of the year Ty and I only drank a couple times, but we weren't fighting about it. Alcohol wasn't consuming my thoughts because God was. We discussed our plans for our anniversary and tried to come up with ideas. Due to Ty's work schedule, I ended up booking the same Jacuzzi room we had on our wedding anniversary for February 28th, March 1st and the 2nd. It was three days away and I was so excited. I bought two tickets for Row 19 to the 'WHAT NOW' tour with Kevin Hart. I also bought two tickets to a Pacer game through a friend for my sport fanatic husband. It was going to be his first live NBA game. I planned to surprise Ty at our hotel with the tickets, but I was so excited I couldn't wait and ended up spoiling it and told him about the tickets. He didn't react the way I thought he would, but I had grown used to that.

I had talked to Ty about if we should bring alcohol to the hotel or not. I just wanted to have a good time away with Ty and not a repeat of our last anniversary. He said we should and promised he wasn't going to get upset about anything. The day we were to leave for the hotel, I had everything packed for us. I had maxed out both of my credit cards, but it was worth it. Ty and I were doing good so I figured it wouldn't take long to pay them off. I had even ordered a two-burner electric tabletop stove so I could cook steak for my man while we were gone. I was ready for the best getaway weekend a woman could have with her husband. I had plans to spoil my man with all the love I could give him.

Unfortunately, Ty had a pretty bad cold during our entire stay at the hotel, but it didn't stop us. We had so much fun and not at one point did we fight about anything. We laid around in the Jacuzzi for hours and enjoyed one another in ways we hadn't in a long time. We talked about our marriage and how we could make things better. I asked him if there was anything I could do to make him happier and he told me, "No, baby, you're perfect." I even asked if he wanted to stop drinking altogether or if he felt like things were okay. He reassured me that we were good. I was so happy and felt loved by Ty.

I did express to him it would be nice to be spoiled a little more. I asked him to please put a little effort into maybe flowers or cards to show his love and he agreed to try harder. We even discussed the book, "Men are from Mars and Women are from Venus," written by John Grey. I ordered it right there from our room on my phone. We committed that, when it came in, we would read it together. Things were going so good I was starting to feel like nothing could ever break us. We really enjoyed one another's company and affection the entire time we were there.

Even though Ty was sick, he still loved it when I cooked him a New York Strip and served him in bed. I always loved doing things that pleased Ty. My problem was that, in trying to please Ty, I hurt myself. He didn't seem to ever appreciate my effort or notice it, however, it was finally starting to feel like Ty was really receptive to my love and affection and even returning it. I admit it really seemed like we were finally on the right path. Things for months had been going so good, and I just knew that life was going to get better. I was feeling closer to God. I was actually praying every day and my marriage was starting to take a turn for the best. Nothing was going to tear us down now.

MONDAY, March 2, 2015: When Ty and I got home in the afternoon all was well. Bree came home after staying with her best friend for the weekend and the house was still in one piece. We were all sitting in the living room when around 10 p.m. that evening Ty stood up and started to put his jacket on. When I asked him where he was going, he said he was going to get a bottle. It was really odd for Ty to decide just out of the blue like that to go get a bottle, especially because we had been drinking over the weekend. I didn't think too hard on it and just told him to be safe.

After Bree went to bed, Ty got back with a fifth. We sat down at the table and started talking as we took our shot after shot. Once the bottle was close to being gone, Ty tried really hard to pick a fight with me. I felt really good from the shots we drank, but I wasn't blacked out or trashed. We argued back and forth for little bit, but Ty wasn't upsetting me as much as I believe he was trying to. The fight had no basis and there was no point to it. It was so weird to come out of such a wonderful and love-filled weekend to just come home and fight. He ended up getting mad at me. I think it was because I refused to give the argument any merit. I didn't want to fight and I refused to. I didn't even raise my voice once and stayed calm through the whole thing. Ty ended up just going upstairs and going to bed. I laid in my recliner, pushed it back and sat there thinking about why he just tried to fight with me. I convinced myself he was just being silly and would get over it.

TUESDAY, March 3, 2015: After the morning started, Ty and I apologized to one another. I was usually always the one who initiated every apology or talk after an argument with Ty. He was too stubborn to admit he was wrong about much of anything. I learned a long time ago it was easier to take the fall or blame for most of our fights because he was really good at holding a grudge. The day was a normal busy day spent catching up on laundry from our weekend getaway and taking care of the kids running around the house.

That night at 10 p.m. I was waiting for my last child to be picked up when, out of the blue, Ty did the same thing as he had the night before. He stood up and put his coat on. When I asked him what he was doing, he said he was going to buy a bottle. It was really strange; not only was he going to buy a bottle again, but he was okay with us drinking for the fifth day in a row. I don't remember drinking that many days in a row since we had first got together.

It was so abnormal of Ty that, even as she was headed to bed, Bree made a comment about how it was weird dad wanted to drink again. I just agreed with her. We usually never drank the next day after already drinking. It wasn't anything normal, especially for Ty. He was always telling me he was afraid I would start drinking daily, as I did when we first met, and I was always assuring him I would never go back there again. Now here he was, and here we were drinking for the fifth day in a row.

When he got home it was crazy how everything replayed. The same situation occurred. As soon as the bottle was near the bottom he began to start a fight with me. It didn't even make any sense and I still didn't want to fight. When Ty went to run away to our room after starting the fight this time, I stopped him. Reflecting on it now, I think Ty was actually trying to get me drunk and then make me go off on him. I truly believe with all my heart it was his escape plan and I had no idea.

I didn't want to fight with him ever, but he really seemed to like fighting and all the angry feelings it stirred up. I still wasn't drunk or blacked out. I was feeling good and I wasn't allowing another fight to happen over nothing. This time, before he had a chance to head up the stairs, I grabbed him and kissed him passionately. It was a 'take me now' kind of kiss. I then proceeded to pull him in the kitchen and pull some 'Fifty Shades of Grey' on him. Okay, maybe not that intense, but I took my husband and did with him as I pleased. Needless to say it was a good night, the fight was squashed and we slept well.

WEDNESDAY, March 4, 2015: The day began as every other day. Ty and I had no problems and even flirted all day about how much fun we had in the kitchen the night before. I teased Ty about wanting to fight with him again because it was fun the way it all ended and he just smiled at me. The day was good and just another normal day filled with kids, cartoons and chores around the house.

Ten p.m. came around and Bree went to bed. One of the children I babysat for was being picked up when Ty headed out the door for another bottle. It was really getting me confused and I didn't understand why he was continuing to want to drink, but he did. I was starting to have a hard time because drinking every day brings me to a point where I don't want to stop drinking and makes me crave alcohol. Drinking six days in a row was not the best thing for me; however, I hadn't been blacking out and my body seemed to be okay. But it was like I was stuck in the movie, "Groundhog Day". He did the same thing. When the bottle got close to empty, he started a fight with me.

What was crazy were the things Ty was trying to fight about weren't even issues. It was so strange. We would take a shot and he would ask why I drank so much. We would take another shot and he would ask why I got drunk so fast. It was confusing and he was just nitpicking at me. He was trying to argue about anything he could come up with. I didn't understand why he was behaving the way he was, but I wasn't going to try to figure it out. He was already extremely confusing when it came to things he wanted to argue about and his opinion on how things should be. Again, I didn't put much thought in it. We ended up going to bed mad at one another.

THURSDAY, March 5, 2015 and FRIDAY, March 6, 2015: I thought life was good and everything seemed to be going better. Ty didn't go get a bottle out of the blue and we were back to a normal level. Ty was back to work and I was back into the swing of things. There was nothing really exciting or interesting that occurred throughout these days. I did notice my body wanted alcohol, but I prayed and just pushed the thoughts aside. We were back to watching television as a family at night and just enjoying the kids when they were there.

SATURDAY, March 7, 2015: The day started off good. I didn't have any kids the entire day, so I thought I would catch up on the rest of my house cleaning. As I was drinking my hot tea and scrolling down my Facebook page, I noticed that Dean, Paul's son, had wrote a post about something going on with his health. I ended up letting him know I would keep him in my prayers and that I loved him. It wasn't long after that when Dean asked me to give him a call. Of course, I did. As we talked, I could feel my heart aching, my stomach began to curl and I couldn't stop the tears.

Dean had been to the doctor and they feared he had cancer, the same kind as Paul. Dean said he hadn't told anyone but me and asked me to please not tell anyone. I told him that it wasn't fair to not tell the people that love him and his mom needed to know what was going on, but it was his choice. I explained it wasn't right the way his dad handled the cancer by not letting anyone know how bad it was and he shouldn't do the same. Dean was crying, I was crying and I felt so helpless. I knew I couldn't help him in any way. I asked him if he wanted me to come up to Michigan to spend time with him, but he said he wanted me to wait to see what the results were from the biopsy the doctor had done.

Dean and I talked for a long time about everything from the past to the future. When we hung up, I couldn't stand any longer and just dropped to my knees in prayer and tears. I couldn't believe that Dean was going through this at such a young age. He was only in his early twenties at this time. I was alone at the house this day because Bree was at her friend's and Ty was at work. I ended up going to pick up Bree so I could let her know what was going on.

She was the only one around me as close to Dean and loved him as much as I did. We held one another and cried for a long time. We both ended up in prayer for Dean. As the morning went on, Bree asked if she could go stay at her best friend's house and I was fine with that. She always had support from her best friend and the entire family. They have always been so good to Bree and me both. I am very thankful for them even now.

After a few hours of tears and getting Bree to her friend's house, I went up to the liquor store and grabbed a half pint of Goldschlager. When I got home I ended up calling Dakota and he came over to talk to me. Once he got to the house, I told him what happened with Dean and I couldn't stop crying. The whole thing brought back so much of the same emotions I had from when Paul passed away. Dakota knew Dean too. He just hugged me and listened as I tried to explain what Dean had told me. Dakota's friend was with him and they ended up leaving for a bit to do something. When they came back after about an hour they brought a fifth of Goldschlager with them.

I can't say I remember much else of the afternoon. Dakota stayed until Ty got home so he could explain everything that happened with Dean and why I was completely hammered and passed out. Looking back on it, I ran to alcohol often after Paul passed away and things got hard on me. Truth is, when I would wake in the morning after drinking, the same problems were always there and usually more. The alcohol never helped.

Dakota knew how angry Ty got if I drank without him. So in Dakota's mind he was trying to help me so Ty didn't go off on me. By the time Ty got home from work, I was passed out on the kitchen floor and Ty ended up helping me to bed. I remember looking at him and crying. Even though I was drunk, I couldn't stop thinking about Dean. I couldn't believe that Dean could be dying just like his father had. It killed me to even think about it. I asked Ty if he knew about Dean and he told me Dakota had explained everything to him. I believe, if it wasn't for Dakota staying around that night, Ty and I would have been in the fight he was looking for because I was that drunk.

SUNDAY, March 8, 2015: This day was spent under complete recovery. I had drank way too much the entire week and my body wasn't handling it well at all. Ty wasn't even upset and acted like things were okay. He wasn't happy, but he wasn't mad at me and actually acted like he understood my pain. The alcohol never helped me, it honestly hurt me more than it ever did anything else.

When Bree came home that evening things were okay. My heart was heavy and my mind wouldn't stop thinking about Dean, but I did talk to Ty and reassured him that, if anything did happen to Dean, I wasn't going backwards. I explained to Ty I didn't know if my heart could handle it if anything happened to Dean, but I wouldn't turn to alcohol as an out. I tried so hard to prepare myself for whatever the results were and continued to pray for Dean's health.

Now here we are and I am taking you back to the beginning of this crazy story. Remember the woman in the long blue trench coat? It was the next day that I was blessed enough to meet her, March 9th. It was Tuesday, March 10th, that my little brother came over and we drank. Of course, it was that night that Ty walked out of our marriage and you know what happened next.

FRIDAY, March 13th-March 19th: The results did end up coming in and Dean did not have cancer, praise God. As the days passed, I was able to begin moving around again. I had no idea what I was going to do. I tried to talk to Ty and wanted to make things work even after everything that happened. I kept telling myself if he just came home we could pull through this and make things right. Truth is, the entire past week was throwing me off. I didn't understand how we ended up here. After our anniversary weekend this was the last thing I ever expected.

Ty and I began talking mainly through Instant Messenger. I asked him if he was willing to give our marriage three months and then see where we should go from there. He agreed he would. I didn't realize Ty already had a place set up and was in his own apartment already. I never wanted to believe that Ty was always making a plan to leave, but now I see. I was very blind and ignorant as to what was truly going on throughout our entire relationship. Even at this moment it still didn't register to me that Ty used me. I was simply unwilling to see or believe it.

Dakota came and checked on Bree and me often. Dom also ended up coming over and stayed with Bree and me for a couple nights. He just wanted to make sure we were safe and he was always so respectful.

Money was tight the moment that Ty walked out. Ty knew exactly what he was doing. Dom ended up surprising Bree and me by bringing over two handfuls of groceries. I'm not sure that I would have even been able to provide what Bree needed if it wasn't for the few dear friends that helped us. I just couldn't accept the fact that Ty did it again. After all his promises and commitment to our marriage he left again. I counted on what money Ty gave me for our bills. My credit cards were maxed out from our anniversary and I didn't know what I was going to do financially. The daycare I was running could not support our bills alone and I was unable to provide for the kids. I ended up shutting the daycare down to figure out what my next step should be.

I really didn't think Ty would stay gone. I convinced myself he would come home, but, what I didn't realize was, he had what he was truly after. Ty said he needed to re-evaluate if marriage was for him, and I argued he should have done that before he asked me to marry him. Seriously, after the years together and now having his Green Card for less than a month and a half, he needed to re-evaluate if marriage was for him? I just couldn't wrap my head around it. What was he talking about?

I again started digging into any information I could find about rebuilding our marriage. I found a dedication to rebuilding a marriage and Ty even agreed to do the devotional with me. It was designed to help us both heal and it went really well at first. We even made a date and planned to get together on March 20th. The week was spent with apologies and asking forgiveness for things that had been wrong in our marriage. I asked Ty to forgive me for thinking he could somehow complete me and for putting too much pressure on him to give me attention. He apologized for his stubbornness and for not being the husband he should. As we continued talking to one another, I felt like we were really going somewhere by getting things out.

Neither of us were perfect and, even though he ran every time things got bad, he always came back. This time was different. He had already arranged a place to live. I started wondering when did he do that? He had no intention of coming back. He actually led me on the entire week letting me believe we had a chance to get through this. He acted like fixing our marriage was important to him. Yet, again, I wanted to do nothing, but believe him.

March 19, 2015 and on: It was the day before our date and I have to admit I was nervous. I hadn't seen Ty in weeks and was ready to just give him a hug. I missed him and still wanted to do nothing else but make it work with him. We started texting in the evening and things were good. I asked him if he was really dedicated to making our marriage work or if he was dedicated to staying gone for three months. His response shot through my heart like a knife as he told me he fully intended to stay gone. I didn't argue, but I expressed that I felt like a fool because I was always chasing him. I explained I was thinking more along the lines of him coming home and us going to marriage counseling or even going to the church and speaking with an elder or pastor. Ty replied by telling me he was over it and didn't want to deal with my bullshit anymore. He said he wanted a divorce and didn't want to be with me. I didn't understand. We had been trying to work things out, or at least I had. I began to realize that Ty never wanted to work things out, he just wanted his citizenship and it didn't matter who he hurt along the way.

After Ty said he wanted a divorce he hung up on me. I tried to call him back to find out why he was even saying those things. We were doing good talking, and I thought we were healing wounds in order to move forward. He ended up telling me to not bother him again and he wouldn't bother me. He was so hateful and his words hurt me. He wanted a divorce, then so be it. I decided right then I didn't want to spend my life continually chasing a man that didn't even want me.

After crying and praying for a while, I ended up deleting all of my social media and just went into hiding. The only time I heard from Ty was on Saturday, March 21st. He texted and threatened me that, if I filed for a divorce, he would remove my daughter and me from his insurance. I didn't respond because I didn't know what to say. This wasn't the man I thought I had fallen in love with and don't believe he ever was. Ty was a monster. I just continued to seek answers within my Bible.

As the days passed, the fog began lifting and I wasn't captured by thoughts of losing Ty or being without him - I was consumed by thoughts of realism. I began seeing things for what they were and how they got there. I was in the weakest moment of life when I met Ty and he knew it. Ty moved in on me and used me to get all he wanted and needed from the first day he arrived. I simply didn't know what to say or think about the entire relationship. As I continued to pray and read my Bible, I started to see how blind I had been. All the events that happened in our marriage, all the fights, all the drinking and blaming; it was so obvious he never completed me and how much he took advantage of me. The fog was lifting, and I couldn't believe I had given Ty so much control for so long.

Angel helped me through so much during this time. She was truly a shoulder to lean on when I came to realize how blind I had spent the last several years of my life. I started to see Ty for who and what he was. We didn't talk or text again until April 3rd when Ty sent me a long apology for the way he had talked to me. He finished it with asking if I needed money. I needed all the help I could get. Ty did end up helping me twice with very little money after he left, but I knew there was no way I was going to be able to make it financially on my own at this point in my life.

As I continued to pray and keep my head stuck in my Bible every day, I began to feel a sense of comfort. I didn't know how, but I kept telling myself that things would work out as they should. I wasn't drinking or thinking about drinking. It wasn't even close to my thoughts or wants. I was so confused how I allowed things to get to this point. How was I this crazy drunk lady when I didn't even want to drink? I didn't say no to drinking with Ty when he was there and continued to encourage me to drink. Not at one point did I realize Ty was keeping alcohol near us so he could use it against me until this time. I could see that now.

I gave so much of me to Ty that I forgot who I was without him. He had convinced me I was unworthy of complete forgiveness and I was beneath him. Ty made sure I stayed in that realm of thinking throughout most of our marriage. The man would drag me through the mud, stand me up, rinse me down, to just drag me through it again. I felt like I needed to get away from that house and from Indiana altogether. I needed a break. I began to hate being in the house I was once in love with and thought of as home. It wasn't a home anymore, it was a prison.

I didn't want to pretend to be okay. I turned to church, and on Sunday just sat alone trying not to cry. The leader of my Bible study group ended up sitting down with me and embracing me. She prayed over me and, before I knew it, there were several women from my group surrounding me. They held me and continued to pray over me. The emotions were so strong and the tears seemed to heal my heart.

You see, Ty may have hurt me bad and used me the entire time; but, when I saw clearly, I realized I really had done it to myself. My choices are what led me to where I am today and where I was then. Sometimes we need to stand back from a situation before we can see things clearly. Do you ever feel like people come at you sideways all the time, meaning that when we are friended or start a new relationship we have to be leery of the other person's intentions? I was the one standing in a corner and overanalyzing new people the moment my custody case began. I was cautious of new people in my life at all times. With Ty, I let all my guard down because my walls were already broken. He found me at my weakest moment after Paul died and I didn't take any time to stand back and question Ty's intentions. I embraced and welcomed him the moment he came into my life and even begged him to stay with me because I wanted to believe he was the answer to my healing.

My choices and behavior throughout the years were not Ty's fault, they were my own.

Ty didn't force me to love him, I wanted to.
He didn't force me to want to make him happy, I wanted to.
He didn't force me to drink, I chose to.

I began to see that there was never blame to be given. It wasn't Ty's fault that I drank, even if he was the one to bring the bottle in the house. I made the decision every time not to say no or even be the one to buy the bottle. I lifted the shot glass, no one forced me. I had made my decisions that brought me to this point in my life.

The Lord began to lead me and show me I was worthy. I am loved, and I didn't need anyone but Him to be complete. I was being pulled so hard to start writing. I had the desire for many years to write a book, but my attempts were never successful. Honestly, I never knew where to begin because of how much I had been through. Once I sat down and said, "Okay Lord, I surrender. You lead and I will follow", the words began to flood out of me as if they were always there. It amazed me how every word I typed made me feel as if I was losing weight off of my shoulders. I began to feel good and centered again. No more heartache. No more holding in the pain. Here was my story and getting the truth out was setting me free.

I completely cut Ty out of my life. I made no attempt to text, write, or call him and, of course, he didn't try to reach out to me either. He wanted out of our marriage, and I was not going to chase him anymore. I was done the moment he said he wanted a divorce. I made the decision that was exactly what I was going to give him. I finally saw that I was chasing a man that used me for what he needed and there was no need to waste my time anymore.

One day in early May Ty did end up texting me and asking me if we could still be friends. I told him no. He got upset and said it wasn't right we couldn't be friends just because we didn't work out. Did I miss something? We didn't work out because he never wanted or planned to. I am pretty sure it was just a ploy to get something else from me. I thought he was trying to stop me from filing the divorce for as long as he could so it didn't look bad for him with his citizenship being so fresh.

About a week after Ty's text it was Mother's Day. Bree made me an omelet, served me in bed and we watched one of my favorite comedians, Kat Williams. After we were done laughing our morning away, Bree and I decided that we both needed a break and we wanted to get out of Indiana. We instantly began loading up the truck with all that we could grab and left Indiana in the dust that same day. Bree and I ended up at Ina's home and our adventure began.

Being in Michigan brought so much healing that I never expected. I can't express how thankful I am the good Lord led Bree and me there. I was able to heal through prayer and was blessed enough to be made aware of things I needed to face and come to terms with. The Lord brought people to me that I was able to talk to about things I never thought I would discuss again.

Bree and I got ahold of Dean soon after we arrived and he told me he was going to come see us. We were both so excited and Dean said it was important that I meet the girl he wanted to put a ring on and spend his life with. Dean and his lovely girlfriend came to see us and she was so sweet. They truly complimented one another. We talked about Paul a lot and some of the memories we shared with him. There was never a dull moment with Paul. Dean didn't know the story of what happened to Paul's best friend who he was named after. I shared with him the story and we ended up in tears. Our visit was one that I not only needed, but I think Dean needed too. It sounds strange, but it was like Paul was right there with us at certain moments and it brought a warmth to my heart. I couldn't help but picture the little blond-headed boy with blue eyes that Dean once was. Now Dean is handsome and all grown up and looks just like his father. Time goes so fast, so enjoy your children. Before you know it, they will be grown and not need you to lead them anymore. Time goes by too fast. I am honored and blessed to be a part of Dean's life. I love him as my own and I will always be here for him.

It was refreshing to be around all the kids and the love from my nephews and niece was incredible. After staying with Ina and the kids for a while, Bree and I headed over to Brandon and Sadie's house. Being around everyone made Bree and I not want to leave Michigan. Neither of us wanted to ever go back to Indiana. I was desperate for a fresh start and Bree was thinking the same. My intentions were always to put Bree back in school for her Junior and Senior year, but I knew I didn't want to do that in the town we lived in Indiana.

Brandon and Sadie offered to allow Bree and me to stay as long as we needed. I took the time to figure out my next move. Bree, and Brandon's entire family, encouraged me and lifted me up. I can't express my gratitude for their support and help. One day Bree ended up coming to me in tears and begged me not to make us go back to live in Indiana. She really wanted to stay and, frankly, I did too. I felt safe. In Michigan we weren't half an hour away from Jade and Chad, and I knew I didn't have to worry about anyone trying to tear me down. We were near family and friends that we had missed for a long time and it felt good for both of us.

Bree, like myself, was ready for a change and a fresh start where we could actually live and not worry about being under attack all of the time, whether it was Chad and Jade, his family or just the house that was now a prison. We both needed a change, and I was 100% ready to do so. Bree wanted to be in Michigan more than anything, and I knew the school was a small town school that she could really enjoy and finish out her high school years without many problems.

I kept thinking about how I was about to lose our home and had no way to get out of the debt I was in. Ty left us with nothing but debt. I decided to call the courts just to see if I needed to do anything because it had been four years since Chad had seen or even spoke to Bree. I was told I would have to file an Intent to Move and Chad would have 60 days to dispute it. Knowing anything I wanted to do would be objected by Chad and Jade, I asked what would occur if they disputed the move. I was told Bree would be appointed another Ad Litem and the case could start all again. It didn't make sense to me Chad would have a say in our lives since he had nothing to do with Bree. Reopening the custody case was not an option for me. I was not providing them another opportunity to hurt Bree in any way. I didn't want to bring them back into our lives just so they could try to cause more heartache. I talked to Bree about the issue and all she could do was cry. She begged me not to make us go back. She just wanted to start her junior year in Michigan and start over. I wanted her to finish her last two years in a public school so she could make more friends, enjoy high school and prom. I had no idea what I was going to do, but I knew I was going to lose our home and had to figure something out. In Michigan, we had the support of Ina and the boy's, Brandon, Sadie and all their children, plus a few older friends I had reconnected with. We were welcomed and loved with open arms. I tried to figure out a way to stay without having to go through court with Jade and Chad all over again. After speaking to a few attorneys, I realized if Chad and Jade wanted to take me to court for moving I had a fighting chance to win. I decided I wasn't going to ask their permission to make my decision.

On June 17th Bree and I reluctantly headed back to Indiana. The "WHAT NOW" tour with Kevin Hart was on June 19th and I ended up asking a girlfriend of mine to go with me. We had an absolute blast. Kevin Hart is hilarious. Soon after, I gathered all the paperwork for my divorce and contacted Ty so we could meet and sign the papers. We agreed to meet at a bank where a notary public was available. Ty rolled up in a nice brand new jeep and was pimped out in all new name-brand clothing. He was obviously doing great. I didn't worry about it because I knew my success wasn't going to be based on a man. Once the papers were signed, I filed for our divorce. About two weeks later Ty posted all over Facebook that he was in a relationship with some girl and he shared all kinds of pictures of the two of them. It really hurt, but it was what it was.

On the verge of losing our home, Bree and I started packing what we wanted and let go of many years of hurt and pain. We turned our house into a shopping center and sold everything we could. We were both really excited, but I admit I was nervous about what Chad and Jade might do. From the sale we made enough to purchase an older fifth-wheel travel trailer and made arrangements to have it parked on Brandon and Sadie's land. After we stopped by to see Margaret and say goodbye to her, we soon found ourselves traveling back to Michigan ready to start over. For the first six months I called the courts every week to see if Chad and Jade had tried to file anything against me, but they never did.

EPILOGUE

I realize that you may have been hoping this book could provide some answers on how to get through the tough times in life. Perhaps you were hoping for some grand happy ending. The truth is, I am simply a Child of God struggling to do what he wants for my life. I continue to daily hand God my praise and ask him to lead me as I take on what may come. I strive to make others smile and do for others as I want done for me. I have no answers except I have found there is freedom when you surrender trying to control everything. I find peace when I allow God to lead and don't let go of the fact that He is with me.

Everyone always says, "God only gives you what you can handle." I just assume that means I am a beast warrior. He must really love me to have brought me through so much. I was knocked down and beaten, but I got up and was always ready to go another round. We are products of our childhood, but we can choose to allow that to make us a victim or a survivor. We do have a choice to rise above our past and present mistakes.

Pressure to be perfect and fit in are mainly from people who are insecure with themselves. Stand up, be you and make your own path. You will find it amazing how things turn around and how even the mistakes from your past can become your most important lessons. We all make mistakes, every single one of us. If you have someone always shoving your mistakes in your face, just brush it off. No one can define you, but you.

I wish I could provide some great knowledge and specific answers to all the tough questions, but I can't. I believe the only place to find those answers are in prayer and in diligently searching them in God's Word.

He provides comfort even in the worst storms. Don't underestimate the power of God's love for you. Perhaps your struggles are God preparing you for your purpose. Don't give up on yourself. Believe in yourself and the rest will come.

As for what happened to Bree and me? How did it all turn out? Where are we now?

We are together, safe and living each day as it comes. We say our prayers each day and we love with all our hearts. Bree is doing great in school, and I am enjoying my time as a single mom trying to continue doing the best I can to be here for my daughter. I am still trying to find my way every day and stay on a path that will be pleasing to God. I hold no anger or resentment toward anyone that has hurt me; and, for those I hurt along the way, all I can do is beg your forgiveness. This book is just the beginning of my story. My past is now exposed and my future is welcome. One thing I do know is the Lord has his hand on Bree and me. I'm ready and have no fear of what's to come next.

I know I have been freed from all the hurt and abuse life has thrown my way throughout the years. I have come to a point in my life that alcohol doesn't cross my mind, but, if it does, I am strong enough to say no. Life's too short for all of us to be so filled with so much anger and to continue to judge one another only because of the way someone has treated us or done us wrong. We need to get over it, forgive and move on. No one is better than the other and we are all equal. Some of us just accidentally wander off into darker spots than others. Be a light for those people. Don't hide your light so that you're the only one that can see it. If you keep staying solely focused on yourself you will never see the wonderful things God is doing around you and you might miss out on the beautiful people he is trying to place in your life.

It is only you that can make the difference in your life. As Kat Williams says in one of his shows, "It is called self-esteem. It's esteem of your mutha fukin self." Treat others as you want to be treated, but don't base your worth on what others think. You'll never live up to your full potential if you base everything you do on pleasing someone else or on what others want you to be. I pray that you find your way and that you never give up. Even when you find yourself knocked down, bruised and broken, you get up and go another round. You, my friend, are worth fighting for. You may be broken, but you are not shattered.

About the Author

Born in Michigan, Kyna Bryn is a mother, aspiring author and woman who has done it all. From being a waitress, to owning her own business, Kyna has become a self-made, educated woman who does not let anything hold her back. After overcoming many challenges in life, Kyna Bryn has now dedicated her life to inspiring others to know that their past does not define their future. Hurt or broken, used or abused, Kyna focuses on lifting others to know that they are not alone and have the power to be victorious and not victims.

brokennotshattered.com

Made in the USA
Lexington, KY
26 April 2018